The Illustrated
EARTH GARDEN
HERBAL

Title page from John Parkinson's *Paradisi in Sole Paradisus Terrestris*, 1629

The Illustrated
EARTH GARDEN
HERBAL
a herbal companion

text and illustrations gathered from
ancient sources and the classic herbals
by

Keith Vincent Smith

A LOTHIAN BOOK

To Irene & Melissa

A Lothian Book

Thomas C. Lothian Pty Ltd
11 Munro Street, Port Melbourne, Victoria 3207

First published in 1978
Copyright © Keith Vincent Smith, 1978
Revised edition, 1994
Parts of this work are based on material which first
appeared in *Earth Garden* magazine

National Library of Australia
Cataloguing-in-Publication data

Smith, Keith, 1939 – .
The illustrated earth garden herbal.

New ed.
Includes index.
ISBN 0 85091 623 2.

1. Herbs. 2. Herb gardening. I. Title. II. Title: Earth garden (Sydney, N.S.W.).

635.7

Printed in Australia by McPherson's Printing Group

CONTENTS

Disclaimer   ix

The Principal Authorities from which this work is drawn   x

Acknowledgements   xii

Preface – to the gentle reader   xiii

1 THE DELIGHT OF HERBS & GARDENS   1

2 WHAT IS A HERB?   3
       definitions . . . classifying herbs . . . propagation

3 THE HERB GARDEN   8
       ordering the garden . . . your herb garden . . .
       weadyng and watering . . . herbal sprays . . .
       harvesting and drying herbs . . . herb powders . . .
       vinegars . . . oils . . . ointments and salves . . .
       scented candles . . . pot-pourri

4 MAN and HERBS   16

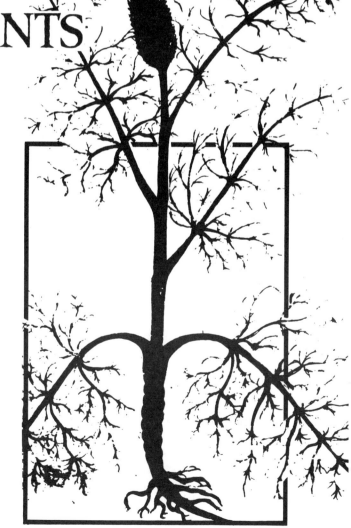

Fennel

5 THE HERBALS   18

Manuscripts . . . Charlemagne's list . . . Strabo's little
garden . . . Anglo-Saxon leechdom . . . Middle
English manuscripts

The printed herbals . . . Turner's Herball . . . Gerard's
Herball . . . The Earthly Paradise . . . The English
Physician . . . William Coles and the Doctrine of
Signatures

Farm and garden books . . . Thomas Hyll . . .
Literature . . . Language of the herbals

**6 A HERBAL COLLECTION AND MATERIA
MEDICA OF FORTY HERBS AND SUNDRY
SUBJECTS**   33

Agrimony (*Agrimonia eupatoria*)   *34*
Alleis and Herbers (walks and arbours)   *35*
Angelica (*Angelica archangelica*)   *36*
Anise (*Pimpinella anisum*)   *38*
Artemisias   *41*
Balm (*Melissa officinalis*)   *41*
Basil (*Ocimum basilicum, O. minimum*)   *43*
Bay laurel (*Laurus nobilis*)   *46*
Bees   *48*

Pot marjoram

Borage (*Borago officinalis*)   *51*
Burnet (*Sanguisorba minor*)   *53*
Caraway (*Carum carvi*)   *54*
Catnip (*Nepeta cataria*)   *57*
Chamomile (*Anthemis nobilis, Matricaria chamomilla*)   *58*
Chives (*Allium schoenoprasum*)   *60*
Clary (*Salvia sclarea*)   *61*
Comfrey (*Symphytum* species)   *63*
Companion herbs   *66*
Dill (*Anethum graveolens*)   *69*
Fennel (*Foeniculum vulgare, F. dulce*)   *71*
Garlands and Coronets   *75*
Hyssop (*Hyssopus officinalis*)   *76*
Knots   *78*
Lad's Love (*Artemisia abrotanum*)   *79*
Lavender (*Lavandula species*)   *81*
Lavender Cotton (*Santolina chamaecyparissus*)   *88*
Marigold (*Calendula officinalis*)   *89*
Marjoram (*Marjorana hortensis & Origanum* species)   *92*
Mazes   *95*
Mint (*Mentha* species)   *96*
Mugwort (*Artemisia vulgaris*)   *99*
Nasturtium (*Tropaeolum major*)   *101*
Ophelia's Garland   *102*

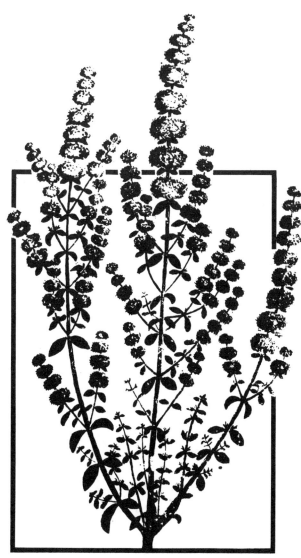

Pennyroyal

Oregano (*Origanum vulgare*) *104*
Parsley (*Petroselinum hortense*) *105*
Pennyroyal (*Mentha pulegium*) *108*
Rosemary (*Rosmarinus officinalis*) *110*
Rue (*Ruta graveolens*) *115*
Sage (*Salvia officinalis*) *117*
Savory (*Satureia hortensis, S. montana*) *120*
Strawberry (*Fragaria vesca*) *122*
Strewing herbs *123*
Tansy (*Tanacetum vulgare*) *124*
Tarragon (*Artemisia dracunculus*) *126*
Thyme (*Thymus* species) *127*
Violets (*Viola odorata*) *130*
Wormwood (*Artemisia absinthium*) *133*
Yarrow (*Achillea millefolium*) *135*
The Zodiac (planting by signs) *136*

7 BIBLIOGRAPHY OF SOURCES   140

8 GLOSSARY OF ARCHAIC WORDS   147

9 INDEX OF PLANTS   151

10 INDEX OF AUTHORS   154

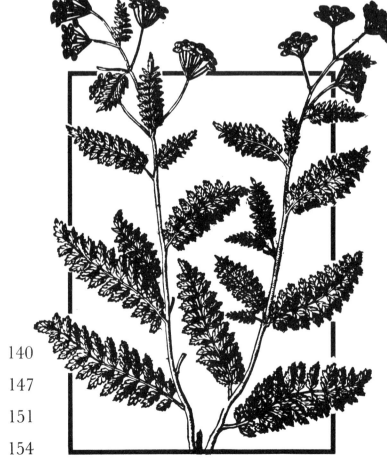

Tansy

Disclaimer

Herbs have been used for thousands of years to treat the ills of mankind. There was a time when they were our only medicine. Folk remedies based on herbs are still in use in many parts of the world, particularly in China. I believe that much valuable knowledge of the properties of herbs is being lost. This work exists as a resource book in which may be found the words of apothecaries, herbalists and cooks of other ages.

However, I am not a doctor, nor a herbalist, and can take no responsibility for the use of plants as medicine. If you are ill, seek the help of professional healers. Many herbs have a 'tonic' effect and contain high concentrations of vitamins, minerals, volatile oils, astringents and other useful medicinal properties – in fact some modern drugs are based on them. But they are not cure-alls. A few may be dangerous, or included in potions based merely on old superstitions.

K.S.

The Principal Authorities
from which this work is drawn

THEOPHRASTUS, 370–255 B.C.(?), *Enquiry into Plants*, translated by Sir Arthur Hort, 1916.

DIOSCORIDES, Pedacius Dioscorides of Anazarba, *De Materia Medica*, 60 A.D., translated by John Goodyer, 1655.

PLINY, Caius Plinius Secundus (Pliny the Elder), 77 A.D. translated as *The Naturall Historie*, by Philomen Holland, 1601.

WALAFRID STRABO, Hortulus, or *The Little Garden*, 840 A.D.

MACER'S HERBAL, 12th century, *Macer Floridus de Viribus Herbarum*, Middle English manuscript.

AGNUS CASTUS, 14th century, Middle English manuscripts.

ANTHONY ASKHAM, *A Lytel Herball*, 1550, represents printed herbals based on Macer and Agnus Castus.

WILLIAM TURNER, *A New Herball*, 1551.

THOMAS HYLL, *A Most Briefe and pleasant treatyse*, 1563; *The Proffitable Arte of Gardening*, 1568; *The Gardeners Labyrinth*, 1577.

THOMAS TUSSER, *Five hundred points of good husbandry*, 1573.

REMBERT DODOENS, *A Niewe Herball*, 1578, translated by Henry Lyte.

THOMAS COGHAN, *The Haven of Health*, 1584.

'Greek apothecary', Nicander of Colophon, 7th century illustration

JOHN GERARD, *The Herball*, 1597.

RICHARD SURFLET, translator of *The Countrie Farme*, 1600, written in French by Charles Stevens and John Liebault.

SIR JOHN HARINGTON, *The Englishmans Doctor*, 1607.

WILLIAM LAWSON, *The Countrie Housewifes Garden*, 1617; *A New Orchard and Garden*, 1618.

JOHN PARKINSON, *Paradisis in Sole Paradisus Terrestris*, 1629; *Theatrum Botanicum*, 1640.

NICHOLAS CULPEPER, *The English Physician*, 1652; *The English Physician Enlarged*, 1653.

WILLIAM COLES, *The Art of Simpling*, 1656; *Adam in Eden*, 1657.

JOHN PECHEY, *The Compleat Herbal*, 1694.

JOHN EVELYN, *Acetaria: A Discourse of Sallets*, 1699.

(A bibliography of the sources is given at the back of this book.)

ACKNOWLEDGEMENTS

The material on the cover is reproduced from the original manuscript of the *Juliana Anicia Codex* (Cod. med. gr. 1) of 512 A.D. by the very kind permission of Dr Otto Mazal, director of the collection of manuscripts and Incunabula of the Austrian National Library, Vienna.

Black and white plant figures from the same work are taken from *Codex Aniciae Juliane*, a facsimile of the original (A.W. Sitjhoff, Leiden, 1906), and produced with permission from the Library Council of Victoria.

The majority of plant illustrations come from herbals from the Richardson Collection, Special Collections, State Library of New South Wales. I wish to thank the State Library of New South Wales for their help in access to the original works and for allowing them to be used here. These sources include *A New Herball*, by William Turner (1551), *A Niewe Herball*, by Rembert Dodoens, translated by Henry Lyte (1578), *Commentorium*, by Petri Andreae Mathioli, Venice (1583), and *The Herball or Generall Historie of Plantes*, by John Gerard (1597).

Decorative headpiece from Edward
Wollaston's *The Religion of Nature*, 1725

PREFACE
To the Gentle Reader

he Earth Garden Herbal has been planned in the spirit of the old herbals
and their authors – who seemed able to bring rare flowers into bloom
from the printed page.

These 'ancient gentlemen' knew the herbs for medicine, for cooking,
for antiseptic perfumes and for adornment. They were full of enthusiasm for their
own gardens and the plants they nourished in them and knew well how to express
their delight.

I have spent many happy hours with dusty books collecting the material about
herbs and the figures of plants for this selection. Much time has been spent with
spade and hoe in the open air growing all the plants mentioned. I am both a herb
gardener and a library gardener, loving equally the living herbs and the exquisite
books about them.

It has taught me that you can learn more by reading the old gardening books and
herbals than you will by looking at a plant. This is because they contain all the
accumulated wisdom and knowledge of 2 000 years of man's association with the
useful herbs.

The idea of this book is to let the ancient writers tell you about herbs in their own
words, about what each herb looks like, its mythology, history and folklore, its
medicinal, culinary and aromatic virtues, how it grows and how more plants are
gained from it.

While telling us about the plants, the herbalists tell us a little about their own
personalities, the life of their times and their customs and pass on some recipes and
gardening hints we can still make good use of today.

The Greek writer Theophrastus, for example, suggested in 300 B.C. that 'basil is
watered even at noon, for it is said that it grows more quickly if it be watered at

April, from *The Kalendar of Shepherds,* 1518, printed in London by Julian Notary

first with warm water'. Salad lovers will agree with Richard Surflet, writing in *The Countrie Farme* in 1600 about the same herb: 'crop it oft with your fingers and not with any yron thing'.

'Put a sprig of pennyroyal behind your ear,' said Walafrid Strabo, a Benedictine monk at the monastery of St Gall in Switzerland, in 840 A.D., 'to prevent the heat from harming your head'.

If you need a breath-sweetener 'chawinge of the fresh and grene Parceleye, doth cause a swete smelling breath,' according to Thomas Hyll in 1568. In his book, *The Proffitable Arte of Gardening*, Hyll repeated an idea of Pliny the Elder (77 A.D.) that parsley leaves would be more 'crysped' if 'before the sowing of them [you] stuffe a Tennis ball with the seedes, and beat the same well agynst the ground . . .'

In this collection you will find herbs to bring up the highlights of fair hair (chamomile), to make the heart merry (borage), to protect against lightning (bay laurel) to 'pierce the senses' with their sweet smell (lavender), to keep away snakes (mugwort or tarragon), to get thin (fennel), to help grow a beard, or stop talking while asleep (lad's love for both) – many uses which will seem curious; and many which will seem practical.

The form of a herbal was established by the early Greek and Latin writers. It dealt with plants and described them and their medicinal virtues, often with illustrations. Plant lore accumulated from one herbal to another, so that from the time of Pedacius Dioscorides, a Greek speaking doctor with the Roman army in the 1st century, to Nicholas Culpeper, an English apothecary of the 17th century, this tradition was unbroken.

There is particular emphasis on the 'classic century' of herbals, which starts with William Turner's *A New Herball* (1551) and includes *The Herball* (1597) the famous

Herbalists' garden from *Le Jardin de Santé*, Paris 1539 (a French version of the *Ortus Sanitatis*)

work by John Gerard, and John Parkinson's utopian *Paradisus* (1629). The period ends with Nicholas Culpeper's *The English Physician Enlarged* (1653).

This was the era when herbals written in English reached a peak as printing and publishing developed and the arts of botany and medicine prepared to go their separate ways.

The herbs themselves have not changed in all the time that herbals have been written. If you look at thyme, sage or mint, you see a plant with the same form, height and colour that Theophrastus, Strabo and John Gerard described. Look at the fine painting of the violet and the other herbs created for Juliana Anicia, a Byzantine princess of 512 A.D. These illustrations compare well with the 16th century woodcuts, or the same herbs in your garden.

It has been a thrill for me to grow something for the first time, such as salad burnet, and see it shoot from the earth, eventually taking on the shape depicted in a herbal 400 years ago. The herbs have become familiar to me. I hope they will fascinate you as you read these pages and grow the herbs yourself. I would like to see herbs used again in all the many ways they can help mankind – to give real flavour to food; to add fragrance in a world of chemical deodorants; for natural dyes, instead of synthetics; as tonic medicines replacing drugs; and with their unique beauty to soften the ugliness of our polluted earth.

For the inspiration of this book I owe a debt of gratitude to Eleanour Sinclair Rohde and her many books about herbs and herbals. They have been invaluable guides to the heyday of herbs. I recommend them highly, particularly *The Old English Herbals* (1922) with its detailed bibliography.

Keith Vincent Smith

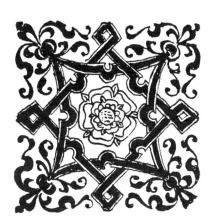

Garden scene from Thomas Hyll's *The Gardeners Labyrinth*, 1577

1
THE DELIGHT of
HERBS & GARDENS

his arte being once knowen, and the use so necessarie esteamed, hath caused wise men, by a kinde of common consent, to place Gardens neere unto Citties, Townes, Villages, as a store house and place, wherein might be kept, as well as such herbes, as are fit for ye health and presarvation of mans bodie, as also al maner of pleasant flowers and delectable herbes, as are daylye sought for, and required to the common people.

THOMAS HYLL, *The Proffitable Arte of Gardening*, 1568

For if delight may provoke mens labor, what greater delight is there than to behold the earth apparelled with plants, as with a robe of embroidered worke, set with Orient pearles, and garnished with great diversitie of rare and costly iewels?
... The delight is great, but the use greater, and ioyned often with necessity. In the first ages of the world they were the ordinarie meate of men, and have continued ever since of necessarie use both for meates to maintaine life, and for medicine to recover health. The hidden vertue of them is such, that (as *Pliny* noteth) the very bruite beasts have found it' out: and (which is another use that he

observes) from thence the Dyars tooke the beginning of their Art.
... And here beside the fruit, to speake againe in a word of delight, gardens, especially such as your honour hath, furnished with many rare Simples, do singularly delight, when in them a man doth behold a flourishing shew of Sommer beauties in the midst of Winters force, and a goodly spring of floures, when abroad a leafe is not to be seene.

JOHN GERARD, Dedication to Sir William Cecil (Lord Burghley), *The Herball*, 1597

God Almighty first planted a garden, and, indeed, it is the purest of human pleasures; it is the greatest refreshment to the spirits of man, without which building and palaces are but gross handyworks ... I do hold it, in the royal ordering of gardens, there ought to be gardens for all the months in the year, in which, severally, things of beauty may be then in season.

FRANCIS BACON, *Of Gardens*, 1625

That there is no place more pleasant, may appear from God himselfe, who after he had made Man, planted the Garden of Eden, and put him therein,

1

Fœniculum. Fenell.

that he might contemplate the many wonderful Ornaments wherewith Omnipotency had bedecked his Mother Earth.

... As for recreation, if a man be wearied with over-much study (for study is a wearinesse to the Flesh as Solomon by experience can tell you) there is no better place in the world to recreate himselfe then a Garden, there being no sence but may be delighted therein. If his sight be obfuscated and dull, as it may easily be, with continuall poring, there is no better way to relieve it, then to view the pleasant greennesse of Herbes, which is the way that Painters use, when they have almost spent their sight by their most earnest contemplation of brighter objects: neither doe they onely feed the Eyes, but comfort the wearied Braine with fragrant smells, which yeild a certaine kinde of nourishment ... The Eares also (which are called the Daughters of Musick, because they delight therein) have their recreation by the pleasant noise of the warbling notes, which the chaunting birds accent forth from amongst the murmuring Leaves.

WILLIAM COLES, *The Art of Simpling*, 1656

Hearbs are those whose root stalkes cannot be reckoned to be wood, but doe for the most part consist of Leaves, as *Fennel, Everlasting, Baulme, Mints & c.* The Seed is that part of the Plant which is ended with a vitall faculty to bring forth its like, and it contains potentially the whole Plant in it.

The Flower is the beauty of the Plant, arising from the most refined and concocted matter, and therefore is most commonly of a different colour from the leaves, as yellow, blew, red, white and sometimes mixed.

The Leafe is that part of a Plant which is sent forth from the main stalks by another lesser stalk, and consists of three similar parts, to wit, veyns, sinnews and flesh.

The Stalk is that part of a plant which riseth up from the root, and is as it were a pipe to convey the nourishment, being more fully concocted to the rest of the parts, within which many times there is the pith, which consists of flesh, and sometimes of fleshy nerves and moisture.

The Root is the lowermost part of a plant, which, answers to the mouth in a man, and being fastened in the earth, drawes convenient nourishment unto it, and supplieth all its parts.

WILLIAM COLES, *The Art of Simpling*, 1656

Fennell from Rembert Dodoens' *A Niewe Herball*, 1578

Left to right: Basil, Chamomile, Lavender, Marjoram from Rembert Dodoens' *Florvm et Coronariarvm* printed by Christopher Plantin in Antwerp in 1568

2
WHAT IS A HERB?
Definitions

hat is a herb? asked Alcuin, the English monk who was an adviser to Charlemagne.

The friend of the physician and the praise of cooks, was the reply given by the Emperor, who loved herbs so much that he ordered that some seventy types should be grown in the gardens of his villas. Alcuin already had his own garden at the Abbey in Tours, France.

Of course this is only one of many possible replies to a question which should be simple, but somehow never is. Theophrastus, the Greek scholar of botany, put it this way in his work, *Enquiry into Plants*, written about 300 B.C. –

A herb is a thing which comes up from the root with its leaves and has no main stem, and the seed is borne on the stem; for instance, corn and pot-herbs.

His definition has been echoed through the ages and today most dictionaries give this type of botanical meaning:

A herb is a plant whose stem is soft and which dies down to the ground after flowering each year.

Many of the plants which we think of as herbs, and which are included in this book, would not fit

this description, for example, rosemary and the bay laurel tree. Thyme and winter savory are familiar culinary herbs which have persistent, woody stems.

The Herb Society of America, founded by dedicated amateur herb gardeners in the 1930s, chose the following definition, which proves that Charlemagne's reply has stood the test of time – more than 1 000 years!

Any plant that may be used for pleasure, fragrance, or physic.

So a herb is usually accepted today as being a plant that is used either for culinary flavouring, for its aroma, for its medicinal uses or for its beauty.

At one time in the English language, the word herb would have served to describe any growing plant. Derived from the Latin, *herba*, it meant grass or herbage, and was applied to all crops. An earlier name was *wort*, which came in time to mean a plant prized for its medicinal use.

The distinction which we are accustomed to making between herbs and vegetables, herbs and weeds and herbs and flowers did not really exist until after the 16th century. Vegetable as a word

replaced pot-herb only in the mid-18th century. This was 'a herb grown for boiling in the pot; any of the herbs cultivated in the kitchen garden'.

On top of all this, the pronunciation of this four-letter word has also changed through the centuries. At first the 'h' was mute (as in Latin and French), until the 19th century. Now it is pronounced by most English speakers, except in the United States, where the 'h' is still dropped. American books often speak of an herb garden, an herbalist, and so on.

Classifying Herbs

The majority of herbs belong to three major botanical families – the mints (*Labiatae*), the carrot or parsley group (*Umbelliferae*) and the daisy clan (*Compositae*). As you can see, these names are taken from a typical family member and given a title in a feminine plural Latin word.

The system of classifying herbs is based on that of Carl Linne (*Carolus Linneaus*), the famous Swedish botanist, which is used throughout the world. In this way, any person may recognise a specific plant, no matter what its local name or the name used in any particular language. Botanists, however, are constantly reclassifying plants. Where the name given by Linneaus has fallen out of favour, the most commonly used and accepted title is given here, just as the herbs treated are among the most usually grown.

The full botanical name includes a generic name, usually Greek. For example, the Pot Marigold – *Calendula officinalis* – in which *officinalis* is the distinguishing plant name and denotes that it has at some time been used for medicine. The term *vulgaris* usually marks out the common or garden variety of a herb.

The division of herbs into their family groups helps the grower to recognise individual plants and to understand their growth habits and requirements. Here is a breakdown into families of the major herbs covered in this book:

Plants of the mint family from *Paradisus*, 1629. (1) Pot Marierome (2) Garden Thyme (3) Savorie (4) Hyssope (5) Penniroyall (6) Common Sage (7) Sage of vertue

Mints

Balm (*Melissa officinalis*)
Basil (*Ocimum basilicum and O. minimum*)
Catnip (*Nepeta cataria*)
Clary sage (*Salvia sclarea*)
Hyssop (*Hyssopus officinalis*)
Lavender (*Lavandula* species)
Marjoram (*Marjorana hortensis, Origanum onites*)
Mints (*Mentha* species)
Oregano (*Origanum vulgare*)
Pennyroyal (*Mentha pulegium*)
Rosemary (*Rosmarinus officinalis*)
Sage (*Salvia officinalis*)
Savory, Summer (*Satureia hortensis*)
Savory, Winter (*S. montana*)
Thyme (*Thymus vulgaris*)

The mints have typical square stems, simple leaves and two-lipped flowers in whorls among the leaves.

Umbelliferae

Angelica (*Angelica archangelica*)
Anise (*Pimpinella anisum*)
Caraway (*Carum carvi*)
Dill (*Anethum graveolens*)
Fennel (*Foeniculum vulgare and F. dulce*)
Parsley (*Petroselinum hortense*)

The parsley group plants have cylindrical stems, which are usually hollow. The flowers form in flat-topped clusters or umbels. The 'seeds' (more correctly 'fruit') are used for flavouring.

Compositae

Chamomile (*Anthemis nobilis and Matricaria chamomila*)
Lad's Love, or Southernwood (*Artemisia abrotanum*)
Lavender Cotton, or Santolina (*Santolina chamaecyparissus*)
Marigold (*Calendula officinalis*)
Mugwort (*Artemisia vulgaris*)
Tansy (*Tanacetum vulgare*)
Tarragon (*Artemisia dracunculus*)
Wormwood (*Artemisia absinthium*)
Yarrow (*Achillea millefolium*)

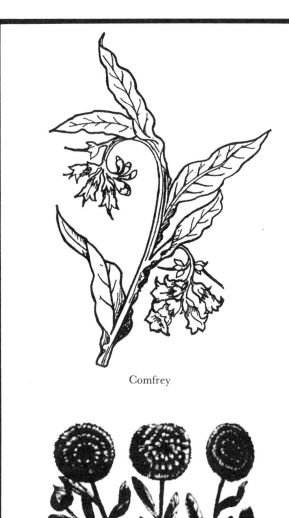

Comfrey

Marigold

Composites have either ray or disc flowers, like daisies and dandelions.

Borage Family (Boraginaceae)

Borage (*Borago officinalis*)
Comfrey (*Symphytum* species)

Rose Family (Rosacea)

Agrimony (*Agrimonia eupatoria*)
Burnet (*Sanguisorba minor*)
Strawberry (*Fragaria vesca*)

Other Groups

Bay laurel (*Laurus nobilis*), *Lauraceae*
Chives (*Allium schoenoprasum*), *Liliaceae*
Nasturtium (*Tropaeolum* species), *Cruciferae*
Rue (*Ruta graveolens*), *Rutaceae*
Violet (*Viola odorata*), *Violaceae*

Propagation

A further breakdown helps in planning the herb garden and gives you an idea of what to expect from your plants. It is into *annuals, biennials* and *perennials*.

Annuals are plants which complete their life cycle in one year. They bloom three or four months after planting, flower by five or six months, then their seeds mature and they die.

Biennials usually live two years, growing from seed the first year. Then they die down, or go dormant, returning to flower and set seed in the second year. Parsley is a well-known biennial, which needs patience to grow because of its slow germination.

Perennials usually live three years, or much longer if they are well cared for. A majority of the herbs, particularly mints, are perennial.

Angelica is strictly neither annual, nor perennial, so it falls into the class of a biennial, though it may not flower until the third year. Usually, it is kept as a perennial by cutting back the topmost stems, except in those plants where flowering is encouraged, either for beauty or to produce seeds. Caraway and clary sage are true biennials.

Most herbs may be grown from the seed, though many are more easily grown by dividing their roots, or by taking layer or stem cuttings.

These annuals grow well from the seed: anise, basil, dill, fennel, marigold, summer savory.

Perennials to grow from seed: catnip, hyssop, lovage, marjoram, rue, sage, thyme, winter savory. Sow after the soil has warmed up in spring, until about late summer.

Some perennials are best propagated by dividing the roots into pieces in spring and replanting. These include: balm, chives, comfrey, germander, hyssop, marjoram, mints, tansy, thyme, violet, wormwood and yarrow. When you split the root clump of Russian comfrey, almost every piece will form a new plant if replanted immediately.

French tarragon, which rarely sets seed, is usually grown by root cuttings or divisions.

Stem cuttings, described as 'slips' in the old herbals and gardening books, are a simple method of growing plants which start slowly from seed, like rosemary and lavender.

Take cuttings, 25 to 75 cm long, from the new growth of healthy plants like balm, geranium, germander, lemon verbena, marjoram, sage, thyme, lad's love and winter savory. Root the stems in pots filled with sand, vermiculite or compost. This is best done in spring. It's a good idea to remove the leaves from the stems in the bottom half of the cuttings before poking them in the sand or compost.

Mints are easily grown by layering and, in fact, a mint bed can easily get out of hand. Many herbs will layer themselves as they send out branches across the ground. This operation is done simply by covering the creeping branches with soil at various points. When roots are formed the stem is severed from the parent plant and repositioned.

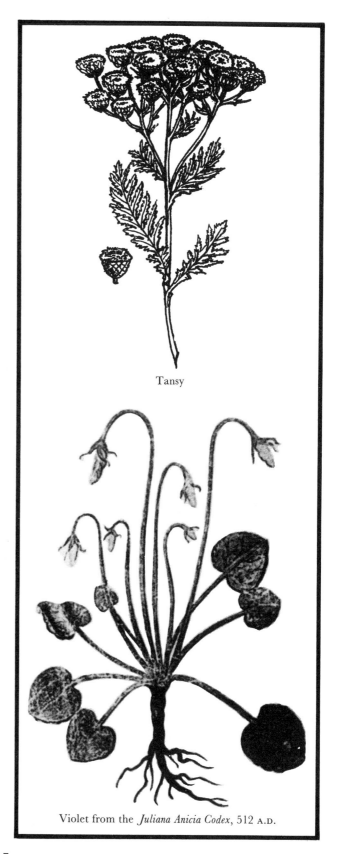

Tansy

Violet from the *Juliana Anicia Codex*, 512 A.D.

7

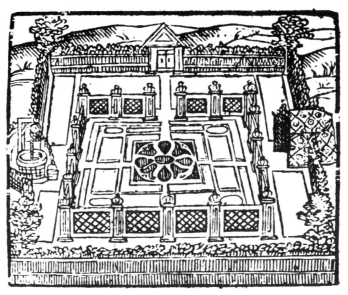

Enclosed garden from Thomas Hyll's *A Most Briefe and pleausant treatyse*, 1563

3
THE HERB GARDEN
Ordering the Garden

Hearbs are of two sorts, and therefore it is meet (they requiring divers manners of Husbandry) that we have two Gardens: A Garden for Flowers, and a Kitchen Garden: or a Summer Garden, and a Winter Garden: not that we meane so perfect a distinction that the Garden for Flowres would or can be without hearbs good for the Kitchen, or the Kitchen Garden should want flowres, nor on the contrary: but for the most part they would be severed: first, because your Garden flowres shall suffer from disgrace, if among them you intermingle onions, Parsnips, etc.

Secondly, your Garden that is durable, must be of one forme: but that, which is for your Kitchen use, must yeeld daily roots, or other hearbs, and suffer deformity. Thirdly, the·hearbs of both will not be both alike ready, at one time, either for gathering, or removing fruit therefrom.

Division of Hearbs

Garden hearbs are innumerable, yet these are common and sufficient for our Countrie House-wives.

Of the Summer Garden

These hearbs and flowres are comely and durable for squares and knots, and all to be set at Michaeltide, or some what before, that they may be setled in, and taken with the ground, before Winter, though they may be set, especially sowne in Spring.

Roses of all sorts must be set. Some use to set slips and twine them, which sometimes, but seldome thrive all.

Rosemary, Lavender, Bee-flowers, Isop, Sage, Time, Cowslips, Pyony, Daisies, Clove Gilliflowers, Pinckes, Southernwood, Lillies, of all which hereafter.

Of the Kitchen Garden

Though your Garden for flowres doth in a sort peculiarly challenge to it selfe a perfit, and exquisite forme to the eyes, yet you may not altogether neglect this, where your hearbs for the pot doe grow. And therefore, some here make comely borders with the Hearbs aforesaid.

The rather because aboundance of Roses and Lavender yeeld much profit, and comfort to the sences: Rose water and Lavender, the one cordiall (as also the Violets, Burrage and Buglos) the other reviving the spirits by the sence of smelling: both most durable for smell, both in flowres and water: you need not here raise your beds, as in the other Garden, because Summer towards, will not let too much wet annoy you – and these hearbs require more moisture.

Yet must you have beds divided, that you may go betwixt to weede, and some what forme would be expected: To which it availeth that you place your hearbs of biggest growth, by walles, or in borders, as Fennell, etc, and the lowest in the middest, as Saffron, Strawberries, Onions, etc.

Hearbs of Greatest Growth

Fennell Angelica, Tansie Hollyhock, Lovage, Elly Campane (elecampane), French Mallowes, Lyllies, French Poppie, Endive, Succory, and Clarie.

Hearbs of Middle Growth

Burrage, Buglas, Parslie, Sweet Sicillye, Flowerdeluce, Stocke Gillyflowers, Wall-flowres, Anniseeds, Coriander, Feather-few, Marigolds, Oculus Christi, Landibeefe, Alexanders, Cardus Benedictus.

Hearbs of Smallest Growth

Pansye, or Harts ease, Coast Margeram, Savery, Strawberries, Saffron, Lycoras, Daffadowndillies, Leekes, Chives, Chibals, Skerits, Onions, Batchelors buttons (double buttercup), Daisies, Pennyryall.

WILLIAM LAWSON, *The Countrie Housewifes Garden*, 1617

Your Herb Garden

The forms and layouts of herb gardens are as varied and numerous as the number of herb gardeners and their way of enjoying their plants. One, in the words of Gervase Markham in his edition of *The Country Farme* (1616), 'whereof is lead by the hops and skips, turnings and windings of his braine', the other 'by the pleasing of his eye according to his best fantasie'.

In the *Herbal Collection* of forty plants in this book, I have given the details of growing and propagating each herb and the height which each will reach, with suggestions sometimes for layout or spacing. Where and how you choose to plant your herbs is up to you. You are limited by the amount of space available and how much sunlight falls there. Most of the herbs originate in the sunny hillsides of the Aegean and Mediterranean, but others like a cool, shady place. Angelica, mints and comfrey will do better in a damp, shaded spot.

The layout may be formal or informal – there is plenty of scope offered by those definitions. Each has its own charm, and the beauty and variety of colour stands out whether it is randomly or deliberately placed. One most practical way to grow herbs is in the vegetable garden, where their pest-repelling qualities are best used in a companion planting scheme. (See *Companion Herbs* page 66). The herbs will also bring the bees to fertilize your plants and improve your harvest.

The Medieval herb garden enclosed all around with walls is the one we picture in our mind when we think of a monastery garden. This was a direct descendant of the Saxon *wortyards*, defended by walls of woven wattles.

The feeling of a cloistered garden may be recaptured in a small way by using beds of raised earth or boxed beds with only one type of plant to each square or rectangular plot. In those days the beds were bordered with oak boards, bricks, tiles, sheets of lead or even sheep shank bones.

Old railway sleepers or wooden planks make the best edges, held in place with wooden pegs or iron spikes at regular intervals. Bricks, stones and tiles may also be used.

A good-sized box bed would be about two metres long and one metre wide, with a depth of twenty-five centimetres or more to allow for root growth. These boxed beds may be set into a lawn. The confined space makes weeding and watering simple.

A row of tall-growing herbs, such as angelica or fennel, or massed sunflowers, would make an attractive screen around the beds.

The illustration of the enclosed garden shown was the frontispiece for Thomas Hyll's *A Most brief and pleausant treatise* (1563). It shows an outer wall of low wooden palings and a hedge and an inner wall of decorative trellis work around a central bed. At the left, between the two walls, is a well with a bucket and rope and opposite a covered *herber* or *arbour*.

In the centre is a knot garden, with rows of compact herbs woven in and out in an elaborate pattern, which suited the more elaborate taste of Tudor and Stuart times. The original intention of knot gardens was that they could be viewed from towers and battlements above. Later in the book, there are special sections on *aleis* & *herbers*, knots and mazes from the old gardening books.

During the late 16th century, the formal garden usually had a feature in the middle, such as a

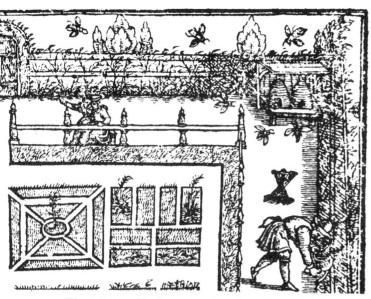

The delights of herbs and gardens from Thomas Hyll's *The Gardeners Labyrinth*, 1577

fountain, or a sundial surrounded by mints to refresh the visitor. Garden plots were divided by pathways leading out from this. In the smaller cottage gardens of the 18th century onwards the focus was often a straw bee skep, or a clump of gnarled rosemary or lavender.

In these old gardens herbs were deliberately planted to be walked upon or brushed past to release their scent into the air. A modern herb border alongside a path should have tall-growing plants at the rear and a front row of lavender, cotton lavender (santolina), rosemary, marjoram, yarrow, chamomile or chives. Occasionally a bigger plant, such as a clump of sunflowers, will break up the aspect. This kind of border may be sited in a confined area such as the courtyard of a terrace house.

If you really don't have much space you can still grow herbs in pots and containers which may be kept on steps, patios or verandahs. Indoors they should be allowed to get as much sunlight as possible and they must be watered regularly. Bush basil is a traditional herb for a pot. Burnet or prostrate rosemary will trail down from a hanging basket.

You could replace your lawn with a ground carpet of the well-trodden chamomile such as Queen Elizabeth has at Buckingham Palace, or peppermint-smelling pennyroyal or tiny Corsican mint. The ancient idea of an earth bank planted with herbs is worth reviving. What a place to rest on a drowsy day to listen to the hum of bees and the song of the birds!

A small culinary herb garden is ideal in the nearest ground to the kitchen door. This gives the cook easy access to basil, chives, marjoram, mint and parsley as it is required.

Gardening is something which can be inspired by books, but in the end you must make your own garden for your own enjoyment and delight.

Weadyng and Watering

When the seedes were thus orderly sowen, and somewhat come up, then they (the auncient Romaines) thoroughly learned, that the often weadying, and watering, of the younge plants, did cause them the faster to come up. And in such places, wher the plantes grew thick together, they (by their painful industrie) learned to set them thinner . . .

And yet every grounde at times convenient, may by the dunging, be made more fruitful and plentifuller, or bigger yealding.

THOMAS HYLL, *The Proffitable Arte of Gardening*, 1568

There is a constant flow or routine in the herb garden which you will soon learn. This involves regular weeding, watering, sowing and setting, dividing and replanting, harvesting and caring for your plants.

It is a fact that herbs grow well in almost any type of garden soil and need very little fertilising. Even compost may be too rich for them at times – it has been found to cause rust in mints at times.

As for artificial fertilizers and poisonous chemical sprays, these must be avoided at all costs. They may burn the roots of some herbs and kill others outright. In any case, they will wipe out the beneficial insects and the earthworms which enrich your soil.

The *Earth Garden* way is the natural, organic method of gardening and follows the basic laws of common sense. The controls over insects pests are companion planting, regular feeding of plants with compost, well rotted animal manure, mulches and blood and bone, or dolomite and lime where it is required in the soil. Herbal sprays may be used if necessary. Any good book on organic gardening will give you the guidelines on how to go about raising your own healthy herbs.

From Pliny onwards, gardeners have observed that many plants have an affinity for one another and help each other's growth when planted together.

Many herbs will discourage insect pests when grown scattered around the garden. These are particularly valuable in the vegetable garden. For example, garlic, chives, spearmint and nasturtium will keep away aphis – the nasturtium acting as a 'trap plant' or 'decoy' to distract the aphis from nearby plants.

Pennyroyal and tansy will discourage ants, sage, hyssop and thyme deter cabbage moth while lavender, lavender cotton, lad's love and wormwood will keep moths away from stored clothes. These uses are detailed under the separate listings of each herb, where you will also find suggestions for growing and propagation.

Herbal sprays

A Garlic spray for white butterfly, potato and tomato blight, apple scab, powdery mildew and fruit tree predators and diseases has been developed by the Henry Doubleday Research Association, a group of amateur gardeners who seek to grow their plants without harm to birds, bees or beasts.

Crush 90 g garlic. Pour over 10 ml paraffin oil. Cover and soak for forty-eight hours. Then make a pure soap solution, perhaps 10 g soap powder in a 500 ml of hot water. Pour over the garlic mixture. Leave for one day, then warm slightly and strain. Bottle. Use 1-to-100 parts with water, or less, depending on the problem.

Other herbal sprays are made simply by preparing an infusion of a particular herb and allowing to cool. Chamomile spray is used against damping off of young seedlings, hyssop against plant diseases, wormwood and tansy to repel pests.

Harvesting and Drying Herbs

'In a cleare and warme daye'

Now it behoves anyone who desires to be a skilful herbalist, to be present when the plants first shoot out of the earth, when they are fully grown, and when they begin to fade. For he who is only present at the budding of the herb, cannot know it when full-grown, nor can he who hath examined a full-grown herb, recognise it when it has only just appeared above ground.

... But herbs which are full of branches, like Stoechas ... should be gathered while they are great with seed; flowers ought to be gathered before they fall; fruits when they are ripe, and seeds when they begin to be dry, and before they fall out.
DIOSCORIDES, 60 A.D.

And nowe those herbes (for the use of Medicine) oughte to be gathered, and cut up, when as they be in a maner come, unto their full growthe, and that before the coloure of the flowers beginne to chaunge, and the seedes somewhat appeare. And this also oughte to be done, in a cleare and warm daye, and that they have been moystened with some showers fallinge two or three days before, so that they ought not to be gathered when any raine moisture, or wet dewe is on them, nor being then drie parched with the heate of the Sunne, nor in a raynie, and cloudie daie: for any of these, doe much hynder the keaping any tyme in their vertue. Also they ought to be gathered, when they be full of iuyce and freshe, and that not the smaller or bigger are to be chosen, but the meaner, and suche besides whiche fall not to whythering. And onely the tender toppes, the leaves, the flowers, are to be gathered and dried in the shadowe, in a place open towarde the Southe, not being moyste, and defended from the duste, and smoke and for the better defending and preserving of theim, to be putte up in bagges close bounde at the mouthe, and in boxes for that use.
THOMAS HYLL, *The Proffitable Arte of Gardening*, 1568

Good huswifes in Sommer will save their owne
  seedes
Against the next yere, as occassion nedes.
One seede for another, to make an exchange,
With fellowlie neighborhood, seemeth not strange.
THOMAS TUSSER, *Five hundred points*, 1573

Dry your flowers in the shadow till they be almost dry, and then sunne them well that they mould not, and so also dry your herbes.
RAMS LITTLE DODOEN, 1606

Of Leavs, chuse only such as are green and ful of Juyce, pick them carefully and cast away such as are any way declining, for they wil putrifie the rest. So shal one handful be worth ten of those you buy in *Cheap side*.

Note in what place they most delight to grow in, and gather them there; for Bettony that grows in the shadow is far better than that which grows in the Sun, because it delights in the shadow: So also such Herbs as delight to grow neer the Water, shall be gathered near it, thought haply you may find some of them upon dry ground ...

The Leavs of such Herbs as run up to Seed are not so good when they are in Flower, as before (some few excepted, the Leavs of which are seldom or never used) in such cases, if through ignorance they were not known, or through negligence forgotten, you had better take the top and the Flowers than the leaf.

Having wel dryed them, put them in brown Papers, sewing the Paper up like a Sack, and press them not too hard together, and keep them in a dry place near the fire.

NICHOLAS CULPEPER, *The English Physician Enlarged*, 1653

Nature in the whole growth of plants tends to the production of their flowers and seed, but when they are ripe the rest begins to decay, having done its Duty, so that the time when the entire Plant is in its most full Perfection, is when it is in the Bud when the Heads are formed for flowering, but not a single Flower has yet disclosed itself. The tops of the plant are always preferable to the whole Plant for immediate use. The time of the Day must be when the morning Dew is dried away. This is a very material circumstance, for if they be cut wet with the Dew, Herbs will not dry well, and if they be cut at Noon Day, when the sun has made the Leaves flag, they will not have their full Power.

Care must also be taken to cut them on a dry day, for the wet of Rain will do as much harm as that of Dew. When the herbs are thus gathered they are to be looked over, the decayed Leaves picked off, and the dead ends of the stalks cut away. They are then to be tied up in small bunches, the less the better, and hung upon Lines drawn across the room where the windows and doors are to be kept open in good weather; the Bunches are to be kept half a foot asunder, and they are to hang till perfectly dry. They are then to be taken softly down, without shaking off the Buds of the flowers, and laid evenly in a Drawer, pressing them down and covering them with paper.

SIR JOHN HILL, *The British Herbal*, 1756

Herb Powder for Flavouring

1 oz. dried lemon thyme, 1 oz. dried winter savory, 1 oz. dried sweet marjoram and basil, 2 oz. dried parsley, 1 oz. dried lemon-peel.

Mode. – Prepare and dry the herbs; pick the leaves from the stalks, pound them, and sift them through a hair-sieve; mix in the above proportions and keep in glass bottles, carefully excluding the air. This we think a far better method of keeping herbs, as the flavour and fragrance do not evaporate so much as when they are merely put in paper bags. Preparing them in this way, you will have them ready for use at a moment's notice.

MRS ISABELLA BEETON, *Household Management*, 1861

You may cut fresh herbs to use in salads and cooking at any time. In fact, constant picking and pinching out of the top stems of herbs will strengthen the plants and make them bush out. Allow some stems to flower and mature to collect seed for next year's garden.

In the autumn comes the task of gathering, drying and storing your herbs to preserve their flavour and aroma and to use in winter for teas, flavouring and sachets.

The best time for harvesting is just as the old herbalists recommend – as the plants are about to flower, for then the essential oils they contain are at their most concentrated, strong in flavour and perfume.

Select only healthy leaves and pick them after the morning dew has dried but before the sun has heated the foliage. If you gather when the moon is waning (as you sow when the moon is waxing), the herbs will dry more quickly because they contain less sap (see *The Zodiac* pages 136–9).

Herbs to be harvested when their blooms are at the fullest include hyssop, lavender, rosemary and thyme.

Though some, like Nicholas Culpeper, suggest herbs be dried in full sunlight, the best results are usually achieved by hanging the herbs in small bunches in a dry, airy, shaded place, such as an attic.

Seed-yielding herbs from *Paradisus*, 1629.
(1) Parsley (2) Smallage (3) Fennell (4) Dill
(5) Sweete Chervill (6) Common Chervill

When they are thoroughly dry, in two or three weeks, strip leaves from the stalks and crumble them finely before packing into airtight jars and tins which are stored in the dark. Avoid oven drying, except in very cold or damp areas, as this tends to evaporate essential oils from the herbs.

With annuals, the whole plant may be plucked from the ground and dried. However picturesque are rows of bunched herbs hanging from the rafters, Thomas Hyll's warning that they will be 'clagged with duste, Copwebs and much other filth', is worth heeding.

Herbs stored in paper bags and boxes won't keep as long and their quality will slowly deteriorate.

Label the jars and add the date of storage. When cooking with dried herbs, you need to use only a small quantity, say one half or one third the amount of fresh herbs in a recipe.

Flowerheads like lavender and chamomile can be separated from the stems and spread in a single layer on a wire rack for a few days until they are brittle.

Harvest seeds of anise, dill, fennel and other seed herbs when they are ripe, but before they are ready to drop. Cut the plants and tie them in bunches. Hang these over sheets of paper to catch the falling seeds. Various methods of harvesting are given under each herb.

Herb Vinegars

Herb vinegars are made by steeping herbs in white wine vinegar, tightly capped, for a week or so. Discard the herb and repeat the process until the vinegar is flavoured strongly enough. Basil, burnet, dill and tarragon are ideal for herb vinegars. Use in salad dressings and whenever a subtle herb flavour is needed.

Herbal Oils

To Make Oyle of Roses or Violets

Take the flowers of Roses or Violets, and break them small, and put them into Sallet oyle, and let them stand in the same ten or twelve dayes and then presse it.
GERVASE MARKHAM, *The English Housewife*, 1615

Oyle of Camomile

To make oyle of camomile, take a quart of sallet oyle and put it into a glasse, then take a handful of camomile and bruise it, and put it into the oyle, and let them stand in the same twelve daies, onely you must shift it every three dayes, that is to straine it from the old camomile, and put in as much of new, and that oile is very soveraine for any griefe proceeding from cold causes.
GERVASE MARKHAM, *A Way to Get Wealth*, 1631

You can make herb oils for perfume, as ointment or for salads and cooking. Use vegetable oils such as safflower, sunflower, peanut or olive oil.

The Greeks and Romans used flowers steeped in oil as perfume.

For a scented oil, collect fragrant flowers, such as rose petals and leaves of sweet-smelling herbs like lavender or rosemary. Crush them to a pulp and add to the oil in a tightly closed glass jar. This is placed in sunlight, or in sand where the temperature is high.

The best proportion is 5 g of flowers or sprigs of herbs to 500 ml of oil. Strain after a fortnight, discard the plants and re-bottle. The herbs scent and colour the oil.

The oil may be used as a skin cleanser, perfume or deodorant. If using olive oil, add a little vinegar and you have an aromatic suntan lotion.

A herb cooking oil is made the same way, using combinations of herbs to make your own personal salad or cooking medium. A quicker way to make herb cooking oil is to add 5 g of herbs, say rosemary and oregano, and two cloves of garlic, to oil in a frypan over a low heat. Cook for ten minutes. Strain through cheesecloth and store for use in a glass jar.

Fragrant rubbing lotions for tired limbs are made by infusing herbs in rubbing alcohol. Place sprigs of thyme, lavender, rosemary, mint or lemon balm into a wide-mouthed jar. Pour over the alcohol and let it stand two weeks, shaking occasionally. Strain and rebottle.

Herbal Ointments & Salves

In William Turner's time, and until the 19th century, ointment was made out of hog's grease mixed up with herbs and flowers ground to a powder in a mortar. Wax and turpentine were often added.

The best way to make a salve these days is to pound up the leaves or roots of the herb needed (such as comfrey, for healing cuts) and mix in with vaseline.

Another method: mix 185 g coconut fat, 125 g of the dried herb and 30 g beeswax in a saucepan (not aluminium) and put over a low heat for $1\frac{1}{2}$ hours. Pour off into containers (old cosmetic or ointment jars).

Scented Candles

Melt refined paraffin, then add either fragrant oils or distilled oils bought at the chemist, or powdered aromatic herbs. Stir thoroughly. Dip the candles quickly in the melted perfumed wax.

You may need to dip candles or tapers several times until you think there is enough covering them. Colour may also be added.

Pot-pourri

The following mixture is said to retain its fragrance for fifty years:

Gather early in the day and when perfectly dry, a peck of Roses, pick off the petals and strew over them three-quarters of a pound of common salt. Let them remain two or three days, and if fresh flowers are added, some more salt must be sprinkled over them. Mix with the Roses half a pound of finely pounded bay salt, the same quantity of allspice, cloves and brown sugar, a quarter of a pound of gum benzoin, and two ounces of powdered orris root. Add one gill of brandy and any sort of fragrant flowers, such as Orange and Lemon flowers, Lavender and Lemon-scented Verbena, and any other sweet-scented flowers. They should be perfectly dry when added. The mixture must be occasionally stirred and kept in close-covered jars, the covers to be raised only when the perfume is desired in the room. If after a time the mixture seems to dry, moisten with brandy only, as essences too soon lose their quality and injure their perfume.
DONALD McDONALD, *Fragrant Flowers and Leaves*, 1895

Rose

4
MAN and HERBS

erbs have nurtured man, cured his ills, dyed his garments and provided perfume and beauty aids since at least the Stone Age. Naturally, early man's first interest in plants was to secure food. Many of his experiments must have ended with painful, or even fatal, results until a body of knowledge was built up. But he learned. Herbs nourished him and they grew close together.

Our first gods were flowers and trees and deities of fertility. Primitive man considered that healing was a gift of the gods, who alone knew the characters of plants. Superstition grew up, with folk stories attached to many herbs. Magic was one aspect of the accumulation of herbal lore. It led to the evolution of both priest and physician.

The story of the close association of man and herbs from the time of writing and keeping records unfolds in these pages, but we know very little about this in prehistory, though obviously a great deal of verbal tradition and superstition from those times has been passed down in some form.

We can trace the link between humans and the conscious use of herbs and flowers to Neanderthal man following the analysis of pollen clusters by scientists which shows that a funeral bouquet was placed in the grave of a male buried 60 000 years ago at Shanidar Cave in Iraq.

Seven of eight flower species recovered resembled plants still used today for their herbal and medicinal properties. These included yarrow, cornflower, grape hyacinth, horsetail, hollyhock and St Barnaby's thistle.

That Stone Age man showed a similar spirit is evidenced by numerous cave paintings, particularly one of a man wearing a vivid red vest at L'Angles-sur-l'Anglin in France. This may have been dyed with dandelion, sorrel or Galium (also called Lady's Bedstraw).

In Egypt official schools of herbalists existed as long ago as 3 000 B.C. Imhotep, a priest physician, became the god of medicine.

'In Egypt the men are more skilled in medicine than any of human kind,' wrote Homer in the Fourth Book of the *Odyssey*. The Egyptians used castor oil, senna, dill, lettuce, gentian, mint and poppy among eighty-five herbs mentioned in medical treatments in a papyrus dating to 2000 B.C. This medical document was discovered by Dr George Ebers in 1875.

Egyptians placed flower wreaths, often of mignonette, in mummy tombs and planted gardens near the tombs. The head gardener of Pepi I was honoured by a statue when the king's pyramid was built.

On the other side of the fertile crescent, Merodach Baladin, king of Babylon about 720 B.C., grew seventy different herbs in his garden. They were mostly fragrant and included thyme, coriander and saffron.

Most of the herbs in common use today are natives of the lands bordering the Aegean and Mediterranean. Some are from Persia, a few from India, many more are common field weeds of Europe or have been introduced from North America.

The ancient Greeks had many delightful stories in their mythology about the origin of herbs and their uses. They revered Asclepius as the first physician and the founder of medicine. He was the son of Apollo and was said to have learned the arts of healing from Chiron, the Centaur, in his cave. Another version has it that Asclepius was abandoned as an infant on Mt Titthion, famous for the medicinal virtues of its plants.

Chiron was the wise tutor of a galaxy of Greek heroes, including Jason the Argonaut and Pelenus, father of Achilles. He is represented as one of the Zodiacal centaurs, holding the serpent. There is a mosaic of Chiron with Plato and Asclepius at Pompeii and this is how he is depicted in herbals ranging from the *Juliana Anicia Codex* of the 6th century, through to the Anglo-Saxon and Medieval works.

The Greeks thought some herbs, such as rue and yarrow, were given by the gods to mankind to help cure sickness or wounds. It was 'moly' or wild rue (though some identify moly as garlic) which protected Ulysses from the charm used by Circe to turn his men into swine. Achilles healed his comrades wounded with iron in the Trojan wars with yarrow (*Achillea millefolium*).

Other herbs were sacred because they were created by the metamorphosis of a god or legendary figure into a herb – the nymph Minthe into mint and Daphne into the bay laurel. There are many examples of this.

With the Greeks we have arrived at the dawn of botany and the beginnings of the herbals, when the first records were kept of the virtues and growing habits of plants.

Hippocrates, the 'father of medicine' was an early pioneer in this field, basing his treatments on results and ignoring the superstitious attributes attached to the herbs.

Theophrastus studied under Aristotle and inherited his master's garden and library. Though he was a scientific botanist, he passed on many strange beliefs in his *Enquiry into Plants* (300 B.C.) and these were repeated and passed on by Pliny the Elder 400 years later.

Woodcut of plants from *Das puch der natur*, Augsburg, 1475

5
THE HERBALS
Manuscripts

liny the Elder, writing in 77 A.D., said that 'Cratevas, Dionysius and Metrodorus used to depict various plants in colour and add to them a description of their properties'.

This early clue to the form of the first herbals is interesting because it infers that the illustration of the herbs was the first consideration and that the text was attached to it.

This has its own logic. Unfortunately, none of these ancient works exist today. We know that Nicander of Colophon's works of the 2nd century B.C. were illustrated, though he dealt with many other subjects than herbs. Fragments of an illustrated herbal in Greek from the 2nd century A.D. have been found at Tebtunis in Egypt. The text differs from Dioscorides.

Before this there are few references to herbs, other than the stone tablets of Sumeria and the fossils which prove that plants existed millions of years ago. The Egyptians kept the first medical records on papyrus. *The Ebers papyrus*, has 876 remedies which include 500 substances, many of them herbs and plants, including senna leaves, dill, castor oil seeds and goat fat.

Herbs are mentioned only briefly in Homer's *Odyssey*. The most complete and valuable work on herbs to survive from early Greece is that of Theophrastus, already mentioned.

The 'curious Pliny', or the 'worthy Pliny', as he was called in the 16th century herbals, was a great scholar and collector of information, who influenced herbals for centuries with his *Naturall Historie*, written about 77 A.D. The work was a kind of universal encyclopaedia of knowledge, staggering in its range even today.

Born in 23 A.D., Pliny died in 79 A.D. when he was suffocated by fumes while investigating the eruption of Mt Vesuvius. Philemon Holland, a doctor, of Coventry in England, made his translation of the *Naturall Historie* in 1601. Holland made several other translations of the classics during his long life of eighty-five years. He died in 1637.

The oldest existing manuscript of a herbal is a precious example of Byzantine art which was prepared in 512 A.D. for a pious princess, Juliana Anicia, daughter of Flavius Anicus Olybrius, a consul who was briefly Emperor of the West. It combines the famous first century work by Pedacius Dioscorides, usually called the *Materia Medica*, with 400 brush water colour illustrations of plants and some birds, by an unknown Byzantine artist.

It is speculated that some of the plant figures are copied from illustrations made by Cratevas, physician to the Emperor Mithridates VI Eupator (136–63 B.C.). Cratevas is quoted by Galen, Pliny and Dioscorides, but no record of his writings or art exist. One of the less distinct illustrations in the manuscript gives credence to this. It purports to show Dioscorides at work on his book while a figure representing *Epinoia* (Intelligence) holds up a mandrake for Cratevas to draw.

The Dioscorides manuscript, known as the *Codex Vindobonesis* is filed as *Cod. med. gr. I* in the Austrian National Library in Vienna. It is a *Codex*, that is a bound book of fine parchment sheets, and not a *Rotulus* or roll, the more usual form of ancient manuscript. The text is written in fine, even Greek capital letters. The manuscript was seen by a Sicilian traveller named Aurispa at the monastery of St John the Baptist in Constantinople in 1473, some twenty years after the city fell to the Turks.

It was over 1 000 years old when it next turned up in 1562, being offered for 100 ducats to Ogier Ghiselin de Busbecq, a Flemish scholar who was the ambassador of the Emperor Ferdinand I at the court of Sultan Suleiman the Magnificent.

'One manuscript I left behind at Constantinople,' wrote de Busbecq in a letter, 'one much worn with age, containing the whole text of Dioscorides written in capital letters, with painted representations of plants, among which are a few by Cratevas, unless I am mistaken, as well as a small treatise on birds.'

Seven years later the work was in the Imperial Library in Vienna. At the end of World War I, the *Codex* was seized by the Italians and taken to Venice, but it was later returned.

Another version of Dioscorides, also richly illustrated, but with more stylised plant figures, was taken at the same time and is now in the Biblioteca Nazionale in Naples. It is usually dated to the 7th century.

A less beautiful version from the 9th century is in the Bibliotheque Nationale in Paris and another, dated to 800 A.D. was destroyed at Monte Cassino monastery during World War II.

A work which has much in common with the Juliana Anicia manuscript is a 10th century Dioscorides now in the Pierpont Morgan Library in New York. This has 360 pages, of which 199 are included in the herbal, while other sections include plants, flowers, animals, fish and insects. It is speculated that the work, *Morgan Cod. 652*, may be in part a copy of the Vienna manuscript, or be copied from the same source. The plant figures are beautiful, far superior to the intervening versions, and the bird illustrations are more complete.

Dioscorides, of Anazarba in Ciclilia, was a Greek who served as a physician with the Roman Army during the reign of the Emperor Nero. He wrote a treatise on natural history in five parts about 60 A.D. covering 500 plants briefly. Many of these are easily recognised and still in use today, while a number of others cannot be identified. It is laid out in sections covering aromatics, potherbs, oils, resins, pitch, medical, culinary and sharp herbs, roots, vinegar and wine.

For more than 1 500 years Dioscorides was the model and major authority for all the herbals which followed. Later famous works were based on it in the 15th century and others on these, influencing botanical and medical knowledge until the 17th century.

For example, the commentary on Dioscorides by Pierandrea Mattioli, issued in 1544, sold 30 000 copies in the first Italian edition (a large amount at the time) and was subsequently printed in Latin, German, Spanish and French. Mattioli was physician to Ferdinand I and Emperor Maximilian II and was able to base his work on two copies of the Dioscorides Codices given to him by his friend de Busbecq.

Some of the figures of plants reproduced here are taken from a 1583 edition of Mattioli's *Commentorium* printed in Venice, a copy of which is in the Richardson Collection of the State Library of New South Wales in Sydney.

The *Materia Medica* was translated into Latin in the 6th century. The first printed edition, in Greek, was done by Aldo Manuzio in Venice in 1499 with help from Greek speaking scholars.

A great number of manuscript versions still exist, including Arabic translations made as early as the 9th century. The classic manuscripts of Hippocrates, Aristotle, Plato, Galen and Dioscorides probably survived through the European 'dark ages' because they were captured as booty by Islamic victors of clashes with the Byzantines.

At Baghdad manuscripts were collected and

transcribed between 750–800 A.D. in a 'House of Wisdom' and disseminated. The Arabic library at Cordoba in the 10th century, for example, had 600 000 volumes. Monks later translated these 'Arabic' works into Latin, bringing them back into the mainstream of European ideas.

The first human figure included with plant illustrations in a Dioscorides manuscript is in an Arabic volume dated to February, 1083. This is in *Cod. Or. 289*, in the Leiden University Library, The Netherlands. It is said to have been copied from a version of 900 A.D.

Curiously, Dioscorides' herbal was already 1 870 years old before it was published in an English edition in 1933. The translation used was made by John Goodyer, of Petersfield, in a hand-written manuscript of the parallel Greek and English text, between 1652 and 1655.

It was John Goodyer who introduced the Jerusalem artichoke to Hampshire and helped Thomas Johnson revise John Gerard's *Herball* in 1633.

The translation was kept, unpublished, at Magdalen College, Oxford, until it was edited and published by John Gunther, who included line drawing copies of the Juliana Ancia *Codex* in black and white as illustration.

There are manuscript and printed versions of Dioscorides in the libraries at Mt Athos in Greece, including a 12th century copy at the Lavra monastery which shows 'flower girls' collecting violets. There is a story told about a director of the Kew Gardens in London who visited Mt Athos during the 1930s. There he saw a monk, carrying a black bag over his shoulder, out collecting herbs. Inside the bag were four manuscript volumes, copied from Dioscorides, to help identify the plants!

Christian monasteries kept alive the early works on herbs, as well as those on arithmetic, science and philosophy. Monks copied and recopied manuscripts in many languages, including Arabic, and exchanged works with other monasteries and other countries.

Herb and flower gardens were attached to each abbey and monastery. In a surviving plan of the Benedictine monastery at St Gall, near Lake Constance in Switzerland, the layout is based on the old Roman villas. Very little space was wasted; as the orchards were also used as graveyards! Many of the holy men were notable writers, in prose and poem, usually in Latin, about the virtues of herbs. One of these was Bishop Venantinus Fortunatus of

'Flower girls' collecting violets, from a 12th century Discorides manuscript held at the Lavra Monastery, Mt Athos, Greece

Poitiers who wrote *De Horto Ultragothonis Reginae* in 565 A.D. This was dedicated to Radegonde (or Radegunda), wife of Clothair, king of the Franks, who had fled from the court and become the Abbess of a nunnery in which she laid out a garden.

Fortunatus wrote to her of violets: 'He who offers violets must in love be held to offer roses. Of the fragrant herbs I send none can compare in nobleness with the purple violet. They shine in royal purple: perfume and beauty unite in their petals. May you show forth in your life what they represent.'

The Abbess, later Saint Radegonde, sent flowers and food to Fortunatus in return and entertained him at a dinner at which the tables were strewn with roses and garlands hung from refectory walls.

Charlemagne's List

Charlemagne, king of the Franks and Emperor of the Holy Roman Empire, issued instructions in 812 for some seventy herbs to be planted in the gardens of his villas.

The original manuscript reproduced here of a copy of his *Capitulare* de Villis Imperialibus is dated to 872 A.D.

The herbs are listed in the first two columns and can be identified as:

(Left-hand Col.)   (Middle Col.)

LXX. We desire that they have in the garden all the herbs, namely, the lily

rosas – roses
fenigrecum – fenugreek
costum – costmary
salviam – sage
rutam – rue
abrotanum – lad's love
cucumeres – cucumbers
pepones – peppers
curcubitas – melons
fasiolum – beans
ciminum – cummin
ros marinu (m) – rosemary
careium – caraway
cicerum italicu (m) – chickpeas
squillam – squill
gladiolum – iris
dragantea – arum
anesum – anise
coloquentidas – coloquinth
solsequiam – chicory
ameum – animi
silum – laserwort
lactucas – lettuce
git – black cummin
eruca alba – rocket
nasturtium – nasturtium
parduna – burdock
puledium – pennyroyal
olisatum – alexander
petresilinum – parsley
apium – celery
levisticum – lovage
savinam – sabine tree
anetum – dill
fenicolum – fennel
intubas – endive
diptamnu (m) – dittany
sinape – black mustard
satureiam – savory
sisimbrium – curly mint
mentam – water mint

mentastrum – horse mint
tanazitam – tansy
neptam – catnip
febrefugiam – feverfew
papaver – poppy
betas – beet
vulgigina – asqrabacca
mismalvas – marshmallows
malvas – high mallows
carvitas – carrots
pastenacas – parsnips
adripias – orach
blidas – amaranth
ravacaulos – kohlrabi
caulos – cabbage
uniones – onions
britlas – chives
porros – leeks
radices – radish
ascalonicas – shallots
cepas – garlic
alia – onions
warentia (m) – madder
cardones – artichokes
fabas maiores – big beans
pisos mauriscos – field peas
coriandrum – coriander
cerfolium – chervil
lacteridas – capper spurge
sclareiam – clary

Other plants which may be identified are apple, pear, laurel, pine and fig.

Charlemagne's list of herbs from *Capitulare de Villis Imperialibus*, copy dated 872 A.D.

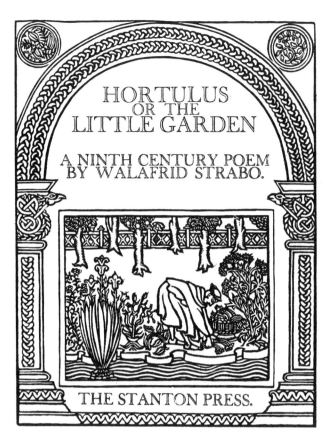

Title page of Hortulus or *The Little Garden*, translated by Richard Lambert and published by The Stanton Press, Wembley Hill, England in 1924

Strabo's Little Garden

Walafrid Strabo, which means 'Walafrid the Squint-Eye', wrote a beautiful Latin poem in 440 hexameters called *Hortulus*, or *The Little Garden*, about 840. The manuscript, written about 875 in another hand, lay at the monastery of St Gall in Switzerland where Walafrid was a monk, for 600 years before it was discovered and first printed in 1510 at Venice.

Walafrid was born in 809 and became tutor to Charles, son of Louis the Pious, Charlemagne's successor, in 829. He became Bishop of Richenau at the age of thirty, but died in 849 by drowning, aged only forty. These simple little verses tell about the seasons and the peacefulness of the monastery garden and its many herbs. I quote him often.

An English monk, Alexander Neckham, became the Abbot of the Augustinian monastery at Cirencester in 1215. He mentions herbs and gardens in his two works, *De Naturis Rerum* and *De Laudibus Divinae Sapientiea*, in which the seventh book of ten books is on herbs. His list of plants included roses,

lilies, peonies, costmary, fennel, lad's love, coriander, parsley, hyssop, sage, savory, mint, rue, dittany, lettuce, mercury, sorrel and garden cress. Neckham mentioned 'Dioscorides and Macer, in which the nature of herbs is dealt with'.

Anglo-Saxon leechdom

Even with the Anglo Saxon leech books, we are dealing with ancient wisdom filtered and diffused into another age and culture. The powerful figure of Chiron the Centaur is present among recipes for the 'elf-shot', those struck by a shaft from an elf or other supernatural creature of the woods and marshes.

The *Leech Book of Bald*, dated to about 900–950 A.D. is the oldest book on herbs written in Anglo-Saxon. The leech was the wort or herb doctor of the day. Though it includes much knowledge about native British herbs like waybroad (plantain), water dock, mugwort, betony and vervain, many passages have been found to be direct translations into the vernacular from Latin and Greek texts.

These include works by Paul of Aegina, 7th century (a compiler of Galen), Alexander of Tralles, 6th century and Petrocellus, all of whom influenced the medical school at Salerno in Italy.

The 109 vellum leaves were written by a scribe named Cild for Bald, a leech. Two other doctors, Dun and Oxa, are mentioned as contributing prescriptions. The Leech Book is thought to have been written during the reign of King Alfred, or shortly afterwards, and contains letters sent to the king by the Patriarch of Jerusalem, Elias III (879–907), while the holy city was under Moslem rule.

The Herbarium of Apuleius is an Anglo-Saxon translation and adaptation of a Latin original which also includes a section taken from the Greek of Dioscorides. The original *Herbarium Apuleii Platonici* is dated to the 4th or 5th century and the Anglo-Saxon manuscript to 1050 A.D.

The author's name is fictitious, a Christian rendering of the names Apollo and Plato. The herbal, often called the *Pseudo-Apuleius*, is illustrated with figures of plants copied from older volumes, with the Juliana Anicia *Codex* a possible source. The frontispiece is a coloured picture which shows Asclepius and Chiron the Centaur, with herbs in his arms, presenting a large volume to Plato. It stresses plant sorcery and magic and

Title page from Gerard's *The Herball*, 1597

Macer is now thought to have been written (or collected) by Odo de Meung, or Odo Magdunesis, who lived at Meung on the Loire River in the 11th century. It was a Latin poem written in hexameters, which described seventy-seven plants.

This was translated into many Middle English manuscripts, including one 'tornyd into Ynglis' by a schoolteacher, Johannes Lelamour of Hereford in 1373 which is in the British Museum.

The first printed version is thought to be *Macer floridus De viribus herbarum* published in Latin at Paris about 1491.

Agnus Castus (the name comes from a type of willow) is a series of manuscripts, nowhere complete, the main manuscript being in the Royal Library at Stockholm and others in the British Bodleian and Ashmolean libraries. It dates from the 14th century.

These two works have the attractive lilt of Middle English, with all the remedies for bites of serpents and cures for eye troubles of the day. They have both been edited and published by scholars at Uppsala in Sweden (see *Bibliography*, page 140).

describes 132 herbs. Other illustrations include snakes, scorpions and strange winged creatures.

The Lacnunga is another early Anglo-Saxon manuscript of magic and medicine. The Anglo-Saxon text and translations were collected and edited by the Rev. Thomas Oswald Cockayne in *Leechdoms, Wortcunning and Starcraft of Early England* (1866), recently reissued in three volumes.

Middle English Manuscripts

A later vernacular manuscript, *MS 136*, Medical Society of London, seems to represent a transition between the Anglo-Saxon leechdom and the printed herbals which followed a century later. Of ninety-eight folios on vellum, it includes many surgical directions, but is still based on Dioscorides, Pliny, Galen and others. Warren R. Dawson, who edited the manuscript in 1934, dates it to 1444.

The link between the handwritten manuscripts on parchment and vellum and the first printed herbals of the late 15th century were two popular works, *Macer's Herbal* and the *Agnus Castus*.

Printed Herbals

Johann von Cube, a Frankfurt physician, realised that many of the plants described by Dioscorides and Pliny could not be found growing along the Rhine (despite prevailing views that they did). He set out southwards with an artist 'cunning and subtle of hand' to have the plants drawn 'with their true colours and form'.

Von Cube made a long and difficult journey through Italy, the Balkans and Greece, visiting Corfu, Crete and Rhodes, then Cyprus and the Middle East, including Egypt and Jerusalem. The result of his study was the *Herbarius zu Teutsch*, or the German Herbarius, printed at Mainz by Peter Schoffer in 1485. The figures of plants drawn from nature made this one of the first illustrated printed herbals. It recorded 380 plants.

The arrival of printing in England had an almost revolutionary effect on the thinking of the times. English for the first time began to be standardised, partly due to William Caxton's adoption of the East Midland or London dialect as standard. His famous pupil Wynken de Worde followed this precedent in his edition of *De proprietatibus rerum*,

NOMEN HERBAE MANDRAGORA

Mandragora (mandrake) from *Herbarium Apuleii Platonici*, 1480

by an English monk, Bartholomaeus Anglicus (1495).

This was a universal 'wonder book' like Pliny's Natural History. Consisting of nineteen books, the seventeenth book was a treatise on herbs which was composed in Latin in the 13th century. The work is usually dated to 1260 and there is a Latin version of 1296 at Oxford. Wynken de Worde used the translation made by John de Trevisa in 1398.

The style is simple, original and naive, as shown by this example:

> Spryinging time openeth the earth, that hath been long closed and bound with cold, and bringeth forth mosses, rootes and herbs that were hid in the earth, and bryeth the earth, and reneweth it with floures and herbs, and exciteth birds and fowles to chertering and to love, and clotheth, and bryheth all the over parts of the earth with a wonderful fairness ... for then hearbs and trees beginne to spring and to wear greene, with burgenings and twiggs.
>
> Spryngyne tyme is the time of gladnesse and of love; for in the Sprynging tyme all thynge semeth gladde; for the erthe wexeth grene, trees burgynne and sprede, medowes bring forth flowers, heven shyneth, the sea resteth and is quyete, foules synge and make theyre nestes, and al thynge that semed dead in wynter and widdered, ben renewed, in Spryngyne tyme.

Printing multiplied the available copies of works of the ancient authors, caused an upsurge in scholarship and generally gave impetus to the revival of learning. In this climate a demand developed for practical books, either original or in translation.

Among the popular works which began to roll off the hand presses were the herbals, with their rough woodcuts of plants, and gardening and farming treatises, most of which went into several editions.

The plant figures in *The Grete Herball*, printed by Peter Treveris at Southwalk, were copies of later, pirated editions of the *German Herbarius* printed at Augsburg, much inferior to the originals. This seems to have set the pattern for future herbals in which illustrations were either copied from earlier works, or the woodblocks used in one herbal were borrowed or bought for use in another.

The preface of *The Grete Herball* is based on the German work, though most of the text is a translation from the French *Le Grand Herbier*. The French work in turn can be traced to *Circa Instans*, a 12th century Latin manuscript.

The first edition of *The Grete Herball* is thought to have been 1516, but the earliest extant copy is dated 1526.

The oldest printed herbal in English consequently is *Banckes' Herball* published by Richard Banckes in 1525 (as Bartholomaeus Anglicus' work was not strictly a herbal). The compiler is unknown, but this is the first in a series of herbals based both on *Macer* and *Agnus Castus*.

These include *Redman's Herball* (1530), *Macers Herbal Practysyd by Doctor Lynacro* (1535), printed by Robert Wyer, and *A Lytel Herball* (1550). This last is attributed to Anthony Askham, priest, physician and scholar. It seems, however, that Askham was responsible only for the addition of an astrological treatise to the text – and this is not found in

Capital letter from *Macers Herbal . . .*, 1535

any of the surviving copies. At any rate, Askham thus became the first Englishman to have his name on the title page of a herbal.

I have chosen *A Lytel Herball* to represent this group, with occasional quotes from the other works, most of which are identical in text. None are illustrated, though Wyer's *Macer* of 1535 included some decorative capital letters.

Turner's Herball

The 'classic century' of herbals begins with William Turner's *A New Herball* (1551) and stretches to Nicholas Culpeper's *The English Physician Enlarged* (1653), taking in the outstanding works of John Gerard, a barber-surgeon (1597), and John Parkinson, apothecary to two kings (1629 and 1640).

It is a thrill to hold in your hand a worn, calfbound book which was printed some 425 years ago, and only about sixty years after Caxton first began printing in England. Some of the pages are stained or torn and parts are missing, but the first edition of William Turner's *A New Herball* (1551) is still in good condition.

The type is black letter, angular and hard to read. The woodcuts come mainly from Leonhard Fuchs' *De historia Stirpium* (1545) and his *Neue Kreuterbuch* (1543), though a few were specially cut.

'The woodcuts are very good and much better than in many modern botanical works,' said Nelson M. Richardson, of Weymouth, England, who owned this copy in 1923. He compared it with his copy of *The Grete Herball* in which, he said: 'The pictures as well as the descriptions are very quaint, something like the trees in a child's Noah's Ark and about as recognisable.'

Said Eleanour S. Rohde: 'Turner's notable work, his Herbal, is the only original work on botany written by an Englishman in the sixteenth century'. Turner's plant descriptions and observation are original and vigorous and earned him the title of the 'father of English botany'.

William Turner, the son of a tanner, was born at Morpeth in Northumberland in 1510. He studied at Cambridge and was a minister with strong Protestant views. This made him an exile from England between 1539 and 1547, when he wandered in Holland, Germany, Italy and Switzerland, where he studied under Conrad Gesner, author of *Catalogus plantarum* (1542), in Lucerne.

Rembert Dodoens

'The seconde parte' of William Turner's *Herball* was printed at Cologne in 1562 and a combined herbal of three parts, dedicated to Queen Elizabeth I, came out in 1568, the year of the author's death.

Agnes Arber, a great historian of herbals, says her interest in them was first sparked when, in 1894, she read a copy of Henry Lyte's translation of Rembert Dodoens' *Kruydeboeck*. The first edition in the Richardson collection of the State Library of New South Wales has delightful illustrations, more than half of them taken from the octavo edition of Leonhard Fuchs' *Primi de Stirpium historia commentariorum*, printed in Basle in 1545.

Dodoens, born in Malines about 1517, was physician to Maximilian II and Rudolf II successively and later professor of medicine at Leyden, Holland, where he died in 1585. His original work was

APOLLO

ÆSCVLAPIVS

GENTIVS

METHRI
DATES

ARTHEMISIA

LYSIMACHVS

A NIEVVE HERBALL,
OR HISTORIE OF PLANTES:

wherin is contayned

the vvhole difcourfe and perfect defcription of all fortes of Herbes
and Plantes: their diuers & fundry kindes:
their ftraunge Figures, Fafhions, and Shapes:
their Names, Natures, Operations, and Vertues: and that not onely of thofe whiche are
here growyng in this our Countrie of
Englande, but of all others alfo of
foyrayne Realmes, commonly
vfed in Phyficke.

Firft fet foorth in the Doutche or Almaigne
tongue, by that learned D. Rembert Dodoens, Phyfition to the Emperour:
And nowe firft tranflated out of
French into Englifh, by Henry Lyte Efquyer.

AT LONDON

by my Gerard Dewes, dwelling in
Pawles Churchyarde at the figne
of the Swanne.
1578.

HESPERIDVM HORT...

translated into French by Charles de L'Ecluse, then translated from the French into English by Lyte, who added some notes. Eleanour S. Rohde says the French copy Lyte used, now in the British Museum, has this inscription: 'Henry Lyte taught me to speak Englishe'.

The original woodblocks did not come to England – the book was printed in black letter by Henry van de Loe in Antwerp and published in London by Gerard Dewes.

Ram's Little Dodoen, which appeared in 1606, was a compilation of recipes by William Ram, designed 'for the poorer sort'. Some of the matter was abridged from Dodoens.

Gerard's Herball

Of all the herbals, the most charming and delightful to me is John Gerard's *The Herball or Generall Historie of Plantes* (1597). It was the first herbal I ever saw and the impression of its vast scope and individuality is still with me.

I know that the basis of *The Herball* was a translation, made by a Dr Priest, of Rembert Dodoens' *Pemptades* (1583) for John Norton, the Queen's printer. Gerard rearranged the matter, but did not acknowledge his use of Dr Priest's manuscript. He was caught out in this deception by overlooking an introduction made by Stephen Bredwell which acknowledged: 'Dr Priest for translating so much as *Dodonaeus*, hath hereby left a tombe for his honorable sepulture. Mr *Gerard* coming last, but not the least, hath many waies accomodated the whole worke unto our English Nation . . . '

Norton, who published the work, borrowed most of the 1 800 woodcuts used in it from Nicolas Basseaus of Frankfurt. They had first appeared in Jacob Theodor's *Eicones* (1590).

Among the sixteen original illustrations was the first published figure of the potato, which Gerard gave the name of the 'Virginian' potato. In the title page portrait he holds the potato plant in his hand.

Gerard made so many errors in matching the illustrations of the plants to their descriptions that the Dutch botanist Matthais de l'Obel (*Lobelia*), who was asked to correct it said he had made changes 'in a thousand places'. Gerard is also

Title page from Dodoens' *A Niewe Herball*, 1578

John Gerard

accused of taking material from de l'Obel's own *Stirpium Adversaria Nova* (1571).

Eventually the herbal was enlarged, amended and corrected by Thomas Johnson, a London apothecary, in 1633. I have made a point in this work to quote from Gerard's 1597 edition, retaining its text and spelling and, I believe, its disarming personality, acute observation and a good deal of English plant folklore.

Gerard loved herbs and flowers and grew 1 000 varieties in the garden which he called 'the little plot of myne owne especiall care and husbandry', planted with rarities like the potato and white-flowering thyme. It lay beside the River Flete, near Fetter Lane in the London suburb of Holborn.

How often he can boast: 'These be strangers in England, yet I have them in my own garden, where they flourish as in their natural place of growing'.

Most of the quotations selected have been drawn from the second of the three books into which *The Herball* is divided, which contains 'the Description, place, time, names, nature, and vertues of all sorts of Herbes for meate, medicine, or sweet smelling

John Parkinson

guage of the day. The illustrations of plants are accurate and interesting because they are grouped together.

Born in 1567, Parkinson had his own garden at Long Acre and was Apothecary to James I. He was named *Botanicus Regis Primarius* to Charles I after the publication of *Theatrum Botanicum* (1640). This was more aptly a herbal and dealt with 3 800 plants. Produced when the author was aged seventy-three, it seems less original than the *Paradisus*, which Parkinson himself described as 'a speaking garden'.

He called the new work 'A Theatre of Plants or a Herball of a large extent,' adding 'From a Paradise of pleasant Flowers, I am fallen (Adam like) to a world of profitable Herbes and Plants'. He died in 1650 at the age of eighty-three.

Thomas Coghan was an 'orator' at Oxford University. He seems a wise and gentle person, much concerned with the health of his students, outlining for their benefit many simple remedies in his work, *The Haven of Health* (1584).

Sir John Harington (born 1561) was a cousin of Queen Elizabeth I, being a grandson to Henry VIII by one of the king's illegitimate daughters. His translation of the medical advice of the School at Salerno in Italy, reads like quaint jingles or rhymed proverbs. It was published in 1607 as *The Englishmans Doctor*.

The English Physician

Nicholas Culpeper, a famous and controversial apothecary and herbalist was an eccentric character, a recluse and a ranter at 'Papists', who dogmatically believed in the power of astrology over plants and people. (I must confess that I have warmed to Culpeper as I grew more familiar with his *English Physician*, first printed in 1652, and not merely because I discovered that he shared his birthdate [October 18] with me.)

Culpeper was studying Greek and Latin at Cambridge when his fiancée, a young heiress, was struck dead by lightning as she was on her way in a carriage to elope with him. Embittered, he left university and became apprenticed to an apothecary in London. In 1649, Culpeper published the first translation into English of the medical *Pharmacopoea*, thus unlocking to the general public the secrets of doctors and physicians. For this he was

use'. The woodblock figures show the complete plant – root, stem, flower and seeds, to establish its true identity as you will see in the text.

The Earthly Paradise

John Parkinson, a childless man, seems to have poured out all his love on plants and lavished it on his vast and lovely 'flower book', *Paradisi in Sole Paradisus Terrestris* (1629). The title is a pun on his own name – 'Park-in-Sun's Earthly Paradise'.

The title page shows Adam and Eve in the Garden of Eden, a landscape in which the lush flowers are as big as the humans and the weird and mythical 'vegetable lamb' is suspended in the air from a stem.

Parkinson is not a great writer, but expresses himself vividly in the appropriately flowery lan-

NICHOLAS CULPEPER

*View in this face, whom Heaven snatcht from hence,
Our Phisicall and Starrie Influence;
Had not Great Culpeper such order tooke,
In spight of Fate to Live still in this Booke.*

Nicholas Culpeper

bitterly reviled and attacked by the College of Surgeons, who published a satire against him.

Culpeper renounced the 1652 edition of *The English Physician* as a forgery, 'there being twenty or thirty gross errors in every sheet', so I have used the 1653 'Enlarged' edition in this work. This was to prove one of the most popular and well-known herbals ever written, countless editions and forgeries following the first. It is still in print today.

His medical remedies were based on astrology. Treatment was given according to which planets governed the affected parts of the body and herbs were harvested for medical use according to the planet in the ascendant. Culpeper wrote in a lively, vivid style, not afraid to criticise the older authors or his contemporaries if they disagreed with his theories. He spent most of his short life treating the poor of Spitalfields in London's East End and died of tuberculosis in 1654.

William Coles and the Doctrine of Signatures

William Coles, author of *The Art of Simpling* (1656) and *Adam in Eden* (1657), attacked Nicholas Culpeper as being a man 'very ignorant in the form of Simples'. His enmity with Culpeper was due to his own disbelief in the Zodiac and its influence. Coles' little book is full of details about herbs and their folklore and uses for animals and humans. He had a preacher's turn of phrase which is eminently quotable. He himself believed unquestioningly in the ancient *Doctrine of Signatures*.

This, rather simply stated, was the belief that plants could be recognised from their shape or colour or habitat as being beneficial for various illnesses. Lungwort, for example, has mottled leaves shaped like lungs and willow grew near wet places and so must be good for colds and rheumatism. Often these remedies proved effective, especially the bark of willow, from which salacin is now extracted to treat rheumatism. Coles wrote:

> Though Sin and Sathan have plunged mankinde into an Ocean of Infirmities Yet the mercy of God which is over all his Workes Maketh Grasse to grow upon the Mountaines and Herbs for the use of Men and hath not onely stemped upon them (as upon every man) a distinct forme, but also given them particular signatures, whereby a Man may read even in legible Characters the Use of them. Heart Trefoyle is so called not onely because the Leafe is Triangular like the Heart of a Man, but also because each leafe contains the perfect Icon of an Heart and that in its proper colours viz a flesh colour. Hounds tongue hath a forme not much different from its name which will tye the Tongues of Hounds so that they shall not barke at you: if it be laid under the bottomes of ones feet.

Farm and Garden Books
Thomas Hyll

Many of the books quoted are not strictly herbals, but rather works on gardening and agriculture.

The first gardening book printed in England was written by Thomas Hyll, a Londoner. It was a tiny book, just three inches wide and six inches long, but it had a long title: *A most brief and pleasant treatise*, teachynge howe to dress, sowe and set a Garden,

Thomas Hyll

and what propertyes also those few herbes heare spoken of, have to our comodyte: with the remedyes that may be used against such beasts, wormes, flies and such lyke, that commonly noy gardens, gathered out of the principallest Authors in this art by Thomas Hyll Londoner. Short titles were not in vogue in those days. Hyll said he wrote 'to please the common sort', but he obviously knew the classic writers and was a prolific author, also writing on astrology and arithmetic.

The earliest surviving edition of the work is dated 1563, though it is thought to have been printed sooner. Later editions, starting in 1568, were titled *The Proffitable Arte of Gardening*.

Thomas Hyll died before he could complete *The Gardeners Labyrinth*, written under the pseudonym of Didymus Mountain, a play on his own name. It was edited by his friend Henry Dethicke. Hyll's books are full of practical advice on gardening and herbal medicine. He repeats many of the older superstitions about plants from Theophrastus and Pliny, thus keeping within the tradition of the herbals.

The woodcut motif used on the title page of this book is from the title page illustration of Hyll's first book.

Thomas Tusser, who sang as a boy in the choir of St Paul's in London, later became a musician, schoolteacher and farmer, when he retired from the court of King Henry VIII. His *Five hundred points of good husbandry* (1573), written in rhyming couplets, is a calendar of the tasks of a Tudor farm and garden through the twelve months of the year.

Charles Stevens (or Estienne) and his son-in-law John Liebault were the authors of the French work, Maison Rustique, which Richard Surflet translated as *The Countrie Farme* in 1600. A treatise on farming and gardening, it gave details of the kitchen garden with its potherbs and a pleasure garden divided into two parts. In one grew flowers for nosegays and garlands and, in the other, the sweet-smelling herbs. It had a section on beekeeping, including ways of protecting the 'little pretie wretches' from 'home and tame beasts'.

Gervase Markham wrote so many books on horses that he is often accused of being the original 'hackney' or 'hack' writer. He produced an augmented edition of *The Country Farm* in 1616. Markham's knowledge of animal husbandry and agriculture was practical. *The English Husbandman* (1613) reads like a well rounded 'homesteading' book, with directions on ploughing, farm tools, grafting, gardening, vineyards, hops, herbs, fruit preserving and plans for garden knots and mazes.

'I shew a plaine and sure way of planting which I have found good by 48 years (and more) experience in the North part of England,' wrote William Lawson, a Yorkshireman. His little book, *The Countrie Housewifes Garden* (1617), was the first book written in English for women gardeners. Eleanour S. Rohde captured his style and personality when she called him 'the Izaak Walton of gardening writers'. His advice is always brief and to the point, but spiced with a special charm as he writes about plants, fruit trees and bees.

'Your Gardiner,' he advises, 'had not need to be an idle or lazie lubber' . . . and explains the reason for pruning his list of herbs, saying: 'I recken these hearbes only, because I teach my Country Housewife, not skilful Artists . . . Let her first grow cunning in this, and then she may inlarge her garden, as her skill and ability increaseth.' His other work, *A New Orchard and Garden*, was published in 1618.

John Evelyn (1620–1706) was a diarist and essayist. He kept a garden at Sayes Court with a thick-set holly hedge which was vandalised by Czar Peter the Great of Russia, who liked to ride through it in a wheelbarrow. Evelyn's interests may be traced through the titles of his works and display a love of trees, gardens and salads. They are *The*

French Gardiner (1658), *Kalendarium Hortense:* or the *Gardiners Almanac* (1644), *Sylva* (1664), the first work on the conservation of forests and his *Acetaria* (1699) a hymn to salads from which I have drawn occasionally.

Another of John Evelyn's essays, '*Fumifugum* or the Inconvenience of the Aer and Smoke of London dissipated' (1661), put forward a plan to curb the city's air pollution by surrounding it with gardens of 'odoriferous flowers'.

Square plots, each twelve or sixteen hectares, would be planted with woodbine, sweet-briar, jasmine, roses and lavender, 'but above all, rosemary, the flowers whereof are credibly reported to give off their scent above thirty leagues off at sea upon the coast of Spain'.

Literature

Herbs are mentioned frequently in English poems and literature. I have drawn on Cervantes, Robert Herrick and Richard Addison to name a few.

Herbs were a familiar part of the life of Geoffrey Chaucer (1340–1400), who married Phillipa Roet, maid to Queen Phillipa of Hainault, said to be the first person to plant rosemary in Britain.

The glossary in any good edition of Chaucer, such as that of the Oxford University Press, is the key to most of the difficult words in Middle English and his philosophy reflects the age, as in this passage from the *Prologue to the Canterbury Tales* (1386):

With us ther was a Doctour of Phisyk,
In al the world ne was noon him lyk
To speke of phisik and surgerye;
For he was grounded in astronomye . . .
He knew the causes of everich maladye,
Were it of hoot or cold, or moiste, or drye,
And where engendered, and of what humour;
He was a parfait practisour.
The cause y-knowe, and of his harm the rote . . .
Ful redy hadde he his apothecaries,
To send him drogges and his lectuaries . . .
Wel knew he th' olde Esculapius,
And Deiscorides . . .

From the ancient Greeks the belief had persisted into the Middle Ages that health and illness was governed by humours in men, which affected even their mental outlook. The humours were mixtures of air (hot and moist), fire (hot and dry), earth (cold and dry) and water (cold and moist).

Sir Thomas More, who speaks so feelingly of rosemary, had a famous garden on the Thames at Chelsea, where he was often visited by the playwright John Heywood, Erasmus and Henry VIII. After the king sent Sir Thomas to the block in 1535, it was used as a royal residence. Anne of Cleves died there in 1557. After the king's death, Katherine Parr lived there, having charge of Princess Elizabeth, then a child of thirteen.

William Shakespeare mentions twenty herbs in his plays and sonnets and speaks of them as a countryman would. Elsewhere Ophelia's 'garland' is given and Iago's garden 'sermon' is particularly touching:

Our bodies are gardens, to the which our wills are gardeners; so that if we plant nettles or sow lettuce, set hyssop and weed up thyme, supply it with one gender of herbs or distract it with many, either to have it sterile with idleness or manured with industry; why, the power and corrigible authority of this lies in our wills.

Othello, Act I, Scene 3

Shakespeare (1564–1616) and John Gerard were contemporaries, and it is pleasant to think that they might have met, though there is no proof of it. London was a small place in those days and they were near neighbours for several years. Shakespeare lived in a house almost opposite the Barber-Surgeons' Hall, which Gerard often visited.

James Joyce evidently believed that they had met and twice refers to this in *Ulysses*.

Language of the Herbals

At first sight the archaic grammar and erratic word order of the herbals seems obscure, especially in those written before the 17th century.

However, it is even more difficult to read the originals, especially the manuscripts. The Anglo-Saxon texts are certainly a 'foreign' language and need to be translated. Middle English, which dates from 1100 to 1400, has in it all the seeds of our modern language. Before this period, the speech of Englishmen took in Scandinavian words (from the Viking invasions and settlements of the 9th and 10th centuries) and French words, increasingly after the Norman invasion of 1066.

From Middle English onwards I have merely transcribed directly from the originals, or the edited texts of originals, retaining the spelling, word order and punctuation. This usually meant only changing the long 'f' into 's' in the printed works and the symbol þ for 'th' in the manuscripts. For a brief period this was given as 'ye' for 'the', a misreading which lingered on as a mock antique form of the word. It is used in John Goodyer's translation of *Dioscorides*, but thankfully has now fallen out of use.

The earlier printed herbals were composed in black letter Gothic type, also difficult to read in the original, such as William Turner's *Herball* of 1551 and Lyte's translation of *Dodoens* (1578). Gerard's *Herball* of 1597 is printed in italic and roman letters and has a startlingly modern look about it.

The speech patterns and the spelling tell you something about the attitude of the people behind the herbals as well as the folklore and wisdom they contain. There were no hard and fast rules about spelling then, each writer chose his own. Quite often the printer was likely to adapt the words to even up the lines or to suit the metal letters he had left as he neared the end of the page. This accounts for the differing spelling of the same word in the same paragraph or page.

The meanings of words have subtly altered, too. *Physicall* in those days meant *medicinal*. The *Physick* was a doctor, the *apothecary* a herbal chemist. They were most often called upon to treat *woundes*, the *ague* (a fever, *hoate* or *colde*), or a melancholy *humour* – not something which would make you laugh, but a fluid which was thought to affect the mind and body.

With their herbs they cured *akes* or *paines*, using *ius*, *iuce* ('j' was a late arrival in English, about the 16th century), *jus* or *juce*, which was *medled*, *mengled* or *mixte*, then *drank*, *drunken* or *dronken* by the *paycent*, or taken as a *condite* or *confertue* (not jam, but a conserve or preserve).

The *worts*, *herbes* or *hearbes* were *seethed*, *sethed*, or in other words, *boyl'd* or *boyled*, after which they were *sod* or *sodden*. After that the *payne* was *swaged* or *aswaged* (assuaged or soothed), the *yexxing*, *hickocke*, *hikok* was *stayed*, or the blood *stanched* (staunched), the *eies* or *eine* were *quickened* or re-vived, the *stomake* once again *holsom*.

The ill man could then return to his *wyn* and *potage*, his *hart* comforted, his spirits again *merrie* and *ioyfull*!

In the herb garden grew the *plantes*, *grene*, *blak* or *yelowe* of *lef*, *levis*, *leyys* or *leves*, with their *flowris*, *flowrs*, *flowres* or *floures*, *mikel* (much) or *lytle*, their *rootes* and *sede* or *seede*.

Some herbs are *strown* or strewn in chests against *moughes* or moths, or used as *nosegayes* (bunches of herbs or flowers) to smell unto against *evill aires*.

There is a lilt about the Middle English and Old English sections taken from manuscripts, with this piece from Agnus Castus (14th century) a good example:

The vertue of this herbe is if a cat ete thereof it schal conseywyn and brynge forth kytlyngis anon.

A glossary of archaic words is given at the end of the book.

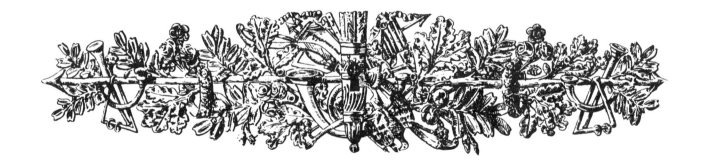

Detail from the title page of *Paradisus*, 1629

6
A HERBAL COLLECTION
and Materia Medica of
Forty Herbs & Sundry Subjects

Here begins
a herbal collection
of forty major herbs~
giving their description,
nature & virtues in quotations,
from the ancient authors & classic
herbals from 300 B.C. to the 20th
~century listing the facts~
~~fantasy and folklore~
of the herbs
to
wh
≈ich
is added a mod~
ern comm~
entary.

Agrimony

'good for them that have naughtie livers'

Agrimony from *A Niewe Herball*, 1578

Agrimony (*Agrimonia eupatoria*). Perennial. Agrimony.

Old form: Egrimony, Egremoine, Egrimoyne, Agrimonie, Argemone, Argemoney, Aaron's Rod, Cocklebur, Stickwork, Church Steeples.

Rose family.

And here in handsome rows you can see my agrimony. It clothes all the fields with its profusion; it grows wild in the woodland shade. If crushed and drunk the draught will check the most violent stomach ache.

WALAFRID STRABO, *The Little Garden*, 840 A.D.

Agrimonia is an herbe that men clepyn egrimoyne. This herbe hast lewys lyk to tansye but the lewys of this herbe are grennere thanne the lewys of tansye. And it beryst a yelow flour and quanne the flour is falle it beryst a seed that wele hange on mannys clothys as burres. This herbe growyst by hegges and in wodys. The vertu of this herbe is if it be etyn with the Rote grene it helyth the akyng of the wombe.

... Also this herbe tempred with esyle is to hole every soort hurt with only yryn.

AGNUS CASTUS, 14th century

And herbes coulde I telle eek many oon,
As egremoine, valerian and lunarie,
And others swiche, if that me liste tarie.

GEOFFREY CHAUCER, *The Chanouns Yemannes Tale*, 1389

The leaves of *Agrimonia*, are long and hairie, greene above, and somewhat grayish underneath, parted into divers other small leaves, snipt rounde about the edges, almost like the leaves of hempe. The stalke is two foote and an half long, rough, and hairie, whereupon grow manie small yellowe flowers one above another upwards towards the top: after the flowes come the seedes somewhat long and rough, like to small burs hanging downwards, which when they be ripe, do catch holde upon peoples garments which passe by it. The root is great, long, and blacke.

The decoction of the leaves of Egrimonie is good for them that have naughtie livers, and for such as pisse bloud upon the diseases of the kidneis.

The leaves being stamped with old swines grease, and applied, closeth up ulcers that be hardly healed, as *Dioscorides* saith.

JOHN GERARD, *The Herball*, 1597

Agrimonie would be planted in a stonie and drie place, and further, craveth no great helpe of hand or husbandrie. The decoction openeth the obstructions of the liver, and strengthneth it: and it being boiled and drunke, doth helpe against the bitings of venemous beastes: the iuice of agrimonie mixt with vinegar and salt liniment, doth cure the itch: Agrimonie is good against the cough of sheepe, and for broken winded horses.

RICHARD SURFLET, *The Countrie Farme*, 1600

It groweth upon Banks neer the sides of Hedges, or Pales. It openeth and clenseth the Liver, helpeth the Jaundice, and is very beneficial to the Bowels, healing al inward wounds, Bruises, Hurts, and other distempers ... Outwardly applied, being stamped with old Swines grease, it helpeth old sores, Cancers, and inveterate Ulcers; and draweth forth Thorns, Splinters of Wood, Nails, or any other such thing gotten into the flesh ...

NICHOLAS CULPEPER, *The English Physician Enlarged*, 1653

The starry yellow flowers covering the stems — or 'church steeples' — of agrimony provided the clue for ancient herbalists of its use in healing yellow jaundice and all liver troubles.

Fantastic as it seems, the *Doctrine of Signatures* has often proved medically correct. Agrimony is also a good example of a magic herb which became a medical herb and contrasts with the herbs which follow, most of which have culinary uses.

The plant grows to about a metre in height, with green, saw-toothed, narrow leaves about 13 cm long and few branches. The yellow flowers cluster about the tough stem. The whole plant is deep green and covered with soft hairs.

It starts well from seed and will self-seed when established. Grow in shade or semi-shade.

Agrimony tea is a popular tonic in France, used for bed-wetting, sore throats, congestion and weakness of the bladder. Pour 500 ml of boiling water over a handful of stems, flowers and leaves. Allow to cool and strain.

Outwardly, the tea is used for sores, sprains and bruises, pimples and blotches.

Agrimonia odorata has a scent like apricots and grows on acid soils.

Alleis & Herbers

Hoom to myn hous ful swiftly I me spedde,
And, in a little herber that I have,
Y-benched new with turves fresshe y-grave,
I bad men shulde me my couche make.
GEOFFREY CHAUCER, *The Legend of Good Women*, 1385

The commodities of these Alleis and walkes serve to good purposes, the one is that the owner may diligently view the prosperitie of his herbes and flowers, the other for the delight and comfort of his wearied mind, which he may by himself or fellowship of his friends conceyve, in the delectable sightes and fragrant smelles of the flowers, by walking up and downe, and about the Garden in them, which for the pleasant sightes and refreshing of the dull spirites, with the sharpening of memorie, many shadowed over with vawting or arch herbers, having windowes properly made towardes the

Wall herber (top) and raised garden beds (bottom) from *The Gardeners Labyrinth*, 1577

Garden, whereby they might the more fully view and have delight of the whole beautie of the Garden.
THOMAS HYLL, *The Gardeners Labyrinth*, 1577

And bid her steal into the pleached bower,
Where honey-suckles, ripen'd by the sun,
Forbid the sun to enter . . .
(Hero), *Much Ado about Nothing*, Act III, Scene I

The green hath two pleasures: the one, because nothing is more pleasant to the eye than green grass kept finely shorn; the other because it will give you a fair alley in the midst, by which you may go in front upon a stately hedge, which is to enclose the garden . . . therefore you are, on either side the green, to plant a covert alley, upon carpenters' work, about twelve feet in height, by which you may go in shade in the garden.
FRANCIS BACON, *Of Gardens*, 1625

Arbours also being both graceful and necessary, may be appointed in such convenient places, as the corners or else where, as may be most fit, to serve both for the shadow and rest after walking.
JOHN PARKINSON, *Paradisus*, 1629

The 'covert alley' or herber along garden walks and walls is a familiar feature of medieval illustrations. It was a bower-like structure, woven and plaited (pleached) with branches such as juniper or willow, arched at the top or else square like the more modern pergola.

Today we would call such a retreat an arbour. Both words derive from the Latin, *herba*, a plant, as does the word herb.

Thomas Hyll suggested that the alleys in herbers be just over a metre wide and strewn with sand. Fragrant plants, such as lavender, rosemary and thyme, lined the way and jasmine, climbing roses and grape vines roofed in the herber.

Often there were raised seats of turf inside this cool bower. Seats were also cut in earth banks and covered with aromatic thyme and chamomile or violets.

If there is enough space, such an arbour may be put next to the herb garden, or along the side of a house. Here the gardener can relax and enjoy the delights of his plants and flowers, read, or enjoy an early dinner.

A more elaborate plan is for an avenue or long archway of apple trees, mixed with pears, grown on either side of the path, the leaders cordoned or tied to form an arch, or trained over wire arches. Intersperse jasmine or wisteria for colour and shade after every tree.

Angelica

'a singular remedie against poison'

Wild angelica from *The Herball*, 1597

Garden angelica from *The Herball*, 1597

Angelica (*Angelica archangelica*). Biennial-perennial. Garden Angelica.
Old form: Masterwort, Holy Ghost Root.
Umbelliferae – parsley family

The garden Angelica hath great broad leaves, divided agayne into other leaves, which are snipt and dented about ... amongst those leaves springeth up the stalke, three yeares after the sowing of the seede, the which stalke is thicke, and ioyntie, hollow within, and smelleth almost like to *Petroleum*.
REMBERT DODOENS, *A Niewe Herball* (trans. Lyte), 1578

The rootes of garden Angelica is a singular remedie against poison, and against the plague, and all infections taken by evill and corrupt aire; if you do but take a peece of the roote and hold it in your mouth, or chew the same between your teeth, it doth most certainly drive away the pestilential aire, yea although that corrupt aire have possessed the hart, yet it driveth it out againe by urine and sweate as Rue and Treacle, and such like *Antipharmaca*.
JOHN GERARD, *The Herball*, 1597

Angelica would be sowen in well tilled ground, oftentimes wed [weeded] and reasonably watered.
The roote is soveraigne against the plague and all sorts of poyson: whosoever shall keepe a little piece of it in his mouth, or which shall drinke only in a winter morning a little draught of wine and

rose water, wherein it hath been steept, he cannot be infected of any evill aire all that day. Englishmen use the leaves and rootes of this herbe in sauce with all their meats, because it correcteth grosse humours, and a stinking breath, and furthereth digestion very much.

The root put into a hollow tooth asswageth the paine: being chawed, it maketh the breath sweet, and concealeth the smell of garlicke, or any other such meat which causeth an ill breath.

RICHARD SURFLET, *The Countrie Farme*, 1600

Angelica is renued with his seed, whereof hee beareth plentie the second yeare, and so dyeth. The leaves distilled, yeeld water soveraigne to expell paine from the stomacke. The root dryed taken in the fall stoppeth the poares against infections.

WILLIAM LAWSON, *The Countrie Housewifes Garden*, 1617

The Use of Angelica

The distilled water of Angelica, eyther simple or compound, is of especiall use in swounings, when the spirits are overcome and faint, or tremblings and passions of the heart, to expell any windy or noysome vapours from it. The green stalkes or the young rootes being preserved or candied, are very effectuall to comfort and warme a colde and weak stomacke.

JOHN PARKINSON, *Paradisus*, 1629

In times of Heathenism when men had found out any excellent Herb, &c. they dedicated it to their gods. As the *Bay-tree* to *Apollo*, the *Oak* to *Jupiter*, the *Vine* to *Bacchus*, the *Poplar* to *Hercules:* These the Papists following as their Patriachs, they dedicate them to their Saints, as our *Ladies Thistle* to the *Blessed Virgin*, *St. John's Wort* to *St. John*, and another Wort to *St. Peter*, &c. Our Physicians must imitate like Apes (though they cannot come off half so cleverly) for they Blasphemously call Pansies, or Harts-ease an *Herb of the Trinity*, because it is of three colours ... and therefore some call this, an Herb of the *Holy Ghost*, others more moderate call it ANGELICA, because of its Angelic Vertues, and that Name it retains still, and al Nations follow it so neer as their Dialect will permit.

In al Epidemical Diseases caused by *Saturn*, this is as good a Preservative as grows. It resists Poyson by defending and comforting the Heart, Blood, and Spirits; it doth the like against the Plague and al Epidemical Diseases.

– The Stalks or Roots candied and eaten fasting, are good Preservatives in time of Infection, and at other times to warm and comfort a cold Stomach. The Root also steeped in Vineger, and a little of that Vineger taken sometimes fasting, and the Root smelled unto, is good for the same purpose.

NICHOLAS CULPEPER, *The English Physician Enlarged*, 1653

It is grown abundantly near London, and may be cultivated in our gardens. Its peculiar resin, 'angelicin' is stimulating to the lungs. Some writers have said this plant – the Archangelica was revealed in a dream by an angel to cure the plague; others aver that it blooms on the day dedicated to Michael the Archangel (May 8th, old style), and is therefore a preservative against evil spirits and witchcraft. Angelica taken somewhat freely as a sweetmeat will cause a distaste for alcoholic liquors.

DR W.T. FERNIE, *Meals Medicinal*, 1899

To Candy Angelica

Boil the stalks of Angelica in water till they are tender; then peel them and put them in other warm water and cover them. Let them stand over a gentle fire till they become very green; then lay them on a cloth to dry; take their weight in fine Sugar with a little Rose-water and boil it to a Candy height. Then put in your Angelica and boil them up quick; then take them for use.

JOHN NOTT, *The Receipt Book*, 1723

Angelica Incense

Take a root of Angelica, dry it in the oven or before the fire, then bruis it well and infuse it four or five days in white wine vinegar. To make use of it heat a brick red hot and lay the Angelica root upon the brick. The vapour that exhales therefrom is a powerful corrective of putrid air. The operation must be repeated several times.

TOILET OF FLORA, 1755

From pagan times angelica was famed as a safeguard against evil, especially witchcraft, and used as a cure-all for infections or 'evill and corrupt aire'. In Christian times it held the same virtues, which were ascribed to the intercession of Michael the Archangel, whose feast day fell on 8 May (old form) when the plant was said to be in bloom.

Another story said that an angel presented the plant to mankind as a cure for the plague. It was recommended for that reason in the Great Plague of 1660.

Angelica is one of the tallest herbs, towering to two metres or more when in flower. The seeds, stem, leaves and root are aromatic and edible and the whole plant is used for flavouring. A native of damp places and river banks, it thrives in cold countries such as Iceland, Lapland and northern Europe. It is a handsome plant. The leaves are deeply cut and three-parted, the small, yellowish flowers are borne in large rounded umbels.

Strictly it is neither a biennial, nor a perennial plant because it may take two years to send up a stalk and flower. It is treated as a perennial by regular clipping of the heads and cutting of the stalks. After flowering it dies quickly. Keep a few plants for seeds and the beauty of their flowers.

The seed is used in flavouring liqueurs, wines and bitters and crushed for an oil used in perfumes and in flavouring custards. The tall, hollow stem and the stalks are candied with sugar, or made into jam, usually mixed with rhubarb stalks.

The midribs blanched and eaten like celery are tasty – the Finns used to eat the stems baked in hot ashes.

The leaves were often boiled in the pot with fish, or with spinach and other vegetables, or added sparingly to salads.

Angelica is difficult to propagate by seed, which must be very fresh, not more than a week old, one herb nurseryman says. Sow the ripe, fresh seed as soon as it is ready in late summer, in loose, moist soil shaded by trees. Transplant when about 15 cm high and space about a metre apart.

Each plant will last several years, but they should be replaced about every three years. Plants grown from root division and offsets are often inferior, so use seeds or buy a first plant from a nursery.

A resinous gum used in pot-pourri in place of gum benzoin or musk is gathered by making a cut in the stems and crown of the root in spring.

Angelica tea is made by pouring 500 ml of boiling water over 30g of the leaves, or 15g of the seeds. It is pale green, rather bitter like China tea, and was used by village herbalists for colds, and indigestion and to purify the blood.

Warning: Angelica is dangerous for diabetics, as it raises the sugar level in the urine.

Anise

'sweet breath-making'

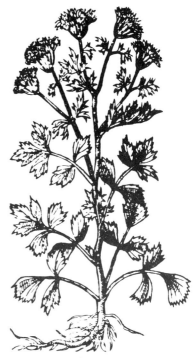

Anise from *The Herball*, 1597

Anise (*Pimpinella anisum*). Annual.
  Aniseed.
  Old form: Anyse, Annise, Anece, Anisum.
  Umbelliferae – parsley family.

Anisum hath generally a warming, drying, sweet breath-making, paine easing, dissolving, ureticall, discussing faculty ... It is good also both for outcasting ye poison of venemous beasts & for inflation ... and being suffited to ye nostrils, it quieteth ye headache.

DIOSCORIDES, 60 A.D. (trans. Goodyer, 1655)

Annise and Dill are as appropriate to the kitchen for Cookes, and the Apothecaries shop for the Physician.

The rusticall peasants of the countrey were wont to guild or glaze (as it were) the upper crust of their loaves of bread with yolkes of egs, and then to bestrew it with Poppie seed, which would cleave fast unto it, having first underlaied the bottome crust with Ammi, or Annise seed and Gith: and then they put them into the oven being thus seasoned; which gave a commendable tast to their bread when it was baked.

PLINY, *Naturall Historie*, 77 A.D. (trans. Holland, 1601)

Ach of the modre (womb) seth ij littil bundell of anece in wyne and make thereof a playstyr and lay abowt his navyl. *et sanabitur* (he will be cured).

MS. 136, MEDICAL SOCIETY OF LONDON, 1444

Anyse sede. Maketh swete breth, provoketh urine, and bringeth downe thinges, cleavynge to the raynes or bladder, styreth up courage and causeth abundance of mylke.

SIR THOMAS ELYOT, *The Castel of Health*, 1541

And washinge your face with the distilled water of this herbe, it doth much clere the same, so that this water be measurably used, for that the often using of it, doth make the face yealowe. And against the blacke and blew of stryepe, and especially if the same be in the face, about the eyes, let the seedes with the cummyn be brused together, and that wrought with waxe, applye hot to the grieved place.

And the eatinge of the annys seedes doth both heate the liver, and helpeth digestion.

THOMAS HYLL, *The Proffitable Arte of Gardening*, 1568

Anise hath leaves like to yong Persley, that is new sprong up: his stalkes be rounde and hollow, his leaves at the first springing up, are somewhat round, but afterwarde it hath other leaves cut and cloven like to the leavs of Persley, but a great deale smaller & whiter. At the toppe of the stalkes groweth divers faire tuftes, or spokie rundels with white floures, like to the tuftes of the small saxifrage, or of Coriandre. After the floures are past there cometh up seede, which is whitish, and in smell and taste, sweete and pleasant.

REMBERT DODOENS, *A Niewe Herball* (trans. Lyte), 1578

The seed wasteth and consumeth winde, and is good against belchings and upbraidings of the stomacke, alaieth gripings of the belly, provoketh urine gently, maketh abundance of milke, and stirreth up bodily lust . . .

Being chewed it makes the breath sweete, and is good for them that are short winded, and quencheth thirst, and therefore it is fit for such as have the dropsie: it helpeth the yeoxing or hicket, both when it is drunken or eaten drie: the smell thereof doth also prevaile very much.

The same being dried by the fire and taken with honie, clenseth the brest very much from flegmatike superfluities: and if it be eaten with bitter almonds it doth helpe the old cough.

JOHN GERARD, *The Herball*, 1597

Anise craveth a well batled, tilled, fat and manured ground: it must be sown in March and oft watered. Every man knoweth how good and profitable the seed thereof is, eaten in the morning: for such as are subject to the gripes of the stomack and guts, to the hicket, belchings, stinking breath, and which desire to have a beautiful and comly contenance: after meat, it also helpeth digestion: it is good for nurses to cause them to have much milk.

RICHARD SURFLET, *The Countrie Farme*, 1600

Some *Annis-seed* be sweete, and some more bitter, For pleasure these, for medicine those are fitter.

SIR JOHN HARINGTON, *The Englishmans Doctor*, 1607

Annyseedes make their growth, and beareth seedes the first yeare, and dyeth as *Coriander*, it is good for opening the pipes, and is used in comfits.

WILLIAM LAWSON, *The Countrie Housewifes Garden*, 1617

Seed Biscuits (Anise or carraway)

Ingredients – 1 lb. flour, $\frac{1}{4}$ lb. sugar, $\frac{1}{4}$ lb. butter, $\frac{1}{2}$ oz. seeds, 3 eggs.
Mode – Beat the butter to a cream, stir in the flour, sugar and seeds; and when these ingredients are well mixed, add the eggs, which should be well whisked. Roll out the paste, shape out the biscuits with a round cutter, and bake them in a moderate oven from 10 to 15 minutes. The tops of the biscuits may be brushed over with a little milk or the white of an egg, and then a little sugar strewn over.

MRS ISABELLA BEETON, *Household Management*, 1861

Mankind has been using the seeds of anise as food and medicine for at least 5 000 years. We know this because its recorded history starts with the tablets of Nineveh and it is included in the Egyptian Ebers papyrus.

In the 6th century B.C., Pythagoras said that a spray of anise held in the hand would prevent an epileptic fit. In 812 A.D. it was on the Emperor Charlemagne's list of herbs to be planted in his villa gardens.

However, this is not the plant often mistranslated in the Bible from *anethon*, the Greek term for dill.

In 1305 aniseed was taxed by the English King Edward I when it was carried across London Bridge (and therefore 'imported'). The revenue earned was used to maintain the bridge.

Edward IV, who reigned from 1461 to 1483, had the linen of the royal household perfumed with a mixture of anise and orris root (the dried and powdered bulb of the Florentine iris), sewn into sachets.

In northern America, the First Assembly of Virginia declared in 1619 that 'each man unto whom a division (land) is granted must plant thereon six anise seeds'.

The name *Pimpinella* is derived from *dipinella*, or twice-pinnate, a description of the plant's two different types of leaves. The lower leaves are like celery, bright green at the base, round and toothed, about 20 mm long. The secondary leaves are finely cut at the top, feathery and wing-shaped.

Anise grows to about 45 cm (18 inches) high. It has a white, fibrous root and slender stems. The flowers are small, white, or yellow-white, borne in umbels and ripen into the fruit or seed about four months after planting.

Stems are weak and often need hilling up or staking when in flower.

Anise seeds are sweet and spicy. They were used by the Romans in the spiced cake described by Pliny, which was a forerunner of our modern spiced wedding cakes.

Today it is used for flavouring cakes, soup, bread, apple sauce and stews. The French chop up green anise leaf to sprinkle over buttered baby carrots and to garnish salads. The powdered seed is used in curry.

Sow seed in place early in spring in a sunny position or sow thickly and thin out to 30 cm each way. Allow the seeds to ripen on the plant and place a brown paper bag over the umbels held in place with a rubber band. When the seeds are crisp, remove the heads and separate the seeds for storage.

Anise tea is used for catarrh. Pour 250 ml of boiling water over 15 g of bruised seeds (or fresh leaves). Sweeten with honey. This may be used as a baby's 'gripe water'.

Anise seeds steeped in hot milk makes a soothing bedtime drink to help you sleep.

Star anise (*Illicium anisatum*) is a small Asian tree with a very similar flavour used in Chinese cooking.

Anise flavours liqueurs like *anisette* and Turkish *raki*, which warm the stomach and promote digestion.

Artemisia and Chiron the Centaur from *De vertutibus herbarum*, 12th century (Sloane 1975, British Museum)

Artemisias

Verily of these Worts which we named Artemesia, it is said that Diana should find them, and delivered their powers and leechdom to Chiron the Centaur, who first from these Worts set forth a leechdom, and he named these Worts from the name of Diana, Artemis, that is Artemisias.

HERBARIUM APULEIUS (trans. Cockayne), 1050 A.D.

The snake or adder wyll not lodge in that Garden, where either wormewoode, Mugworte, or Sothernwood, be aptly planted in the corners, or rounde about the Garden.

THOMAS HYLL, *The Proffitable Arte of Gardening*, 1568

The artemisias are an important group of herbs, used since ancient times in magic and medicine. See the individual herbs:

LAD'S LOVE (*Artemisia abrotanum*)
MUGWORT (*A. vulgaris*)
TARRAGON (*A. dracunculus*)
WORMWOOD (*A. absinthium*)

Balm

'bees do delight in ye herb'

Balm from the *Juliana Anicia Codex*, 512 A.D.

Balm from Mattioli, 1583

Balm (*Melissa officinalis*). Perennial. Lemon balm, Melissa.
Old form: Balsam, Bawme, Baulme, Baulm, Pentarie, Melittena.
Mint family.

Apiastrum, which some call Melittena . . . because the bees do delight in ye herb. But ye leaves being drank with wine, & also applied are good for the Scorpion-smitten, & ye Phalangium-bitten, and ye dog-bitten & ye decoction of them, by way of fomentation for ye same purposes.

DIOSCORIDES, 60 A.D. (trans. Goodyer, 1655)

Mellisa is an herbe that men calle bawme or pentarie. This herbe hast levys lyk to the levis of nepte and it is strong in savour and it hast lytl yelow flour and it beryth the flour on eyther syde of the stalke as doth mynte and many braunches comyn out of one stok and it growith in gardyngis and the brawnches are lengere thanne a cubyte. This herbe is hot and drye.

ANGUS CASTUS, 14th century

Bawme drunk in wine is good against the bitings of venemous beasts: comforteth the hart, and driveth away all melancholie and sadness.

41

... The hives of Bees being rubbed with the leaves of Bawme, causeth the bees to keep togither, and causeth others to come unto them.

... Bawme maketh the hart merrie & joiful, and strengtheneth the vitall spirits.

JOHN GERARD, *The Herball*, 1597

Baulme is often used among other hot and sweete herbes, to make baths and washings for mens bodies or legges, in the Summer time, to warme and comfort the veines and sinewes, to very good purpose and effect, and hath in former ages beene of much more use than now adaies. It is also used by divers to be stilled being steeped in Ale, to make a Balme water, after the manner they have been taught, whiche they keep by them, to use in the stead of *Aqua vita*.

For the hearbe without all question is an excellent helpe to comfort the hearte, as the very smell may induce any so to believe. It is also good to heale greene wounds, being made into salves.

It is also an herbe wherein Bees doe much delight, as hath beene found by experience of those that have kept great store; if the Hives bee rubbed on the inside with some thereof, and as they thinke it draweth others by the smell thereof to resort thither. *Plinie* saith, it is a present remedy against the stinging of Bees.

JOHN PARKINSON, *Paradisus*, 1629

This Herb is so wel known to be an inhabitant almost in every Garden that I shal not need to write any Description thereof, although the Vertues thereof which are many, may not be omitted.

It is an Herb of *Jupiter*, and under *Cancer*, and strengthens Nature much in al actions: let a Syrup made with the juyce of it and Sugar, be kept in every Gentlewomans house, to releeve the weak stomachs and sick Bodies of their poor sickly neighbors, as also the Herb kept dry in the house that so with other convenient Simples you may make it into an Electuary with Hony according as the Disease is. The *Arabian* Physicians have extolled the Vertues hereof to the Skies, although the *Greeks* thought it not worth mentioning. *Serapio* saith, It causeth the Mind and Heart to become merry, and reviveth the Heart fainting into swoonings, especially of such who are overtaken in their sleep, and driveth away al troublesome cares and thoughts out of the Mind arising from Melancholly, or black Choller.

NICHOLAS CULPEPER, *The English Physician Enlarged*, 1653

Baulm, hot and dry, cordial and exhillirating, sovereign for the brain, strengthening the memory, and powerfully chasing away melancholy. The tender leaves are us'd in composition with other herbs (in salads); and the sprigs fresh gather'd, put into wine, or other drinks, during the heat of summer, give it a marvellous quickness.

JOHN EVELYN, *Acetaria*, 1699

Balm, with its delicious lemon scent, is by common consent one of the most sweetly smelling of all the herbs in the garden. Balm-wine was made of it and a tea which is good for feverish colds. The fresh leaves make better tea than the dry.

FRANCES BARDSWELL, *The Herb Garden*, 1911

Melissa or lemon balm rivals sage as a promoter of long life. John Hussey of Sydenham, England, breakfasted each day on balm tea sweetened with honey until the age of 116. Llewellen, Prince of Glamorgan in Wales, who lived to 108, attributed his great age to it.

Honeybees love the plant for its abundant nectar (Melissa is the Greek word for a bee). If you rub the inside of a beehive after hiving a new swarm, the bees will never leave. We humans love the strong minty-lemon fragrance and fresh taste of balm.

In earlier times, bunches of lemon balm (also marjoram and sweet cicely) were rubbed over heavy wooden furniture to give it scent and gloss. Thus, Ann Page in *The Merry Wives of Windsor*:

The several chairs of order look your scour
With juice of balm, and every precious flower.

Balm is a woody perennial, growing almost a metre high, which sends out runners like other members of the mint family. These or the roots may be divided for propagation. It will do best in a dampish spot in semi-shade. The lush, crinkly, deep green leaves are heart-shaped and scalloped around the edges, growing smaller towards the top of the plant. Flowers are tiny and yellowish.

Use the leaves and tops to flavour salads and fruit salads, jellies, iced tea, punch and other summer drinks. Use sparingly in soups, stews and sauces.

Balm tea is a tonic credited with clearing the head, helping against fevers and as a heart stimulant. Pour 500 ml of boiling water over 30 g of leaves and infuse for 10 minutes. Allow to cool and sweeten with honey and lemon.

A mixed tea of balm and marjoram is given to strengthen and content cows after calving.

Dry balm leaves quickly on a hot summer day, but in the shade, or they will blacken. They are used in pot-pourri.

For indigestion: Toast a slice of bread until it is charred black. Put the charred bread and some fresh balm leaves in a cup, adding boiling water, and let steep for about five minutes. Pour the liquid off, and it is ready to drink.

Basil

'good for the heart and for the head'

Basil   (*Ocimum basillicum*). Annual.
  Sweet Basil.
  Old form: Basill, Herb Royal, Basyll, Bazil.
Bush Basil   (*Ocimum minimum*). Annual.
  Mint family.

Most herbs are watered in early morning or at evening, so that they may not be dried up; but basil is watered even at noon, for it is said that it grows more quickly if it is watered at first with warm water.

Basil turns pale about the rising of the dog-star, and coriander becomes mildewed.

THEOPHRASTUS, *Enquiry into Plants*, 300 B.C. (trans. Hort, 1916)

Great Basill gentle.

Bushe Basill, or small Basill gentle.

Sweet basil (left)
and bush basil from
The Herball, 1597

Isabella and the pot of basil by William Holman Hunt

She wrapped it up, and for its tomb did choose
A garden pot, wherein she laid it by,
And covered it with mould, and o'er it set
Sweet Basil, which her tears kept ever wet.

JOHN KEATS, *Isabella; or, The Pot of Basil*, 1818

Ocimum is commonly knowne, being eaten much
it dulls the eye-sight, but it is a softner of ye belly,
a mouer of flatulencies, ureticall, and calling out
of milke. It is hard of digestion. Being applyed
with the flour of Polenta, & Rosaceum, & urnegar,
it doth help inflammations, & ye stroke of ye Sea
dragon, and of ye Scorpion. Of itself with Chian
wine (it is good) for ye griefs of the eyes. But ye
iuyce of it, doth take away the dimnesse that is
in the eyes, and drie up the rhumes. But the seed
being dranck is good for such as breed melancholy,
& for ye Dysureticall and for the Flatulent. It
causeth also many sneesings, being drawn vp by
the smell, & the herb doth the like. But the eyes
must be shut whilst ye sneesing holds. Somme also
doe avoyd it and doe not eate it, because that
being chewed, and set in the Sunne, it breeds
little wormes. But the Africans have entertained
it, because they which eate it & are smitten of a
Scorpion, yet remaine without paine.

DIOSCORIDES, 60 A.D. (trans. Goodyer, 1655)

The best time of the day to water gardens, is
morning and evening, to the end that the water
should not be overheat with the Sunne. Basill onely
would be watered also at noone. And moreover,
some thinke, that when it is new sowen, it will make
hast to come up very speedily, if it be sprinckled
at the first with hote water.

Also *Chrysippus* mightily crieth out upon Basill,
as being hurtfull to the stomacke, supressing urine,
and an enemie to a cleare sight.

Some there be who have not done with it so:
but adde moreover and say, That if Basille be
stamped and put under a stone, it will breed to a
Serpent: if it be chewed in ones mouth and laid
abroad in the Sunne, it will engender woormes and
maggots.

Contariwise, the later writers and modern Phy-
sictions defend and maintain the use of Basill as
stoutly as the other blamed it: for first they avouch
constantly, That Goats use to feed thereupon.
Secondly, that no man was ever knowne to goe
besides himselfe, who did eat thereof. Thirdly,
that Basill taken in wine, with a little vinegre put
thereto, cureth as well the sting of land Scorpions,
as the venome of those in the sea.

PLINY, *Naturall Historie*, 77 A.D. (trans. Holland,
1601)

The Basyll for his excellent smell and savour, hathe
bene greatlye cownted upon, in aunciente tyme,
in so much that kynges, and princes, for the great
delight whych they conceyed, in that herbe, did
plant the same in their garden.

THOMAS HYLL, *The Proffitable Arte of Gardening*,
1568

44

Basil if it be taken plentuously in mete, dulleth the eysyght. It softeneth the belly, moveth the spirites, & dryveth out pisse and bryngeth milk to the brests. But it is hard to be digested.

It is good for the strykying of a sea dragon, and the stynge of scorpiones. The sede dronken is good for them that brede melancholi; and for them that are puffed up with wynd. If it be put to the nose-thrills it maketh a man nese. The which thyng the leves do also.

The most part use Basil and eat it with oyle & (vine) gare, sauce for a fowl or kitchen.

WILLIAM TURNER, *The first and seconde partes of the Herbal*, 1568

Fine basil desireth it may be her lot,
to grow as the gelliflower, trim in a pot;
That ladies and gentles, to whom ye do serve,
may help her, as needeth, poor life to preserve.

THOMAS TUSSER, *Five Hundred Points*, 1577

The smell of Basill is good for the heart and for the head ... it taketh away sorrowfulnesse, which commeth of melancholie, and maketh a man merrie and glad.

Garden Basill is of two sortes, differing one from another in bignes. The first hath broad, thicke and fat leaves, of a pleasant sweet smell, and of which some one here and there are of a blacke reddish colour, somewhat snipt about the edges, not unlike the leaves of French Mercurie. The stalks groweth to the height of half a cubite, dividing it selfe into divers branches, whereupon do stand small and base flowers, sometimes whitish, and often tending to a darke purple. The roote is threddie, and dieth at the approach of winter.

The middle Basill is very like unto the former, but it is altogether lesser. The whole plant is of a most odoriferous smell, not unlike the smell of a Limon, or Citron.

Bush Basill, or fine Basill, is a low and base plant, having a threddle roote, from which rise up manie small and tender stalkes, branched into divers armes or boughes, whereupon are placed many little leaves, lesser than those of Pennie royall. The whole plant is of a most pleasing sweet smell.

Basill is sowen in gardens, and in earthern pots. It commeth up quickly, and loveth little moisture, except in the middle of the day; otherwise if it be sowen in rainie weather, the seede will putrifie, and growe into a jellie or slime, and come to nothing.

JOHN GERARD, *The Herball*, 1597

It must be watered at noone-tide, cleane contrary to other herbes which would be watered at morning or evening. To cause it to grow great, it is good to crop it oft with your fingers and not with any yron thing. Some report a marvellous strange thing of basill, as namely that it groweth fairer and higher, if it be sowen with curses and injuries offred unto it ...

RICHARD SURFLET, *The Countrie Farme*, 1600

The ordinary Basill is in a manner wholly spent to make sweet, or washing waters, among other sweet herbes, yet sometimes it is put into nosegays. The Physicall properties are, to procure a cheerfull and merry heart, whereunto the seed is chiefly used in powder, & c. and is most used to that, and to no other purpose.

JOHN PARKINSON, *Paradisus*, 1629

This is the Herb which all authors are together by the Ears about, and rail at one another like Lawyers: *Galen* and *Dioscorides* hold it not fit to be taken inwardly; and *Chrysippus* rails at it with downright *Billingsgate Rhetoric*; *Pliny*, and the Arabian physicians defend it.

... Being applied to the place bitten by a venemous Beaste, or stung by a Wasp or Hornet, it speedily draws the poison to it; *Every like draws his like*.

... Something is the matter; this Herb and Rue will not grow together, no, nor near one another: and we know Rue is as great an enemy to Poyson as any that grows.

To conclude: it expelleth both Birth and After-Birth; and as it helps the deficiency of *Venus* in one kind, so it spoils all her actions in another. I dare write no more of it.

NICHOLAS CULPEPER, *The English Physician Enlarged*, 1653

Basil imparts a grateful flavour, if not too strong, somewhat offensive to the eyes; and therefore the tender tops to be very sparingly us'd in our sallet.

JOHN EVELYN, *Acetaria*, 1699

Sweet Basil is the right herb for flavouring turtle soup. It has a warm taste resembling clove, and is a great improvement to sauces and to 'cups'. Two hundred years ago French cooks were just as devoted to it for their *Ragouts* as they are today.

FRANCES A. BARDSWELL, *The Herb Garden*, 1911

The best known story about this legendary herb is the grisly tale of *Isabella and the Pot of Basil*, told first by Boccacio in the *Decameron* and later in Keats' poem, but best known to all by the painting of William Holman Hunt.

Isabella kept the head of her dead lover, Lorenzo, in a pot of basil at her bedside, as Salome was supposed to have preserved the head of John the Baptist. This weaves together some early beliefs: that basil thrives on the brains of a murdered man; that it could cause a scorpion to grow inside a man's head; and that it draws out venomous poisons because it is itself a poison. On the other hand, a pot of basil was often placed in the window by a lady as a signal that she was expecting a lover. It was the herb of grief and death.

All this points up the confusion in superstition and folklore about this herb, which caused one modern writer to call it 'a plant with a split personality'.

Basil is a native of Asia, the Pacific Islands and India, where it is known as Tulasi (*Ocimum sanctum*), sacred to the Hindu deity Vishnu and his wife, Lakshmi. It has been used in cooking for over 2000 years.

The name comes from the Greek, *basileus*, a king. In France it is called Herbe Royale. Known in ancient times in southern Europe, basil was not introduced into England until the 16th century.

The early herbalists thought that basil could not be eaten. The Greeks and Romans believed that cursing the plant when sown would ensure germination. The French proverb *semer le basilic* is still used to signify a slander. If you're feeling bad, perhaps you could take it out in a healthy way by heaping abuse on the basil!

Slowly the sweet scent and savour of basil overcame the nasty legends associated with it. It was said that the flamboyant Plantagenets used it as their royal scent. In the 17th century people flocked to Fleet Street, near the site of John Gerard's garden, to buy the famous Fetter Lane sausages which were spiced with basil.

Today we know basil as a favourite flavouring for many dishes. It goes particularly well with tomatoes, in salads, soups and sauces, omelettes and stews. The flavour is quite strong. Only a pinch is needed to pep up omelettes, cucumber, peas, cheese, fish, spinach, zucchini, potato salad and bean soup. It makes a fine herb oil or vinegar.

Chopping basil with 'any yron thing', as Richard Surflet noted, spoils the flavour. It is better to shred the young leaves with the fingers.

Sweet basil is the annual, growing to about half a metre high, with green or purple shiny leaves which are fragrant. The flowers are usually white or purple, but some types have yellow and red blooms.

Bush basil is more branched and compact, usually only about 20 cm high. It is hardier and has a clove-like flavour. Both basils are easily raised from seed and need to be grown in semi-shade. In the garden they are good companions with tomatoes (as on the plate), though *basil does not like rue, nor rue basil*. Keep them well apart.

Used as a strewing herb in the Middle Ages, basil still has a reputation as a discourager of fleas and flies. Harvest the leaves before the flowers open for a finer taste.

Bay Laurel

'appropriate unto triumphs'

Bay laurel from *The Herball*, 1597

46

Bay Laurel

Bay Laurel (*Laurus nobilis*). Evergreen.
  Sweet Bay, Laurel.
  Old form: Baie, bayes, lorer, lawrell, laurell.
  Laurel family.

Lawrell is appropriate unto triumphs, and besides groweth most pleasantly before the gates of the Emperor's court, and Bishops pallace . . . This tree alone both adorneth their stately houses, & also keepeth watch and ward duly at the dores.

With this Lawrell (the Delphicke) were they wont to be crowned at Delphos, who woon the prise at any tournoy or solemne games; as also the victorious captains who triumphed in Rome.

The Lawrell betokeneth peace: insomuch, as if a braunch thereof be held out among armed enemies, it is a signe of quietnes and cessation from arms. Moreover, the Romans were wont to send their missive letters adorned with Lawrell, when they would give advertisement of some speciall good newes or joifull victorie: they used besides to garnish therewith thier launces, pikes, and speares.

It is reported that *Tiberius Caesar* the Emperor used ever to weare a chaplet thereof when it thundered, for feare of being strucken with lightening.

PLINY, *Naturall Historie*, 77 A.D. (trans. Holland, 1601)

To make oyle of lorer tak the bayes of lorere and grynd hem and seth hem wt oyle and cole it or streyne it and this is clepid *oleum laureum*.

This oile is gude for male deflanke (mal de flank = pain in side) and all so when a man felith nat his awn lymmes.

MS 136, MEDICAL SOCIETY OF LONDON, 1444

The leaves of the Bay tree are alwayes grene and in figure and fashion they are lyke unto periwinckle. They are long and brodest in the middle of the lefe. They are blackishe grene namely when they are olde. They are curled about the edges, they smell well. And when they are casten into the fyre they crake wonderfully. The tre in England is no great tre, but it thryveth there many partes better and is lustier than in Germany. The berries are all moste round but not altogether. The kirnell is covered with a thick black barke which may well be parted from the kirnell.

WILLIAM TURNER, *A New Herball*, 1551

'Tis thought the King is dead: we will not stay,
the Bay trees in our country are all wither'd.
(Captain), *King Richard II*, Act II, Scene 4.

The Bay or Laurell tree commeth oftentimes to the height of a tree of a meane bignesse; it is full of boughes, covered with a greene barke: the leaves thereof long, broad, hard, of colour greene, sweetely smelling, and in taste somewhat bitter: the flowers amongst the boughes and leaves are of a greene colour; the berries are more long than round, and be covered with a blacke rinde . . .

JOHN GERARD, *The Herball*, 1597

The Bay leaves are of as necessary use as any other in the garden or orchard, for they serve both for pleasure and profit, both for ornament and for use, both for civil uses and for physic, yea, both for the sick and for the sound, both for the living and for the dead . . . so that from the cradle to the grave we have still use of it, we have still need of it.

JOHN PARKINSON, *Paradisus*, 1629

Neither witch nor devil, thunder nor lightning, will hurt a man in the place where a Bay tree is. Galen said that the leaves or bark do dry and heal very much, and the berries more than the leaves . . .

The berries are very effectual against all poisons of venemous creatures, and the sting of wasps and bees, as also against the pestilence, or other Infectious diseases, and therefore put into sundry treacles for that purposes . . .

A decoction likewise of equal parts of bay berries, cumin-seed, hyssop, origanum, and euphorbium, with some honey, and the head bathed therewith, doth wonderfully help distillations and rheums, and settleth the palate of the mouth into its place.

NICHOLAS CULPEPER, *The English Physician*, 1652

The Sweet Bay bush in the farmer's or cottage garden comes with its story from the streams of Greece, where it seeks moisture in a thirsty land along with the wild Olive and the Arbutus. And this Sweet Bay is the Laurel of the poets, of the first and greatest of all poet and artist nations of the earth – the laurel sacred to Apollo, and used in many ways in his worship, as we may see on coins, and in many other things that remain to us of the great peoples of the past.

WILLIAM ROBINSON, *The English Flower Garden*, 1883

The sweet bay is the true laurel of ancient Greece. Its leaves were used to make crowns for triumphant heroes, distinguished poets and victors of the Pythian games at Delphi. The title, Poet Laureate, comes from this use.

In Greek myth, Apollo was pursuing a mountain nymph named Daphne. The gods changed her into a laurel tree to escape him. Apollo consoled himself by weaving a garland from 'her' branches and, after this, the tree was held sacred by Apollo.

The bay has always been said to confer the gift of prophecy. Originally, it was probably chewed as a drug to procure visions. Leaves, berries and oil are narcotic. Bay leaves were worn as a protection against thunder. A sprig placed under the pillow ensured pleasant dreams. A withering laurel tree was an omen of disaster.

Caesar wore a crown of Alexandrian laurel (*Ruscus racemosus*). Its broader leaves went further in covering his bald head.

Today the bay laurel is the 'herb tree' of modern gardens, growing to a height of around ten metres if allowed, as it does in its native Mediterranean. Usually, it is kept in a tub and trimmed in triangular or global shape as a small shrub.

'Of all growing things', wrote Gertrude Jekyll, 'there is nothing more beautiful in detail than a little branch of Bay, the leaves are so well set on the stems and their waved edges give a satisfying impression of graceful strength'.

A jar or packet of bay leaves is kept in most kitchens. The fragrant leaves are added fresh or dry to stews, stuffings, spaghetti, meatloaf, fish, herb vinegars and the inevitable rice pudding. Only half a leaf or at most a full leaf is needed to give its spicy taste.

Dry the leaves in thin layers in a shady place. Then press them under a board with bricks for two weeks to stop them curling. Store in glass jars.

Bay rum was once made with the distilled bay oil and rum as an astringent and hair dressing. Alcohol and even methylated spirits later replaced the real spirit.

Increase bay by root cuttings. Keep the tree in a shady place in hot areas and move indoors in winter in cold areas if kept in a tub. Be careful not to use the leaves of the Cherry Laurel, which are shinier and produce poisonous prussic acid when cooked.

A bouquet garni, used in French cooking, is a mixture of fresh herbs, usually a bay leaf and sprigs of parsley and thyme, which are tied in a cheesecloth bag and added to soups and stews while cooking. They are removed before serving.

Bees

A swarm of bees from Mattioli, Lyons edition, 1579

The owners of Hives have a parfite forsight and knowledge what the increase or yeeld of honye will be in every yeare, by the plentiful or small number of floures growing and appearing on the Tyme about the Sommer solstice.

For this increaseth and yeeldeth most friendly floures for the Bees which render a coloure and savoure to the Hony.

THOMAS HYLL, *The Proffitable Arte of Gardening*, 1568

Go looke to thy bees if the hive be too light
Set water and honie, with rosemarie dight,
Which set in a dishful of stickes in the hive
From danger of famine ye save them alive.

THOMAS TUSSER, *Five Hundred Points of Good Husbandry*, 1573

Bawme is much sowen and set in Gardens, and oftentimes it groweth of itself in Woods and mountaines, and other wilde places: it is profitable planted in Gardens, as Pliny writeth, about places where Bees are kept, because they are delighted

with this herbe above others, whereupon it hath beene called Apiastrum: for, saith he, when they are straied away, they doe finde their way home againe by it ...
JOHN GERARD, *The Herball*, 1597

You shall perfume the Hive with Juniper, and rub it all within with Fennel, Hyssop, and Time-flowers, and also the stone upon which the Hive shall stand ... for in all clenlinesse and sweetnesse the Bees are much delighted.
GERVASE MARKHAM, *The English Husbandman*, 1613

There remaineth one necessary thing prescribed, which in my opinion makes as much ornament as either Flowers or forme or cleanliness, and I am sure as commodious as any of or all the rest, which is Bees, well ordered. I will not account her any of my good Housewifes, that wanteth either Bees or skillfulness about them.
WILLIAM LAWSON, *The Countrie Housewifes Garden*, 1617

Honey in Spaine smelleth (apparently) of the Rose-Mary of Orenge, from whence the Bee gathereth it.
FRANCIS BACON, *Essay on Gardens*, 1625

Melrosette, or Honey of Roses

Melrosette is made thus, take faire purified hony and newe redde roses, the white endes of them clypped away, than chop them smal and put them into the hony and boile them menely togither, to knowe when it is boyled ynough, ye shall knowe it by the swete odour and the colour redde. Five yeres he may be kepte in his vertue, by the Roses he hath vertue of comfortinge, and by the hony he hath vertue of clensynge.
ANTHONY ASKHAM, *A Lytel Herball*, 1550

Hydromel As I Made It Weak for the Queen Mother

Take eighteen quarts of spring water, and one quart of honey, when the water is warm put the honey into it. When it boileth up, skim it very well and continue skimming it as long as any scum will rise. Then put in one Race of Ginger (sliced in thin slices), four Cloves, and a little sprig of green Rosemary.

Let these boil in the liquor so long till in all it have boiled one hour. Then set it to cool, till it be blood-warm, and then put to it a spoonful of Ale-yest. When it is worked up, put it into a vessel of a fit size, and after two or three days, bottle it up. You may drink it after six weeks or two months.
SIR KENELM DIGBY, *The Closet Opened*, 1669

A Moslem story tells of a princess who was ill. A wise man said she would recover only if she were given 1 000 plants. A herb seller heard about the problem. 'Give her honey,' she advised, 'that comes from 1 000 plants.' Of course the princess soon recovered!

Honey goes as well with herbs as bees go with the herb garden. If you have the space, keep your own bees to increase your delight and to pollinate your plants.

The bees will follow the herbs, buzzing about the borage and lavender or hedge of hyssop. They love the mints and all the plants which are listed below.

Against Bee-stings

After flicking out the sting with the back of your fingernail, rub the wound with the leaves of either balm, marigold, rue, dock or burnet — whatever is closer. If you squeeze a bee sting you only force more painful poison from the dead bee's sac.

Herbs and Plants for a Bee Garden

Alfalfa	Marjoram
Balm	Mints
Basil	Rosemary
Bergamot	Sage
Borage	Savory
Chamomile	Stock
Clover	Sweet cicely
Cornflower	Sunflower
Fennel	Thyme
Fruit trees	Vines
Hyssop	Violets
Lavender	Wattle
Marigolds	Woodruff

49

Borage

'borage for courage'

Borage (*Borago officinalis*), Annual.
Borage, Beebread, Starflower.
Old form: Borago, Borrage, Burrage.
Borage family.

This growyth in gardynggis and it hast a scharp lef and a blew flour. The vertu of this herbe is that it wele clense the rede colour in mannys face. Also this herbe medled in wyn wyl make a man glad and merye. Also it is good to putte in potage for it is holsum for the body.

AGNUS CASTUS, 14th century

Borage is called in shops *Borago: Pliny* calleth it *Euphrosinum* because it makes a man merry and joyful: which thing also the old verse concerning Borage doth testifie:

> *Ego Borago gaudia semper ago.*
> I Borage bring alwaies courage.

Those of our time do use the floures in sallads, to exhilerate and make the minde glad. There be also many things made of them, used for the comfort of the heart, to drive away sorrow, & increase the joy of the minde.

The leaves and floures of Borrage put into wine make men and women glad and merry, driving away all sadnesse, dulnesse, and melancholy.

Syrrup made of the floures of Borrage comforteth the heart, purgeth melancholy, and quieteth the phrenticke or lunaticke person.

JOHN GERARD, *The Herball*, 1597

Although Borage and Buglosse might as fitly have been placed, I confesse, in the Kitchen Garden, in regard they are wholly in a manner spent in Physicall properties, or for the Pot, yet because anciently they have been entertained into Gardens of pleasure, their flowers having been in some respect; in that they have always been enterposed among the flowers of womens needle-work. I am more willing to give them place here (in The Garden of Pleasant Flowers), then trust them into obscurity, and take such of their tribe with them also as may fit for this place, either for beauty or rarity.

. . . Borage and Buglosse are held to bee both temperate herbes, beeing used both in the pot and in drinkes that are cordiall, especially the flowers, which of Gentlewomen are candid for comfitts.

JOHN PARKINSON, *Paradisus*, 1629

Shade to some plants conduceth to make them large and prosperous more than the sunne. As in *Strawberries* and *Bayes & c.* Therefore among *Strawberries* sow here and there some *Borage* seed, and you shall finde the Strawberries under those leaves farre more large then their fellowes.

WILLIAM COLES, *The Art of Simpling*, 1656

The tender leaves, and flowers especially, may be eaten in composition; but above all, the sprigs in wine, like those of baum, are of known vertue to revive the hypochondriac, and chear the hard student.

JOHN EVELYN, *Acetaria*, 1699

Borage, which is alleged to make people brave, is a herb to use in 'cups'; it grows violently from seed, needing less than no encouragement. Its misty blue flowers and grey velvet leaves are of great value where blots of cool colour are needed in the herbaceous borders.

MARIAN CRAN, *The Garden of Ignorance*, 1917

Do you know borage? Borage for courage. It's an old, old herb and the flowers come all the winter, beautiful blue flowers, most extraordinary flowers. They look like little blue shooting stars. They taste of cucumber. A touch of oil and salt just corrects the flavour . . .

NEIL DOUGLAS, *Earth Garden 2*, 1972

Vivid as any flower, borage will brighten your spirits and bring bees to your garden. The Welsh called it Llanwenlys, or 'herb of gladness' and modern researchers have discovered that it stimulates the adrenal gland.

Borage is an annual which grows well from seed and will easily self-sow, coming up every year once started. The stalk and branched stems are hairy and coarse, the wrinkled leaves pulpy, and the clusters of flowers a brilliant sky blue,

Plants of the borage family. 'They have alwaies been enterposed among the flowers of women's needlework' from *Paradisus*, 1629.
(1) Cowslips of Jerusalem (2) Narrow leafed cowslips of Jerusalem (3) Borage (4) Everlasting borage (5) Anchusa (Sea Bugloss) (6) Bugloss or *Alkanet*

Borage from *Herbarus zu Teutsch*, 1496

or sometimes pink. There is also a white-flowering variety.

The plant grows to about three quarters of a metre and does best in a sunny spot. A few borage plants will shade the strawberry patch, as William Coles suggested. They look stunning in clusters, especially in a high bank, as the starry flowers hang down. They also make fine borders.

The leaves and flowers, tasting faintly of cucumber, are delicious fresh in salads or added to cider, punch, white wine, Pimms, or even lemonade. They add flavour to soups, especially cabbage, green pea and bean soups. They can be made into fritters, cooked in butter like spinach, or chopped up on bread and butter.

The flowers alone are candied by dipping quickly in egg white, then sugar, and drying on wax paper. Add to sweets and jellies. The flowers are also dried carefully on wire racks to use in pot-pourri.

Borage contains calcium, potassium and saline mucilage which is cooling.

Borage tea soothes the throat. It is made from the leaves, dried and stored in air-tight jars, 5 g of herbs to 500 ml of water. Or steep the fresh leaves in boiling water. Add honey and lemon if desired.

Borage fritters are made in the same way as comfrey fritters (page 66). They make a delicious sweet, sprinkled with sugar and honey.

A cool tankard: Mix cider, water and lemon juice, or white wine and lemon juice and add borage leaves and flowers for a cooling summer drink.

To Make a Tart of Borage Flowers

Take Borage flowers and parboile them tender, then strayne them with the yolkes of three or foure egges and sweete curdes, or else take three or fouer apples, and parboyle with all, and strain them with sweete butter, and a little mace, and so bake it.

RICHARD PYNSEN, *A proper new Booke of Cookery*, 1575

To Make Conserve of Borage Flowers

Take of your Borage flowers well coloured and picke the blacks from them, then weigh them, to every ounce of flowers you must take three ounces of suger, and beat them together in an Alabaster morter with a wooden pestle untill they be verie fine, so that you cannot discerne any suger in lumps, then take them out and put the conserve into a pipkin, and heat it through hot, and having thus done put them up & keepe them all the yeare.

A Closet for Ladies and Gentlewomen, 1608

Conserve of Borage Flowers after the Italian Manner

Take of fresh Borage flowers 4 ozs. fine sugar 12 ozs, beat them well together in a stone Mortar, and keep them in a vessel well glazed.

W.M., cook to Queen Henrietta Maria, *The Queen's Closet Opened*, 1655

Burnet

'leaves like unto the wings of birdes'

Burnet from *The Herball*, 1597

Burnet (*Sanguisorba minor*). Perennial.
   Salad burnet, Pimpernel.
   Old Form: Pimpernell.
   Rose family.

That salad is not good nor fair,
If Pimpinella is not there.
ITALIAN PROVERB

This herbe hast a blew flour as hast heyhoue and lewys lyk to tansye but thei ben not so grete and the vertue of this herbe is that he wele drye and dustroye the humures and the laxatyf with-inne a man. Also it helyth a man of the yelow jawndees.
AGNUS CASTUS, 14th century

It has two little leaves like unto the wings of birdes, standing out as the bird setteth her wings out when she intendeth to flye. Ye Dutchmen call it Hergottes Berdlen, that is God's little birds, because of the colour that it hath in the topp.
WILLIAM TURNER, *A New Herball*, 1551

Garden Burnet hath long leaves made up together of a great many upon one stem, every one whereof is something round, nicked on the edges, somwhat hairie: among these riseth a stalke that is not altogether without leaves, something chamfered: upon the tops whereof grow little round heads or knaps, which bring forth small floures of a browne purple colour, and after them cornered seeds, which are thrust up together. The root is long: the whole plant doth smell something like a Melon, or Cucumber.

   Burnet is a singular good herb for wounds and commendeth of a number: it stancheth bleeding, and therefore it was named *Sanguisorba*, as well inwardly taken, as outwardly applied.

   The lesser Burnet is pleasant to be eaten in sallads, in which it is thought to make the heart merry and glad, as also being put into wine, to which it yeeldeth a certaine grace in the drinking.
JOHN GERARD, *The Herball*, 1597

Those which perfume the air most delightfully, not passed by as the rest, but being trodden upon and crushed, are three, that is Burnet, Wild Thyme, and Water Mints, therefore you are to set whole alleys of them, to have the pleasure when you walk or tread.
FRANCIS BACON, *Of Gardens*, 1625

Burnet hath many winged leaves lying upon the ground, made of many small, round, yet pointed green leaves, finely nicked on the edges, one set against another all along a middle ribb, and one at the end thereof; from among which rise up divers round, and sometimes crested brown stalks, with some few such like leaves on them as grow below, but smaller: at the tops of the stalks grow small brown heads or knaps, which shoot forth small purplish flowers turning into long and brownish, but a little cornered seed: the root groweth down deep, being small and brownish: the whole plant is of a stiptick or binding taste or quality, but of a fine quick sent, almost like Baulm.

   The greatest use that Burnet is commonly put unto, is to put a few leaves into a cup with claret wine, which is presently to be drunk, and giveth a pleasant quick tast thereunto, very delightful to the palate, and is accounted a help to make the heart merry. It is sometimes also while it is young, put among other sallet herbs, to give a finer relish thereunto. It is also used in vulnerary drinks, and to stay fluxes and bleedings, for which purposes it is much commended in contagious and pestilential agues.
JOHN PARKINSON, *Paradisus*, 1629

Salad burnet has serrated leaves which add a cool, nutty, cucumber taste when snipped into salads and cool drinks.

A perennial, burnet grows in a clumpy rosette to a height of half a metre with its fernlike cut leaves radiating outwards from the centre. The flowers have white and rosy round heads, but these should be nipped off if the leaves are needed for salads, to encourage new leaf growth.

For the same reason the plant is usually treated as an annual, being started easily from seed and self-seeding if allowed to flower. It is best planted in full sun, where it will flourish for years.

Its compact growth makes salad burnet ideal for city dwellers to use in window boxes and pots.

The leaves are added fresh (they don't dry well) to fruit and potato salads, iced drinks, white wine, claret or beer in the same way as borage. Add the leaves as a garnish to soup. I have found that chewing the young leaves freshens the breath.

In former times, burnet had a reputation as a wound healer and the mashed up leaves were said to staunch bleeding. King Chaba of Hungary was reputed to have used its juice to cure the wounds of 15 000 of his soldiers after a bloody battle against his brother. Burnet contains magnesium.

Burnet vinegar is made by steeping the leaves and seeds (if available) in heated vinegar. Keep for two to three months in a stoppered jar before using.

Caraway
'a dish of carraways'

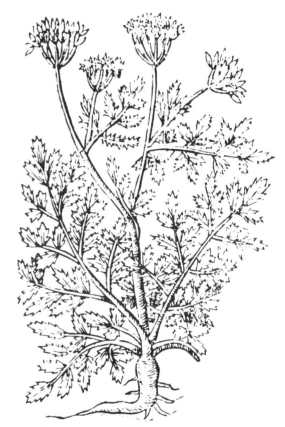

Caraway from *Paradisus*, 1629

Caraway (*Carum carvi*). Biennial.
Old form: Carraway
Umbilleferae – parsley family

Caria is an herbe called Caraway, it hath leves lyke somwhat to fenell, and a long stalke & round sede; more then the sede of persely. The vertue of hym is that he dystroyeth wycked wyndes and the coughe, & heleth men that hath the frensy, and bytynge with venemous beestes ... This herbe is hote and drye, & groweth in gardaynes.

Macer's Herbal Practysed by Dr Lynacro, 1535

Karia or Caraway from the
Juliana Anicia Codex, 512 A.D.

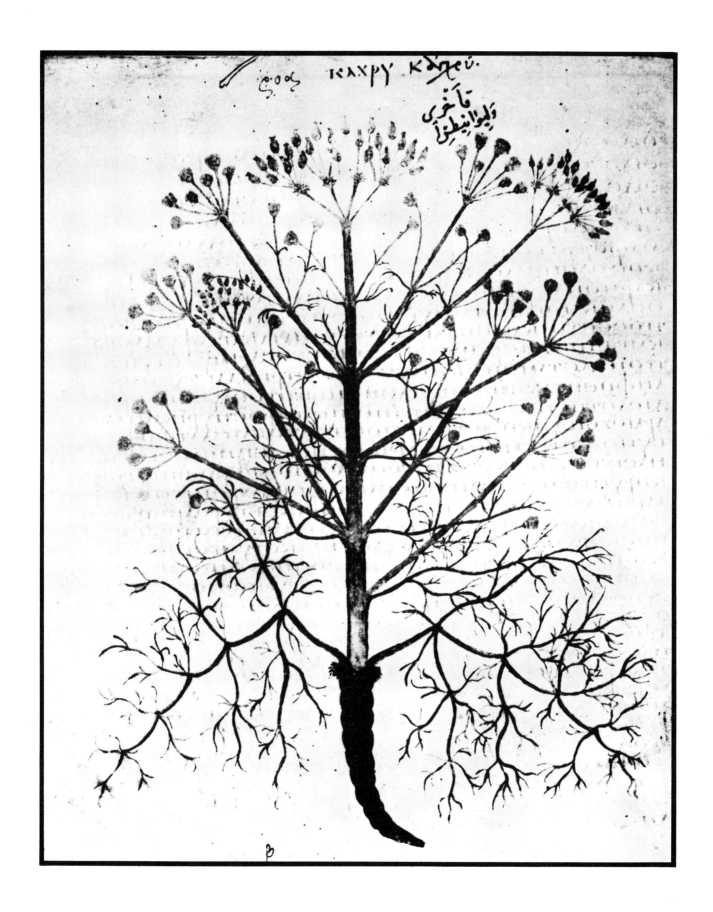

Nay, you shall see mine orchard, where in an arbour, we will eat a last year's pippin of my own graffing, with a dish of carraways, and so forth . . . (Shallow to Falstaff), *Henry IV*, Act V, Scene 3

Wife, sometimes this weeke if that all things go cleare,
an ende of wheat sowing we make for this year,
Remember you therefore though I do it not
the Seede Cake, the Paties, and Furmenty pot.

THOMAS TUSSER, *Five Hundred Points*, 1577

The seedes confected or made with sugar into Comfits, are very good for the stomacke, they helpe digestion, provoke urine, asswage and dissolve all windines: to conclude in a worde, they are answerable to Anise seede in operation and vertues.

JOHN GERARD, *The Herball*, 1597

Caraway hath many very fine cut and divided leaves lying on the ground, being alwaies greene, some-what resembling the leaves of Carrots, but thinner and more finely cut, of a quicke, hot and spicie taste: the stalke riseth not much higher than the Carrot stalke, bearing some leaves at the ioynts along the stalke to the toppe, where it brancheth into three or four parts, bearing spoakie umbles of white flowers, which turne into small blackish seede, smaller than Aniseede, and of a hotter, quicker taste, the roote is whitish, like un to Parsnep, but much smaller, more spreading underground, and a little quick in taste, as all the rest of the plant is, and abideth long after it hath given seede.

The seede is much used to be put among baked fruit, or into bread, cakes & etc. to give them a rellish, and to help digest winde in them are subject thereunto. It is also made into Comfits . . . taken for the cold and winde in the body, as are served to the table with fruit.

The roots of Carraway, being boiled, may be eaten as Carrots and by reason of the spicie taste doth warm and comfort a cold weak Stomache, helping to dissolve Wind and to provoke Urine, and is a very welcome and delightful Dish to many.

JOHN PARKINSON, *Paradisus*, 1629

Carraway seed has a moderate sharp quality, whereby it breaks wind and provokes urine, which also the herb doth. The root is better food than the parsnip; it is pleasant and comfortable to the stomach, and helps indigestion.

The powder of the seed put into a poultice, takes away black and blue spots of blows and bruises.

Carraway comfits, once only dipped in sugar,

and half a spoonful of them eaten in the morning fasting, and as many after each meal, is a most admirable remedy, for those that are troubled with the wind.

NICHOLAS CULPEPER, *The English Physician*, 1652

Caraway Liqueur

Ingredients – ½ lb. of loaf sugar, 1 oz. of caraway seeds, 1 quart of brandy.
Mode – Boil the sugar in half a pint of water, and put in the caraway seeds while it is still hot, then add the brandy. Cork it immediately. Let it stand for a week, then filter and bottle it.

MRS ISABELLA BEETON, *Household Management*, 1861

Caraway is one of the tribe of aromatic seed-producing umbilliferous plants which also includes anise, cumin, dill and fennel.

It is a biennial. In the first year it has finely-cut, lacy, carrot-like leaves. Next year the stalks grow to almost a metre in height, bearing umbels of tiny white flower clusters. These mature into the fruits or seeds, tasting of liquorice, used for many cooking purposes.

Caraway seeds have been found in the debris of the primitive Swiss lake dwellers. In Britain it was a custom from Medieval times to bake 'seedcakes' of caraways for farm labourers after wheat sowing. A plate of seeds was served with roast pippins (apples).

A predominant superstition was that objects containing caraway seeds could not be taken away or stolen. So pigeons were fed with the seeds to stop them straying. It was thought that caraway seeds were a sure protection against the loss of hair and that a few seeds placed in his pocket would prevent the theft of a husband's heart!

In Germany Kummel liqueur is made from the oil extracted from caraway leaves and seeds. The left-over seed cake has a high fat and protein content and is used as cattle feed. Caraway has been used to flavour perfumes and mouth washes.

The seeds are used especially scattered over rye bread, bread rolls, apple pie and baked apples but also in cakes, cheese, sauerkraut, cabbage soup, beetroot and pork dishes. The young shoots and leaves may be used sparingly in salads.

The root is edible and nourishing prepared in the same way as carrot or parsnip. Roman soldiers mixed the roots with milk to make a bread called chara.

Caraway will grow well from seed. It's a good idea to plant caraway each year because of its biennial habit . . . sown in autumn it will flower the next year.

Peas are often planted in the same row and harvested before the caraways appear. *Don't plant near fennel.*

Collect the seeds in the same way as dill as soon as they darken and ripen — otherwise they will split, or the birds will harvest them before you.

Caraway comfits are the seeds crusted with white sugar.

Caraway Cheese

Take one cup of cottage cheese, add salt and pepper to taste, one teaspoon of caraways, and enough cream to soften the mixture for spreading.

Catnip

'cat's delight'

Catnip from *Paradisus*, 1629

Catnip (*Nepeta cataria*). Perennial.
Catnip.
Old form: Nep, Cat-nep, Nepte.
Mint family.

Great conformitie there is in operation between Penyroiall and Nep: for being both of them boiled in water unto the consumption of a third part, they discusse and shake off the cold in ague fits which causeth the Patient to shake; and besides are of validitie to bring downe womens monethly sicknesse. In Summer time, they assuage the extremitie of heat. Nep also is powerful against Serpents, for the smoke and perfume of this hearb they cannot abide, but will flie from it: which is the cause thatsuch as bee afraid of Serpents, strew Nep under them in the place where they mean to repose and sleepe.

PLINY, *Naturall Historie*, 77 A.D. (trans. Holland, 1601)

Moch folk clepyth it catts gresse ffor cattis will ete it when the bene syk in here wombes.

Ach of womb. Take nepte and stamp it and temp it wt wyne and drynke it off and it shall do away the ach.

MS 136, MEDICAL SOCIETY OF LONDON, 1444

The vertu of this herbe is if a cat ete thereof it schal conseywyn and brynge forth kytlyngis anon.

AGNUS CASTUS, 14th century

That which is usual (and called of many Cat Mint) beareth square stalkes, but not so great as Clarie, having two leaves at every joynt, somewhat like unto Balme or Speare Mintes, but whiter, softer and longer, and nicked about the edges, of a strong sent, but nothing so strong as Clary: the flowers grow at the tops of the stalkes, as it were in long spikes or heads; somewhat close together, yet compassing the stalkes at certain joyntes, of a whitish colour, for forme and bignesse like unto Balme, or somewhat bigger: the rootes are composed of a number of strings, which die not, but keep green leaves upon them all the Winter, and shoot anew in the Spring. It is propagated both by the seed, and by slipping the rootes.

Nep is much used of women either in baths or drinkes to procure their feminine courses: as also with Clarie, being fried into Tansies, to strengthen their backs. It is much commended of some, if the juice thereof be drunk with wine, to help those that are bruised by some fall, or other accident. A decoction of Nep is available to cure the scab in the head, or other places of the body.

JOHN PARKINSON, *Paradisus*, 1629

Cats delight both to smell and eate thereof, and gladly rub themselves against it.

JOHN PARKINSON, *Theatrum Botanicum*, 1640

Common Garden Nep shooteth forth hard four square stalks with a hoarines on them, a yard high or more, ful of Branches, bearing at every Joynt two broad Leavs, somwhat like Balm but longer pointed, softer, whiter, and more hoary, nicked about the edges, and of a strong sweet scent. The flowers grow in large tufts at the tops of the Branches, and underneath them likewise on the Stalks many together, of a whitish purple color. The Roots are composed of many long strings or Fibres, fastning themselves strongly in the ground, and abide with green Leavs thereon al the Winter.

It is only nursed up in our Gardens.

. . . It is . . . used in pains of the Head coming of any cold caus, as Catarrhs, Rhewms, and for swimming and giddiness thereof, and is of especial use for the windines of the Stomach and Belly. It is effectual for any Cramps or cold aches, to dissolve the cold and wind that afflicteth the place, and is used for Colds, Coughs, and shortness of breath. The Juyce thereof drunk in Wine is profitable for those that are bruised by any accident.

NICHOLAS CULPEPER, *The English Physician Enlarged*, 1653

When the *Cat* is sick, she goes to the *Nep* or *Catmint*, of which there is this old Rime;

> *If you set it, the Catts will eate it,*
> *If you sow it, the Catts can't know it.*

WILLIAM COLES, *The Art of Simpling*, 1656

'Tis hot and dry. 'Tis chiefly used for Obstructions of the Womb, for Barrenness, and to hasten Delivery, and to help Expectoration. 'Tis used outwardly in Baths for the Womb, and the Itch.

JOHN PECHEY, *The Compleat Herbal*, 1694

Catnip is supposed to make cats playful — something I have yet to see in my own garden. Our neighbour's Burmese cats have never thrown themselves at it, nor eaten it down to the ground.

It is a pretty plant growing to almost a metre high, with heart-shaped leaves toothed at the edges, very much like lemon balm, but with softer tips. It is hardy but gets rather bushy after a couple of years, when it is best to renew the plant. Spikes of tiny white flowers bloom in high summer.

Catnip is easily propagated by seed or root division and does not need much attention, beside regular watering.

The leafy tops make a digestive tea and may be mixed with other mints, particularly lemon balm, in tea or salads.

The leaves are dried to make a toy for cats known as a *catnip mouse*. Cut out two mouse silhouettes in muslin and fill with dried leaves before sewing up.

Chamomile
'the appell of an eye'

Chaomomile from Mattioli, 1579

Chamomile (*Anthemis Nobilis*). Perennial.
  English or Roman chamomile.
  Old form: Camomile, camomile, cammomill.
German Chamomile (*Matricaria chamomilla*).
Annual.
  Composite family.

Much like unto Sothernwood in sent and smell, is Camomile: the flower is white, consisting of a number of pretie fine leaves set round about the yellow within.

PLINY, *Naturall Historie*, 77 A.D. (trans. Holland, 1601)

Asclepius comendith hugely comomylle; this is clepid comomila. This herbe is swete in savour and short in substance.
  . . . Alle they have a yelowe flour in the myddell . . . properly she is seid anthemis, hose flour leves, standying a-boute the yelowe, ben purpure colour. This is the most and strengest.
  . . . Ofte-tyme in the heed risen apostomes or boccles of the humours gederid to-geder, the which boccles the greek clepith exantimata [rash]. Than take grene camomylle and sethe it in oile, and if thou may have noon grene, take dreye and wet it wel in vynegre and therewith oynte the heed alle a-bowte, for there is non oynement that helpith the hede more.

Macer's Herbal, 12th century

This herbe is called Camomyl: the vertue of this herbe is thus yf it be drunke with wine it wyl breke the stone, and destroyeth the yelowe evyl. It helpeth the akinge and the desease of the liver, if it be strained it helpeth and swageth the sores in a mannes mouth, it is good for aking in a mans heade, and for the megrim, this herbe is hote and drye.

ANTHONY ASKHAM, *A Lytel Herball*, 1550

Cammomill, is an Herb used of Physitions to purge the head, and to emptie it of superfluous humour and other grosse matter . . . This hath that laudable preheminence for that the more it is trod and kept under, the more a great deal it commeth up and prospereth.

JOHN MAPLET, *A greene Forest*, 1567

  The Chamomile shall teach thee patience
  That rises best when trodden most upon.

English Saying

. . . For though the camomile, the more it is trodden on, the faster it grows, yet youth, the more it is wasted, the sooner it wears.
(Falstaff to Prince Hal), *King Henry IV*, Part 1, Act II, Scene 4

To comfort the braine smel to camomill, eate sage . . . wash measurably, sleep reasonably, delight to heare melody and singing.

RAM'S LITTLE DODOEN, 1606

Syrup made of the juice of Camomile, with the flowers, in white wine, is a remedy against the jaundice and dropsy. The flowers boiled in lye, are good to wash the head, and comfort both it and the brain. The oil made of the flowers of Camomile, is much used against all hard swellings, pain or aches, shrinking of the sinews, or cramps or pains in the joints, or any other parts of the body.
  Nechessar says that the Egyptians dedicated it to the sun because it cured argues, and they were like enough to do it, for they were the arrantest apes in their religion that I ever read of.

NICHOLAS CULPEPER, *The English Physician*, 1652

It will not be good to Beat, Roll and Mow Carpet-walks and Camomile; for now the ground is supple and it will even all inequalities.

JOHN EVELYN, *Kalendarium Hortense* (October), 1664

No simple in the whole catalogue of herbal medicines is possessed of a quality more friendly and beneficial to the intestines than 'Chamomile Flowers'.

DR W.T. FERNIE, *Herbal Simples*, 1895

There is a remarkable property about the Camomile which some still believe in implicity – that it is the plant's physician. Nothing is thought to keep a garden so healthy as plenty of Camomile about; It will even revive drooping and sickly plants if placed near them.

FRANCES A. BARDSWELL, *The Herb Garden*, 1911

The apple-scented English chamomile (*Anthemis nobilis*) is usually taken to be the Anthemis of Dioscorides, which distinguishes it from its relative Stinking Mayweed (*Anthemis cotula*), an aptly named and much-hated weed.

It looks very much like German chamomile (*Matricaria chamomilla*), which has a similar odour, but coarser leaves. Other differences are that the 'German' plant stands erect, reaching nearly a metre while the 'English' is lower, usually more matted, seldom topping 30 cm in height. This was the type used traditionally for earth seats, paths and carpet lawns. They were regularly clipped and rolled, like the one at Buckingham Palace which is used for garden parties.

Chemical analysis by French scientists of the mummy of Egyptian Pharoah Rameses II revealed traces of chamomile pollen in the stomach contents, which were eighty per cent vegetable matter.

The English and German chamomiles have been used for centuries for their medicinal virtues. Each has a yellow flower centre surrounded by white petals. The centres are rounded and ready to pick when the white ray florets turn back.

The plants spread by runners and are propagated by root division. *Anthemis nobilis* is a perennial; *Matricaria chamomilla* an annual. In the garden, chamomile is thought of as a 'plant doctor', helping to strengthen and revive weak herbs nearby.

Chamomile Tea

Use 15 g of fresh flower heads, less of dried and crushed heads, to 500 ml of boiling water. It is sedative, relieves rheumatism, and was given to babies to help them sleep. It may also be used as a face wash to clear the complexion.

Chamomile Shampoo

Into a basin place one tablespoon of pure soap flakes, 5 ml of borax and 30 g powdered chamomile. Add 250 ml of hot water and beat until you have a thick lather. Wet your hair with warm water, add lather and massage well into the scalp. Rinse and repeat. Brings out the highlights in blonde hair.

Chives
'evill for the eyes'

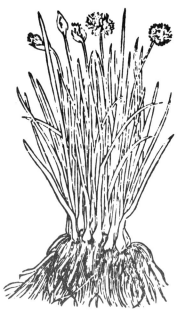

Chives from *A niewe Herball*, 1578

Chives (*Allium schoenoprasum*). Perennial.
  Old form: Cives, Cyves, Civer, Rushe Onyons, Rush Leeks, Chibboll, Chibal.
Garlic Chives (*A. tuberosum*). Chinese chives.
Siberian Chives (*A. ramosum*).
  Lily family.

Cyves or Rushe Onyons, in the Steede of leaves have litle, smal, holowe, & slender piped blades, lyke to smal Rushes, growing thicke together, in taste not much unlyke the taste of Leekes. Amongst the Rushlyke leaves growe smal bowles, or rounde knopped heades, like the bawle in the top of the seede Onyon, but much smaller, and ful of smal purple flowers.

It is set in gardens amongst potte herbes, or wurtes.

Cyves are used in meates and Pottages even as Leekes, which they do resemble in operation and vertue.

REMBERT DODOENS, *A niewe Herball* (trans. Lyte), 1578

Chibals or Chives have their rootes parted as Garlicke, Lillies & c. and so are they set, every third or fourth yeare, a good pothearbe, opening, but evill for the eyes.

WILLIAM LAWSON, *The Countrie Farme*, 1600

Cives. They are also called Rush Leeks, Chives, Civer, and Sweth.

I confess I had not added these had it not been for a Letter I received of a Country Gentleman, who certified me that amongst other Herbs I had left these out; they are indeed a kind of Leeks, hot and dry in the fourth degree as they are, and also under the Dominion of Mars; if they be eaten raw (I do not mean raw opposite rosted or boyled; but raw opposite to a Chymical Preparation), they send up very hurtful vapours to the Braine, causing troublesom sleep and spoiling of the eyesight, yet of them prepared by the Art of the Alchymist may be made an excellent remedy for stoppage of urine.

NICHOLAS CULPEPER, *The English Physician Enlarged*, 1653

Chives, the smallest member of the onion tribe, have a milder, more subtle flavour than either garlic or onions. They are worth growing as well for their dainty pink-purple flower heads.

They grow in clumps of bulbs from which rise the long, hollow, tapering stems of 'grass' to about 30 cm high.

Chives make an excellent edging plant in the kitchen garden and do well in a pot in the windowsill or on the patio if kept well watered. One bed could be left to flower and the other kept for cutting the side spears or shearing off the whole plant close to the ground three or four times a year for cooking. Regular cutting keeps the plant tender. The tops die down in winter. Replant every three or four years.

Use chives finely chopped in omelettes, salads, particularly with cucumber and tomatoes, sprinkle on carrots, mashed potatoes, Vichysoisse and other soups, in sandwiches, sausages and pies and with cottage cheese. You may also pickle the bulbs like small onions.

Raise from seed sown in moist sand in spring or more quickly by dividing the clumps of little bulbs in spring and autumn. Grow in full sun and feed regularly. In the garden, chives are a good companion for carrots and lettuce.

A Chive Spray

To use against apple scab and downy and powdery mildew on cucumbers and gooseberries it is made by pouring boiling water over dried chives. Leave to infuse for fifteen minutes, then dilute with water 2:1 before use.

Clary

'many vertues she havyth'

Clary sage from Petrus de Crescentis' *Opus Ruralium Commodorum*, Basel 1512

61

Clary (*Salvia sclarea*). Biennial.
  Clary sage.
  Old form: Sclarye, Clarie, Clear Eye.
  Mint family.

Sclarye, as leches, seyn, is gode for the hote gowte.
  Sclareye clariefieth her voys that ben hors, and she is right good both to the lunges and to the mawe and the bowell, and many vertues she havyth, of the whyche wise leches tretyn.
Macer's Herbal, 12th century

Wild Clary is called after the Latine name *Oculus Christi*, of his effect in helping the deseases of the eies. The seed put whole into the eies, clenseth and purgeth them exceedingly from waterish humors, rednesse, inflammation, and divers other maladies, or all that happen unto the eies, and takes away the paine and smarting thereof, especially being put into the eies one seed at one time, and no more, which is a generall medicine in Cheshire and other countries thereabout, knowne of all, and used with good success.
JOHN GERARD, *The Herball*, 1597

Clarie is sown, it seedes the second year, and dyes. It is somewhat harsh in taste, a little in pottage is good.
WILLIAM LAWSON, *The Countrie Housewifes Garden*, 1617

Our ordinary Garden Clary hath four square Stalks, with broad, rough, wrinkled, whitish, or hairy green Leavs, somwhat evenly cut in on the edges, and of a strong sweet scent, growing some neer the ground, and some by couples upon Stalks: The Flowers grow at certain distances with two smal Leavs at the Joynts under them, somwhat like unto the Flowers of Sage, but smaller, and of a whitish blue colour. . .
  The seed is used to be put into the Eyes to cleer them from Moats, or other such like things gotten within the Lids to offend them, as also to cleer them from white or red spots in them.
  The fresh Leavs dipped in Batter of Flower, Egs, and a littel Milk, and fried in Butter, and served to the Table, is not unpleasant to any, but exceedingly profitable to those that are troubled with weak Backs, and the effects thereof.
NICHOLAS CULPEPER, *The English Physician Enlarged*, 1653

When tender is not to be rejected in omelets; made up with cream fried in sweet butter, and eaten with sugar and juice of orange or lemon.
JOHN EVELYN, *Acetaria*, 1699

Clary sage is a larger, coarser shrub than the many types of common sage. It has square, brownish stems and reaches 60 to 80 cm in height. The leaves are heart-shaped, about the size of a child's hand, hairy and have a strong scent. The flowers, which are whorled, also have a strong musky aroma.

Clary will start from seed and may be transplanted. It is probably best to plant annually, though in milder climates, it will grow as a perennial.

In older times, clary was added to country wines to give it the flavour of muscatel. It was used in Indian beer and commercially as a perfume fixative.

Pick the leaves as needed to use fresh or dried in the same way as common sage, in omelettes and turkey stuffing. It may be dipped in batter and fried or dipped in cream and eaten with sugar and orange juice.

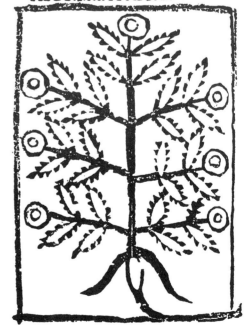

HERBA ARTEMISIA LFPTA, FILOS.I.MATRICALE.

Artemisia from *Herbarium Apulleii Platonici*, 1480

Comfrey, with purple and with white flowers from *The Herball*, 1597

Comfrey

'he shal ben hol in warantyie'

Comfrey (*Symphytum Officinale*). Common comfrey, Medicinal comfrey. Perennial.

Old form: Conforye, Confrey, Consounds, Solidago, Knitbone, Boneset, Bruisewort, Gumplant.

Prickly Comfrey (*S. asperrimum*). German fodder comfrey.

Russian Comfrey (*S. peregrinum*).
Russian's Prayer, Caucasian comfrey, Quaker comfrey. This is a cross between common comfrey and prickly comfrey.

Borage family.

Consolida Maior is an herbe men clepe dayessye or conforye. This herbe hast lewys lyk to horseheine [elecampane] but it is not so qwyth [white] and it growith in watere placis and ther ben ij specis ther-of. The toon [one] hast a qwyt flour the tother a reed and thei han both on[e] vertu. The vertu of this herbe is this that if a man be brokyn or bressed with-inne his body tak the rote of this herbe and roste it wel among hote colys and take it to the seke fastyng with hony and lete hym ete it. And he schal ben hol in warantyie. Also this herbe helyth brokyn bonys. This herbe is hot and drye and it beryth blak seed.

AGNUS CASTUS, 14th century

For the dry couge. Take horehound and comfrey and ete wt hony thre morowes and iij eves.

MS. 136 MEDICAL SOCIETY OF LONDON, 1444

This is named Confrey, it hath leaves lyk to Horse-helme, but they be not so whyte, there be two spyces thereof. One with a why flouer the other with a red. His vertue if yf a man be broken within, take the rotes of this herbe and roste them in the

Ashes and let the sicke eate thereof fastinge iii daies and he shall be hole. Also it helpeth to gather broken bones, it is colde and drye, and it bereth blacke sede. Also it stoppeth al maner of flures of bloude, and specyally for them that hath a veyne broken in the breast and vomiteth bloude, yf the ioyce there be drunke with redde wyne and a lytel masticke.

ANTHONY ASKHAM, *A Lytel Herball*, 1550

Comfrey hath rough hayzie stalkes, and long rough leaves, much like the leaves of common Buglosse, but much greater and blacker. The floures bee round and hollow like little bells, most commonly white, and sometimes reddish. The roote is black without, and white within, very clammie or slymie to touch.

...The roots of Comfrey pound and drunken are good for them that spit bloud, and healeth all inward wounds and burstings.

REMBERT DODOENS, *A niewe Herball* (trans. Lyte), 1578

1. The stalks of this Comfrey is cornered, thicke, and hollowe like that of Sowthistle, it groweth two cubits or a yarde high: the leaves that spring from the roote, and those that growe upon the stalks are long, broade, rough and pricking withall, something hairie, and that being handled, make the hands itch, very like in colour and roughness to those of Borrage, but longer and sharpe pointed, as be the leaves of Elecampagne: from out the wings of the stalks appeere the flowers, orderly placed, hollowe within, of a light redde colour: after them groweth the seed which is blacke: the roote is long and thicke, blacke without, white within, having in it a clammie iuice, in which consisteth the vertue.

2. The great Comfrey hath rough hairie stalks, long rough leaves, much like the garden Buglosse, but greater and blacke the flowers be round and hollowe like little bels, of a white colour: the roote is blacke without, and white within, and very slimie.

Comfrey ioyeth in watrie ditches, in fat and fruitful medowes; they grow all in my garden.

The Vertues

The rootes of Comfrey stamped, and the juice drunke with wine, helpeth those that spit bloude, and healeth all inward wounds and brusings.

The same bruised and laide to in manner of a plaister, doth heale all fresh and greene woundes, and are so glutinative, that it will sodder or glew togither meate that is chopt in peeces seething in a pot, and make it in one lumpe.

The rootes boiled and drunke, doth clense the brest from flegme, and cureth the greefes of the lungs especially if they be confect with sugar in syrupe, it prevaileth much against ruptures or bursting.

The slimie substance of the roote made in a posset of ale, and given to drinke against the paine in the back, gotten by any violent motion, as wrestling, or overmuch use of women, doth in fower or five daies perfectly cure the same...

JOHN GERARD, *The Herball*, 1597

Great comfrey groweth in moist places; and hath the same property that bugle hath, that is to say, to soulder wounde, and this is so great in both of them, as if that you put bugle or comfrey into a pot wherein flesh is boiling, the peeces of flesh will become no more many but one. The roote of great comfrey whiles it is yet greene and newlie pluckt out of the earth, being spred upon linnen, and applied in some forme of a cataplasme, upon gouty or rheumatike places, doth presently appease the paine of the goute, being a thing often prooved and tried.

RICHARD SURFLET, *The Countrie Farme*, 1600

The common great Comfry hath divers very large and hairy green Leavs lying on the ground, so hairy or prickly that if they touch any tender part of the Hands, Face, or Body, it will cause it to itch: The Stalk that riseth up from among them being two or three foot high, hollow and cornered, is very hairy also, having many such like Leavs as grow below, but lesser and lesser, up to the top. At the Joynts of the Stalks, it is divided into many branches with some Leavs thereon, and at the ends stand many Flowers in order one above another, which are somthing long and hollow like the finger of a Glove, of a pale whitish color; after which come smal black Seed. The Roots are great and long; spreading great thick branches under ground, black on the outside and whitish within, short, easie to break, and ful of a glutinus or clammy Juyce of little or no taste.

There is another sort in al things like this, save only it is somwhat less, and hath Flowers of a pale purple color.

They grow by Diches and Water sides, and in divers Fields that are moist, for therein they chiefly delight to grow.

What was spoken of Clowns Woundwort, may be said of this. The great Comfry helpeth those that spit blood, or make a bloody Urin: The Root boyled in Water or Wine, and the Decoction drunk, helpeth al inward hurts, bruises, and wounds, and the Ulcers of the Lungs, causing the Flegm that oppresseth them to be easily spit forth.

... The Roots being outwardly applied, helpeth fresh wounds or cuts immediately, being bruised and laid thereunto; and is especial good for Ruptures and broken bones: yea it is said to be so powerful to consolidate and knit together; that if they be boyled with dissevered pieces of flesh in a pot, it wil joyn them together again.

It is good to be applied to Womens Breasts that grow sore by the abundance of Milk coming into them: as also to repreive the overmuch bleeding of the Hemorrhoids to cool the inflammation of the parts thereabouts, and to give ease of pain. The Roots of Comfry taken fresh, beaten smal, and spread upon Leather, and laid upon any place troubled with the Gout do presently give case of the pains: and applied in the same manner giveth ease to pained Joynts, and profiteth very much for running and moist Ulcers, Gangreans, Mortifications, and the like, for which it hath by often experience been found helpful.

NICHOLAS CULPEPER, *The English Physician Enlarged*, 1653

Comfrey is mucilaginous, and is useful in all chest diseases, spitting of blood, and ulcerated lungs, soreness of the bowels, and all other inward inflammations. It makes a good lotion for ulcers and other sores, being very healing and cooling.

JOHN BROADBENT, *The Australian Botanic Guide*, 1887

Comfrey has been famed as a medicinal herb for thousands of years and known as knitbone and Bruisewort for its capacity to heal cuts, wounds and internal ulcers.

The herbalists from Pliny onwards were describing wild or common comfrey (*Symphytum officinale*). These days the comfrey you are likely to find in gardens is probably Russian comfrey (*S. peregrinum*), a cross between common comfrey and Prickly comfrey (*S. asperrimum*).

This strain has been developed with the aim of getting a high protein plant with higher content of *allantoin*, the active medical constituent, which encourages rapid healing of wounds and knitting of bones.

The figure behind the modern research and use of comfrey is Mr Lawrence D. Hills, founder of the Henry Doubleday Research Association,

a world-wide group of organic gardeners. Mr Hills is the author of *Comfrey, Past Present and Future*, published by Faber & Faber (1976).

Henry Doubleday was a Quaker smallholder of Cogeshall in Essex, who first imported comfrey from Russia to Britain in 1871.

Comfrey is a green stock feed rich in protein and minerals. It is of particular value to vegans because it is the only land plant which contains vitamin B12, necessary for their cheese, egg and meat-free diet.

Scientists recently warned that both borage and comfrey contain toxic pyrrolozidine alkaloids and that the regular eating of small amounts daily may cause cancer of the liver. Caution is also advised in feeding comfrey to stock. It looks as though comfrey fritters should be made a rare treat until more facts are known.

Comfrey is a hairy stemmed, coarse leafed plant with broad, pointed leaves and bell-shaped clusters of mauve flowers. It reaches a height of 60 to 80 cm, spreading out to about 60 cm.

Comfrey rarely sets seed and must be grown from root cuttings or divisions, but it is a perennial plant which will last twenty years. The above earth portion of the plant dies down in winter, but the leaves shoot out early in spring.

Leaves for use should be sheared off several times a year and the plant should not be allowed to flower if needed for regular harvesting. Once you obtain a root piece from a herb gardener or nurseryman you will find that it increases every year. Even the smallest section of root will produce another plant.

Comfrey Tea

This is made from the dried leaves. In Britain, people like an equal mixture of comfrey and ordinary tea with their milk and sugar. In the United States, comfrey tea is mixed half-and-half with mint leaves and sweetened with honey.

Dry comfrey leaves by spreading on wire netting (an old screen window will do) out of the sun in a warm, dry place. Leaves dry slowly because of the high moisture content. When they are crisp and crumble easily, rub them through a sieve and pack into jars tightly closed, or plastic bags sealed with sticky tape.

Comfrey is cooked as a vegetable, like spinach, with just a little water or oil. Use small leaves, or snip off the stringy midribs of the larger leaves. Chop up young leaves to add to salads, soups and stew.

Comfrey Fritters

Make up a batter using one egg, $\frac{3}{4}$ cup plain flour and one cup milk. Sift the flour into a basin and make a well in the centre. Add a pinch of salt.

Break the egg into the flour well, add some milk and beat with a fork, gradually adding the rest of the milk and bringing the dry flour into the centre. Beat well. Wash a dozen comfrey leaves and dip them in the batter before frying quickly in oil or butter until golden brown on each side. They really do look like little golden fishes and are delicious with cheese or meat.

Companion Herbs

Radish is at enmetie with hyssop. The Figtree and Rue are in great league and amitie, insomuch as this hearb, sow and set it when and where you will, in no place prospereth better than under that tree.

Here and there among (onions), there would be Saverey sowne, for the better will the Onions like and prosper with the companie of that hearbe.
PLINY, *Naturall Historie.* 77 A.D. (trans. Holland, 1601)

The strawberry grows underneath the nettle,
And wholesome berries thrive and ripen best
Neighbour'd by fruit of baser quality . . .
(Bishop of Ely), in *King Henry V*, Act 1, Scene 1

This Herb (Basil) and Rue will not grow together, no, nor near one another . . .
NICHOLAS CULPEPER, *The English Physician Enlarged*, 1653

Detail from Thomas Hyll's
The Gardeners Labyrinth, 1577

Among *Strawberries* sow here and there some *Borage* seed, and you shall finde the *Strawberries* under those leaves farre more larger than their fellowes.

WILLIAM COLES, *The Art of Simpling*, 1656

One may sow Reddish and carrots together on the same bed: So as the first may be drawn, whilst the other is ready: or sow Lettuce, purselane, parsneps, carrots, Reddish on the same beds, & gather each kind in their season, leaving the parsneps to winter.

JOHN EVELYN, *Directions for the Gardiner at Says-Court*, 1687

Plants are like people. Some like each other and some don't. Companion planting is a system, evolved since the time of Pliny, which groups together the friendly plants to benefit one another.

Most of the ideas involved, such as setting out shade-loving plants between tall-growing types, were based on observation and practical experience. In time these became interwoven with garden folklore and were passed down from one generation to another.

The value of other good companion groupings is easily explained: some because roots are at different levels in the soil; some which occur in nature; some which secrete a variety of organic substances in their roots which affect micro-organisms about them.

Some plants are mutually *harmful* when kept in close proximity, such as the oft-quoted basil with rue, garlic with peas or beans and sunflowers with potatoes, which inhibit each other's growth.

More sophisticated study of what is called plant *symbiosis* (from the Greek meaning 'living together') is still going on. In the United States, the late Dr Ehrenfried Pfeiffer, a scientist following the Bio-dynamic school of thought, closely studied plant affinities for many years, conducting some 5 000 experiments.

His work was outlined and enlarged upon by Helen Philbrick and Richard Gregg in *Companion Plants and How to Use Them*, published by Robinson & Watkins, London (1974), the definitive work on the subject.

In one sense, companion planting imitates nature's diversity. Mixing flowers, vegetables and herbs in the garden gives a certain degree of control over insect pests. Most aromatic herbs (and the onion family) serve as efficient pest repellents. Herbs like chervil, dill, parsley, borage, sage, tarragon and thyme scattered throughout the vegetable garden will protect plants from various predators.

Insects have a specialised sense of smell which guides them to their food. A wide range of conflicting odours will baffle them, acting like a kind of aromatic 'camouflage'.

The following list has been compiled from the herbals and from the modern experience of organic and Bio-dynamic gardeners and *Earth Garden* readers.

No plants grow well near wormwood, due to its toxic leaf and root excretions. A tea made from this herb will repel slugs, aphis and fleas and keep away weevils in stored grain.

Fennel should also be planted away from the garden as most plants dislike it.

Herb	Companions and effects	Herb	Companions and effects
ANISE	Mutually benefits coriander. Dislikes wormwood. Attracts cats and rats.	**LAD'S LOVE**	Deters cabbage moth.
BALM (*Melissa*)	Brings the bees, benefits plants nearby.	**MARIGOLD** (*Calendula*)	Likes tomatoes. Deters asparagus and cucumber beetles.
BASIL	The tomato herb — keeps disease and pests away from tomatoes. Dislikes rue. Repels flies and mosquitoes.	**MINTS**	Good with cabbages and tomatoes. Deters white cabbage moth, flea beetles, mice, ants and fleas.
BORAGE	Likes tomatoes, squash and strawberries. Deters tomato worm.	**NASTURTIUM**	Likes radish, cabbage, potatoes, tomatoes, broccoli, beans and curcubits. Deters squash bugs, striped pumpkin beetle. Plant under fruit trees as a trap plant for woolly aphis and whitefly.
CARAWAY	Likes peas. Will cross-pollinate with fennel.		
CATNIP or CATMINT	Deters flea beetle and mice — but attracts cats!		
CHAMOMILE	The 'plant's physician'. Benefits all nearby herbs and plants, particularly cabbages (it deters cabbage worm and moths), onions and nasturtiums.	**OREGANO**	Deters cucumber beetle and cabbage butterfly.
		PARSLEY	Grow with tomatoes and asparagus. Deters rose beetles.
		PENNYROYAL	Repels ants and mosquitoes.
CHIVES	Likes carrots. Deters aphis on roses and scab in apple trees. Dislikes peas and beans. A chive tea infusion is useful for downy and powdery mildew on gooseberries and cucumber.	**ROSEMARY**	Likes cabbage, beans, carrots and sage. Deters carrot fly, cabbage moth and bean beetles.
		RUE	Likes figs, roses and raspberries. Deters fleas, ants and flies. Dislikes basil.
DILL	Likes cabbages. Dislikes carrots and tomatoes.	**SAGE**	Plant with rosemary, cabbage and carrots. Deters cabbage moth, repels carrot fly. Retards growth of cucumbers.
FENNEL	*Plant fennel near your kennel* or stable to drive away fleas and to keep it out of the main garden. It has a bad influence on most plants, particularly coriander. Powdered leaves or seeds sprinkled about drive away fleas.		
		TANSY	Goes with cabbages, roses, raspberries, fruit trees. Deters beetles, ants and aphis, cabbage moth, cutworm and peach tree borer.
		SAVORY	The 'bean herb'. Deters bean beetle. Companionship with onions in doubt.
GARLIC	Beneficial to roses, raspberries and stonefruit. Repels aphis and cabbage moth. Dislikes peas and beans.	**THYMES**	Deter cabbage moth.
		WORMWOOD	Likes radish. Deters cabbage moth, carrot fly, black flea beetle, wild and tame animals.
HYSSOP	Grow with grapes. A trap plant for cabbage moth. Dislikes radish.	**YARROW**	Increases the aromatic qualities of medicinal and fragrant herbs.

Dill

'it stayeth the hickets'

Dill from William Turner's *A New Herball*, 1551

Dill (*Anethum graveolens*). Annual.
  Old form: Dyll, Anetum.
  Umbelliferae – parsley family.

Of Anethum, the decoction of the dried hair & of the seed being drank, draws down milk & assuageth the tormina and inflations & stops both the belly & the vomitings that float on the top of the stomach; it moves urine, it stayeth the hickets, & being drank too long together it both dulls the sight & extinguishes geniture, but the decoction thereof is good by the way of Insession for women troubled with womb-griefs . . .
DIOSCORIDES, 60 A.D. (trans. Goodyer, 1655)

The brothe of the leves and sede of dry dyll dronken bryngeth mylke to the breastes, it stancheth gnawynges in the belly, and wynde in the same . . .
  Dyll as *Galene* sayth swageth ake, provoketh slepe when it is grene, and maketh rype rawe humores. The oyle that is made of dyll is good to be given unto them that are werye in winter, for it softneth and moysteth and is good for them that are sicke of an ague that commeth of small fleme, and for all dyseases that come of a coulde cause.
WILLIAM TURNER, *A new Herball*, 1551

They sowe Dill in al gardens, amongst wortes, and Pot herbes.
  The decoction of the toppes and croppes of Dill, with the seede boyled in water and drunken, causeth women to have plentie of milke.
REMBERT DODOENS, *A niewe Herball*, (trans. Lyte), 1578

Dyll is hotte and drie in the seconde degree. The seedes be chiefly occupied in medicine, and of the greene herbs *Galen* writeth that it procureth sleepe. Wherefore in olde time they used to weare garlands of dill at their feasts.
THOMAS COGHAN, *The Haven of Health*, 1584

Dill doth much grow wilde, but because in many places it cannot be had, it is therefore sowne in Gardens, for the uses whereunto it serveth. It is a smaller herbe than Fennell, but very like, having fine cut leaves, not so large, but shorter, smaller and of a stronger, quicker taste: the stalke is smaller also, and with very few ioynts and leaves on them, bearing spoakie tufts of yellow flowers, which turne into thinne, small and flat seedes: the root perisheth every yeare, and riseth againe for the most part of its owne sowing.
  The leaves of Dill are much used in some places with Fish, as they do Fenel; but because it is so strong many doe refuse it.
  It is also put among pickled Cowcumbers, where-with it doth very well agree, giving unto the cold fruit a prety spicie taste or rellish.
  It being stronger than Fenel, is of the more force to expel wind in the body. Some use to eat the seed to stay Hicock.
JOHN PARKINSON, *Paradisus*, 1629

It stayeth the hiccough, being boyled in Wine, and but smelled unto, being tied in a cloth . . . The decoction of Dill, be it herb or seed, (only if you boil the seed you must bruise it) in white wine, being drunk, it is a gallant expeller of wind and provoker of terms.
NICHOLAS CULPEPER, *The English Physician*, 1652

69

I am always pleased with that particular time of the year which is proper for the pickling of dill and cucumbers, but alas! this cry like the song of the nightingale is not heard above two months. It would therefore be worthwhile to consider, whether the same air might not in some cases be adapted to other words.

RICHARD ADDISON, *The Spectator*, No. 251

Dill and Collyflower Pickle

Boil them till they fall in pieces. With some of the stalk, and most of the flower, boil it in a part of the liquor till pretty strong. Being taken off, strain it; and when settled, clear it from the bottom. Then with Dill, gross pepper, a pretty quantitie of Salt, when cold, add as much vinegar as will make it sharp, and pour all upon the Collyflower.

JOHN EVELYN, *Acetaria, a book about Saletts*, 1699

To Pickle Cucumbers in Dill

Gather the tops of the ripest Dill, and cover the bottome of the vessel, and lay a layer of Cucumbers and another of Dill, till you have filled the vessel within a handful of the top. Then take as much water as you think will fill the vessel and mix it with salt and a Quarter of a Pound of allom to a gallon of water and poure it on them, and presse then down with a stone on them, and keep them covered close.

For that use I think the water will be best boyl'd and cold, which will keep longer sweet, or if you like not this pickle, doe it with Water, Salt and White Wine Vinegar, or (if you please) pour the Water and Salt on them scalding hot, which will make them ready to use the sooner.

JOSEPH COOPER (Cook to Charles I), *Receipt Book*, 1640

Dill grows easily from seed planted in spring, flowering two months after sowing. The seeds mature in seventy days, when the plant has reached a height of about a metre. Plant again in autumn where winters are mild.

Usually there is a single dark green hollow stalk, branching out to soft, blue-green, feathery tendrils (so fine that Dioscorides called them 'hair'), bearing often four delicate umbels of yellow florets which turn into tiny brown seeds (30 g may contain 25 000 seeds). Stem, leaves and seeds are aromatic. Virgil called dill 'a pleasant and fragrant plant'.

The name dill comes from the Norse, *dilla*, to lull. Dill water is still a homely remedy for wind in babies. Dill seed and umbels are traditionally used in pickling cucumbers (see recipes).

The leafy branches may be chopped and added, fresh, to salads, potato salad and cottage cheese, or sprinkled over grilled lamb chops. The young leaves and stalks give a unique flavouring to winter soups.

Dill seed is sprinkled over bread, pastries and apple pie, and is used in butter, or mayonnaise as a spicy sauce for fish. It's nice with Turkish-style salad of yoghurt and cucumber.

Save dill seeds by cutting the umbels when they have turned brown in autumn. Spread over a cloth to dry in the shade for about ten days. Thresh by beating over a cloth, or rub the seeds out between the palms of your hands. Store in airtight jars. The leaves are dried by chopping finely and placing them in a basket and turning often.

Dill contains the minerals potassium, sodium, sulphur and phosphorus and a volatile oil.

Don't plant dill near carrots or tomatoes because it will stunt their growth as they mature. Dill near fennel will cross-pollinate, producing plants which are neither dill nor fennel.

Dill vinegar is made by soaking the seeds in a good vinegar for a few days before use.

Dill butter: Blend in 1.25 ml dried dill leaf (often called dill weed) and 1.5 ml white wine vinegar. Spread on boiled fish, or on cabbage or green beans.

Dill seeds may be used in recipes in place of caraway seeds.

Fennel

'to make one slender'

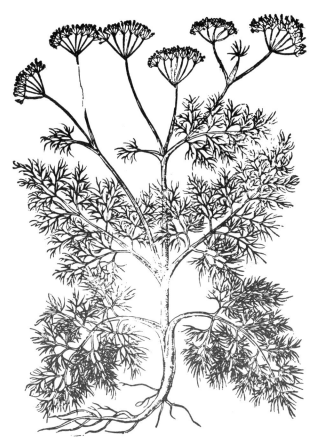

Fennel from Mattioli, 1583

Fennel (*Foeniculum vulgare*). Perennial.
    Fennel.
    Old form: Finkle, Fenel, Fenell, Fenkle, Fennill.
Sweet Fennel (*F. dulce*). Annual.
    Florence Fennel, Finocchio.
Umbelliferae – parsley family.

As for Fenell, the Serpents have woon it much credit, and brought it into name, in this regard, that by tasting thereof they cast their old skin, and by the juice that it yeeldeth doe cleare their eyes: whereby we also are come to know that this hearb hath a singular propertie to mundifie our sight, and take away the film or web that overcasteth and dimmeth our eyes. Now the onely time to gather and drawe the said juice out of Fennell, is when the stalke beginneth to swell and wax big: which, after it is received, they use to drie in the Sun, and as need requireth, make an inunction with it and honey togither.

    As touching the garden Fenell, and the medicinable vertues that it hath, it is holden, That the seed, if it be taken inwardly in wine, is a soveraign drinke for the pricke of Scorpions or sting of other Serpents. The juice thereof, if it be instilled by drops into the ears, killeth the worms there. The hearbe it selfe carrieth such sway in the kitchin, that lightly there is no meat seasoned, nor any vinnegre sauce served up without it. Moreover, for to give a commendable and pleasant tast unto bread, it is ordinarily put under the bottome-crust of our loaves, when they be set into the oven.

PLINY, *Naturall Historie*, 77 A.D. (trans. Holland, 1601)

Fennel deserves high praise both for its taste and smell. It is good for weak eyes.

WALAFRID STRABO, *The Little Garden*, 840 A.D.

Fenell is clepid in greke Maratrum. This herbe drunke with wyn wole destroye alle manere of venyme and hele alle venemous bytinges.

    . . . Wringe out the juus of grene fenel seed and dreye that at the sunne, and that is a gret and mygty medycyn to the sorys of eyen of what cause so it come.

    . . . The decoccion of fenel drunken ofte wole make olde men to seme long yong. This proveth auctours and filisofres, for serpentes, whan they ben olde and wollen waxe strange, mygty and yong a-gen, they goon and etyn ofte of fenel, and so thei becomyn yunglise and mygty.

Macer's Herbal, 12th century

He who sees fennel and gathers it not, is not a man but a devil.

WELSH MYDVAI, 13th century

> Then wente I forth on my right hond
> Doun by a litel path I fond
> O mentes ful and fenel greene.

GEOFFREY CHAUCER, *The Romaunt of the Rose*, 1368

Alewife I have pepper and paeony seed and a pound of garlick, And a farthingworth of fennel-seed, for fasting days.

WILLIAM LANGLAND, *Piers Plowman*, 1377

71

I advise all studentes that be troubled with winde in the stomacke or bellie, to cause Fenell seedes, Anise or Carewaie to be wrought up in their bread. And if they list they may boyle anie sorte of them in white wine.

THOMAS COGHAN, *The Haven of Health*, 1584

Take fennel and seethe it in water, a very good quantity, and wring out the juice thereof when it is sod, and drink it first and last, and it shall swage either him or her.

THOMAS DAWSON, *The Good Housewifes Jewell*, 1587

The pouder of the seed of Fennell drunke for certaine daies together fasting preserveth the eye-sight: whereof was written this *Distichon* following:
Of Fennell, Roses, Vervain, Rue, and Celandine, is made a water good to clear the sight of eine.

JOHN GERARD, *The Herball*, 1597

In Fennel-seed, this vertu you shall finde,
Forth of your lower parts to drive the winde.
Of Fennel vertues foure they do recite,
First, it hath power some poysons to expell,
Next, burning Argues it will put to flight,
The stomack it does cleanse, and comfort well:
And fourthly, it doth keepe and clense the sight,
And thus the seede and herbe doth both excell.

SIR JOHN HARINGTON, *The Englishmans Doctor*, 1607

... Italians especially doe much delight in the use thereof, and therefore as I sayd before transplant it and whiten it, to make it the more tender to please the taste ...

We use to lay it upon Fish or to boyle it therewith and with divers other things, as also the seede in bread ... the leaves or seede boyled in Barley water and drunk is good for Nurses to encrease their milke, and to make it the more wholsome for their Nurse Children to take: the leaves being boyled in water but much more the seede stayeth the hickocke.

Fennel both leaves and seedes or rootes are much and often used in drinkes or brothes, for those that are growen fat to abate their unweldi-nesse and make them more gaunt and lanke.

JOHN PARKINSON, *Theatrum Botanicum*, 1640

Fennel from the *Juliana Anicia Codex*, 512 A.D.

... One good old fashion is not yet left off, viz to boil the Fennel with fish, for it consumes that phlegmatic humour, which fish most plentifully afford and annoy the body with, though few that use it know wherefore they do it ...

NICHOLAS CULPEPER, *The English Physician*, 1652

Fennell seeds are sweet before they ripen, and afterwards grow spicie. *Fennell* increaseth milke in *Nurses*.

WILLIAM COLES, *The Art of Simpling*, 1656

Above the lowly plants it towers,
The fennel, with its yellow flowers,
And in an earlier age than ours
Was gifted with the wondrous powers,
    Lost vision to restore.
It gave new strength, and fearless mood;
And gladiators, fierce and rude,
Mingled it in their daily food;
And he who battled and subdued,
    A wreath of fennel wore.

HENRY W. LONGFELLOW, *The Goblet of Life*, 1846

This elegantly-growing plant grows best in chalky soils, where, indeed, it is often found wild. It is very generally cultivated in gardens, and has much improved on its original form. Various dishes are frequently ornamented and garnished with its graceful leaves, and these are sometimes boiled in soups.

MRS ISABELLA BEETON, *Household Management*, 1861

Prometheus, according to Sophocles, stole the spark of fire from Olympus and brought it to earth hidden inside the stalk of a giant fennel. The ancient Greeks kindled fire with burning charcoal kept similarly in the pith of a fennel plant and I have seen Greek fishermen using the same method to carry fire.

The Greeks revered fennel as giving strength, courage and long life. It was said to improve the sight, clear misty or inflamed eyes, relieve chest pains and promote the flow of mothers' milk. *Marathon*, the Greek name for the plant, meant 'to grow thin' a reputation supported by the later herbalists. The name is connected also to the Plain of Marathon, outside Athens, where the famous battle of 490 B.C. is said to have been fought on a field of fennel.

Botanists tell us that the plant mentioned in myth is the giant fennel (*Ferula communis*). Here we are concerned with its relatives, wild or common fennel (*Foeniculum vulgare*) and Florence fennel (*F. dulce*).

The Latin genus name of *Foeniculum* came from the word for hay, perhaps because of the plant's fresh smell.

In 812 A.D. Charlemagne listed fennel among the herbs he directed to be planted in his gardens. In the Middle Ages, fennel served for fast days and for famine, as well as for slimming, as it dulls the appetite. It helped to make food more palatable, correcting the oily taste of fresh or salted fish like salmon and mackerel.

In the 13th century the household accounts of Edward I show that four kilos of fennel seed were used in one month.

Though fennel is a handsome useful plant, it does not have a good influence on herbs and vegetables nearby. The maxim: 'Plant fennel near your kennel' has two senses – to keep fennel out of the main garden; and a reference to the fact that the powdered leaves and seeds of fennel will drive away fleas.

Common fennel is a perennial, easily raised from seed, or propagated by root division. Because of its bad influences on plants like beans, dill, tomatoes and wormwood, it will do best in a separate block or as a background to the herb garden in a sunny spot. Plant seeds about 30 cm apart.

It grows to about one and a half metres in height, with a smooth, glossy, blue-green stalk, flat at the base and much branched. The leaves are feathery and shiny green, the umbels bearing bright yellow flowers. The seeds which follow are ribbed, a brown-grey colour. They are harvested by cutting the umbels and drying on a tray in the sun or on a stove with low heat.

The leaves are used, cut finely, in salads. The flavour is like *anise*. Leaves and young stalks spice soup and sauce. Plants used for this purpose may be cut back regularly and not allowed

Ladies gardening and garland making from Walafrid Strabo's *The Little Garden*, Nuremberg, 1512

to flower and will last for years. The tender flower stalks, before blossoming, may be peeled like celery and served as a salad with a dressing of vinegar and pepper, or stewed in stock and served with butter sauce. You may use thinnings in this way.

Fennel seeds add flavour to bread, fish sauce, pies, fruit pastries, sauerkraut, coleslaw, spaghetti, meatballs and home-brewed beer and wine. The seeds were also dipped in sugar and eaten as comfits in the same way as coriander, to aid digestion.

Fennel is the fish herb, growing as it does along the sea coast and river estuaries. When boiling fish, tie up some crushed fennel seed with equal amounts of thyme, basil and sage in a cloth. Add this to the saucepan when cooking and remove before serving.

Use fennel leaves in fish marinades or place a sprig inside fish when baking or grilling. Add finely chopped fennel leaves or crushed fennel seeds to butter, white sauce or stock to be served with fish. The crushed seeds mixed with garlic powder make a good dressing for pork.

Florence fennel or Finnochio (*F. dulce*) is a more compact annual plant, grown for its swollen base, which is eaten as a vegetable. You may have seen it in greengrocers and markets, especially in Italian areas.

Finnochio needs richer soil than common fennel and requires regular watering. The soil needs manuring or composting for the base to develop. When it is about the size of an egg, heap up soil about the base to blanch it. Harvest in two weeks.

It has paler stalks than the common fennel, with dense plumes of leaves. It is eaten sliced in salads, or cooked with butter, pepper and salt, or melted cheese.

Carosella or *Sicilian fennel* (*F. var. piperitum*) is another type growing in southern Italy, cultivated for its tender stems, which are eaten raw.

Garlands and Coronets

Cato in his Treatise on Gardens, ordained as a necessary point, That they should be planted and enriched with such hearbes as might bring foorth flowers for Coronets and Guirlands . . . verely there is no painter with all his skill able sufficiently with his pensill to represent one lively guirland of flowers indeed; whether they bee plaited and inter-medled in manner of nosegaies one with another, or set in rankes and rewes one by another; whether they bee knit and twined cordwise and in chaine, work of one sort of flowers, either to wind and wreath about a chaplet, bias, or in fashion of a circle, or whether they bee sorted round into a globe or ball, running one through another, to exhibite one goodly sight and entire uniformitie of a crosse Garland.

PLINY, *Naturall Historie*, 77 A.D. (trans. Holland, 1601)

Beside whiche fountaine, the most fayre lady
La bell Purcell, was gayly sittyng
Of many floures, fayre and royally
A goodly chaplet, she was in makynge.

STEPHEN HAWKES, *Pastime of Pleasure*, 1506

The maide faire hir garland decks with flowers gay
That yeeld a fragrant smel as fresh as somer may;
Mingling sweete Lavender and yellow Marigold
With purple Violet, most pleasant to behold.

VIRGIL, *Bucolics* (30 B.C.), quoted by John Gerard, *The Herball*, 1597

It is not very long since the custome of setting up Garlands in Churches, hath been left off with us; and in some places setting up of *Holly, Ivy, Rosemary, Bayes, Yew, & c.* in Churches at Christmas, is still in use. *Cypresse* Garlands are of great account at Funeralls amongst the gentiler sort, but *Rosemary* and *Bayes* are used by the common both at Funerals and Weddings.

WILLIAM COLES, *The Art of Simpling*, 1656

Hyssop

'purge me with hyssop'

Hyssop from Mattioli, 1583

Hyssop (*Hyssopus officinalis*). Perennial.
Old form: Isope, Hyssope, Hisop, Hissop.
White flowered (*H. albus*)
Rose flowered (*H. ruber*).
Mint family.

Hyssopus, a knowne herb is of 2 sorts, for the one is mountainous, but ye other grows in gardens, but ye best is that which grows in Cilicia. It hath a power of extenuating and warming. Being sod with figgs and water, with honey also & Rue & soe drank it helps in ye peripneumonicall, Asthmaticall, ye internall cough, ye catarre . . . it doth kill also ye wormes, & being licked in honey it doth the same . . . It causeth also a good colour.
DIOSCORIDES, 60 A.D. (trans. Goodyer, 1655)

> Purge me with Hyssop, and I shall be clean;
> Wash me, and I shall be whiter than snow.
Psalms 51, 7

This herbe hast lewys lyk to sawereye but it is nosth so brod and it flourryth as doth sawereye. The vertue of this herbe is good to take the jus and medele it with esyle (vinegar) and tempere it and put it in hys mowth that is sek and it schal distroye alle manere ewelys that he hast in his mowth.
. . . Also if it be drounken grene or ellys be powdre makyth a man well coloured in his face and in alle placys.
AGNUS CASTUS, 14th century

And first the Isope is a fruitful plante, and necessary in the garden, whiche ought to be sowen, or sette in the slips, and whole plantes (neither in a fatte, nor dunged grounde) but in an open, & sunny place . . . And in the Summer, when the herbe beareth his flower, then cut the same, and drye it in the shadowe.
THOMAS HYLL, *The Proffitable Arte of Gardening*, 1568

Of Hisop is made a wine named Hisop Wine, which helpeth by shrinking thereof diseases of the brest, the sides, the lungs, the shortnesse of winde, and an olde cough, all which effects may be wrought by the use of the Syrupe. When I was much troubled with cough and colde, I was wont to make Hisop Ale . . . whereby in that case I have beene much eased.
THOMAS COGHAN, *The Haven of Health*, 1584

Hissope affecteth a place free from shadow, and lying open upon the sunne: it must be dried to put in pottage in winter.
RICHARD SURFLET, *The Countrie Farme*, 1600

Cleane *Hysop* is an hearbe to purge and clense
Raw flegmes, and hurtfull humours from the brest,
The same unto the lungs great comfort lends,
With hony boyl'd: but farre above the rest
It gives good colour, and complexion mends,
And is therefore with women in request.
SIR JOHN HARINGTON, *The Englishmans Doctor*, 1607

Isop is reasonable long lasting, young rootes are good to set, slips better. A good pothearbe.
WILLIAM LAWSON, *The Countrie Housewifes Garden*, 1617

While the gardeners attend to the plants, the herbalist describes and lists the herbs. From *De agricultura sive de commodis invalibus* Petrus de Crescentis, 1471

To Make Syrup of Hysop for Colds

Take an handful of Hysop, of Figs, Raysins, Dates, of each an ounce, French Barley one ounce, boyl therein three pintes of fair water to a quart, strain it and clarifie it with two Whites of Eggs, then put in two pound of fine Sugar and boyl it to a Syrup.

W.M., *The Queen's Closet Opened*, 1655

The modern hyssop is usually associated with the *Azob* or *Ezob* of the Bible, though some herbalists think that this was a type of marjoram (*Origanum maru*) which grows in Israel.

It is a spicy, resinous and bitter tasting herb, too strong to be much used in cooking these days. It was once used in garden knots and mazes because it is a compact, evergreen shrub and stands clipping. Bees love hyssop, which gives a special flavour and aroma to honey.

Hyssop grows 45 cm or more in height, with woody roots, glossy green leaves, dark with spots of oil and clusters of light blue flowers at the top of spikes about 12 cm long. White and rose-pink flowers are more rare.

Hyssop is one ingredient in the liqueur, Chartreuse. Formerly it was used sparingly in soups and salads and with parsley and sage in meat stuffings.

Hyssop grows well from seed or root divisions and likes a sandy or chalky soil. Plant in full sun or semi-shade and renew plants every four years. Hyssop is a bad companion for radishes.

Hyssop tea is an old country remedy for colds, phlegm and mucus, asthma and rheumatism and is used in fevers to produce sweating. Pour 500 ml of boiling water over a handful of the green tops alone, or mixed with horehound leaves; or use 15 g of the dried herb. The tea is also used to bathe bruises and black eyes.

Series of designs for knots from William Lawson's *The Countrie Housewifes Garden*, 1617

Knots

My garden sweet, enclosed with walles strong
Embanked with benches to sytt and take my rest,
The Knotts so enknotted it cannot be espres't,
With arbors and allyes so pleasant and so dulce.
GEORGE CAVENDISH, *Life of Wolsey*, 1520

The number of formes, mazes and knots is so great, and men are so diversely delighted, that I leave everie Housewife to her selfe, especially seeing to set downe many had bin but to fill much paper yet lest I deprive her of all delight and direction, let her view these few, choyce, new formes, and note this generally that all plots are square, and all are bordred about with Privit, Rasens, Feaberies, Roses, thorne, Rosemarie, Bee-flowers, Isop, Sage, or such like.
WILLIAM LAWSON, *The Countrie Housewifes Garden*, 1617

As for the making of knots, or figures, with divers-coloured earths, that they may lie under the windows of the house on that side on which the garden stands, they be but toys: you may see as good sights many times in tarts.
FRANCIS BACON, *Of Gardens*, 1625

The use of Germander ordinarily is as Tyme, Hyssope, and other such herbes, to border a knot, whereunto it is often appropiate, and the rather, that it might be cut to serve for a strewing herbe for the house among others.
JOHN PARKINSON, *Paradisus*, 1629

Knot gardens were a conceit of the elaborate taste of the 16th century. They were meant to be viewed from the tower or battlements of castles and large country houses, displaying a geometric pattern of herbs and plants rather like a tapestry or woven carpet.

The design was laid out on raised garden beds, usually in a set of four square or rectangular plots. The 'knot' effect was gained by the illusion of an under-and-over bow or lacing of the rows of small hedge plants.

In the smaller garden, the knot was a centrepiece and had the practical use on washdays for spreading out linen clothing to dry on lavender or thyme.

There are a few knot gardens surviving in England; one is at Hampton Court Palace. In the United States the knot garden built at the Brooklyn Botanic Garden in 1938 has inspired many other experiments.

Usually, knot gardens are planted with perennials and, once established, the chief maintenance is clipping, though it always seems a shame to me to clip off the yellow buttons of cotton lavender or hyssop or lavender spikes. A knot garden isn't really practical, but quite a small one, say 2 × 1½ metres, can be very decorative.

Plant with neat foliage like germander (*Teucrium chamaedrys*), dwarf lavenders, hyssop and wormwood and the silver-grey artemisias. Fill with bark mulch. You could make a knotted border for a bed of kitchen herbs using parsley, basil, marjoram, chives and thyme.

To lay out the pattern, prepare your garden bed, choose the knot design you like and scale it up, measuring out with sticks and rope. Finally mark the lines of the design with lime as a guide for setting out your herbs. All this of course depends on whether you think knots are beautiful, lacy designs or 'toys' looking like decorated tarts as Lord Francis Bacon did!

Lad's Love

'ffor hem that speke in slepe'

Lad's Love from *The Herball*, 1597

Lad's Love (*Artemisia abrotanum*). Perennial.
Old form: Southernwood, Old Man, Maiden's Ruin, Garde-Robe (Fr.), Sothernwode.
Composite.

Southernwood of the hair-like leaves cures fevers and wounds; it has well-nigh as many virtues as leaves.
WALAFRID STRABO, *The Little Garden*, 840 A.D.

Ffor hem that speke in slepe. Take sothernwode and stamp itt. Medle the juyse with white wyne or wt winegre and gif the syk to drynk when he goth to his bedd.
MS 136, MEDICAL SOCIETY OF LONDON, 1444

The vertue of this herbe is thus: that yf they breake the sede and drynke it with water, it healeth men that have ben bytten with any venemous beast. Also this herbe destroieth wormes i a mans wombe ... also this herbe burnt, and the ashes medeled with oyle, maketh heare growe sooner.
ANTHONY ASKHAM, *A Lytel Herball*, 1550

Southernwood is hoat and drie in the third degree, it is not used in meates, the smell of it is so strong that it will make some mens heads to ake, yet the herbe something dryed and put in a lynnen bagge, and laide as a stomager next the skinne comforteth a colde stomacke well.
THOMAS COGHAN, *The Haven of Health*, 1584

The seed as well as the dryed hearbe, is often given to kill the worms in children, the herbe bruised and

79

laide to, helpeth to draw forth splinters and thornes out of the flesh.

JOHN PARKINSON, *Theatrum Botanicum*, 1640

Clip 4 ounces of the leaves fine and beat them in a mortar with 6 ounces of loaf sugar till the whole is like a paste. Three times a day take the bignesse of a nutmeg of this. It is pleasant and one thing is it in particular, it is a composer and always disposes persons to sleep.

SIR JOHN HILL, *The British Herbal*, 1756

Southernwood, that's very good!

London Street Cries

A common hardy shrub found in old-fashioned cottage gardens, and probably would have gone out of cultivation if it had not been cherished there, yet it is easy to grow, and no collection of scented things would be complete without it; the feathery foliage emits a peculiar fragrance, and it is largely used in the bouquets of country people, and village decorations, it is also extensively employed for keeping the moth away from clothes.

DONALD McDONALD, *Fragrant Flowers and Leaves*, 1895

Old Man, or Lad's-love – in the name there's
  nothing
To one that knows not Lad's-love, or Old Man,
The hoar-green feathery herb, almost a tree,
Growing with rosemary and lavender.

EDWARD THOMAS (1878–1917), *Old Man*

What's in a name? In the case of lad's love, or southernwood, each of its many names tells us something of the attributes it has gathered through the centuries in different countries and cultures.

Lad's Love came from the custom of country boys, who gave a sprig of the plant to their sweethearts on Sundays. It was also used to help them grow their first beards.

Old Man, the most obvious, is suggested by its appearance – a rather hoary, greyish ball of fluff like a seedy old beard. *Southernwood* is said to mean southern wormwood, because it grew in Italy.

Garde-Robe the French tagged it because they used its dried leaves in wardrobes to protect fur and woollen clothing. *Maiden's Ruin* comes from its reputation both as a love charm and as an aphrodisiac.

Lad's love is a low-growing evergreen shrub with woody branches and feathery, threadlike foliage which has a fragrant lemony-pine aroma. It grows between 1 and $1\frac{3}{4}$ metres high and bears whitish-yellow blossoms.

Like wormwood, it is an *artemisia*, named for Artemis, the Greek goddess. Artemisias have been identified with other plants in Assyrian stone carvings dating back to 600 B.C.

Its main use has been as a moth repellent. Sew up the dried leaves in a muslin or cheese-cloth bag to place with clothing stored over summer.

In the garden, lad's love protects against the cabbage butterfly and fruit tree moths when planted nearby. It has one bad reputation, that of repelling bees, so the shrub is usually kept away from the main garden area.

In Italy, lad's love is rubbed over lamb before cooking and young shoots are used to flavour cakes, but there are few culinary uses.

Burn a few leaves on the kitchen stove or in the fire-place to get rid of cooking odours.

Old Woman (*A. stelleriana*), also called Dusty Miller, is a silvery related Artemisia which grows in sandhills in North America.

Lavender
'piercing the senses'

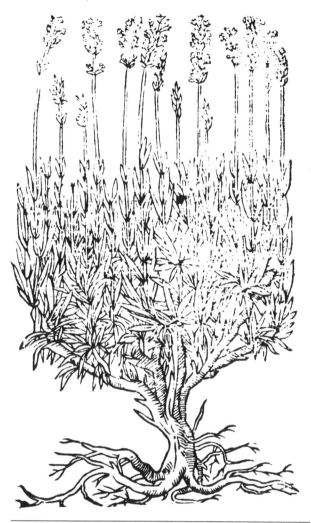

Common lavender spike (left) and white flowered lavender from *The Herball*, 1597

Lavenders

Old form: Lavander.

English Lavender (*Lavandula vera, L. officinalis*). English, sweet, true, or Dutch lavender.

Dwarf varieties of English lavender include L. Munstead, L. Hidcote, L. Seal, white-flowered (*L. alba*) and pink-flowered (*L. rosea*).

Spike Lavender (*L. spica*).

French Lavender (*L. dentata*), grey-leaf (*L. candicans*), wide leaf (*L. latifolia*).

Italian Lavender (*L. stoechas*).

Old forms include Stickadove, Spikenard, Cassidonie, Cassidony, Cast-me-down. Sometimes called Spanish lavender.

Mint family – perennial shrub.

Here's fine Lavender for your cloaths!
Here's your sweet Lavender
Sixteen sprigs to a penny –
Which you will find my ladies
Will smell as sweet as any.
Buy my Lavender! Sweet blooming Lavender!
Lavender! Sweet blooming lavender,
   Six bunches for a penny to-day!
Lavender! Sweet blooming lavender,
   Ladies, buy it while you may.

London Street Cries

Stoechas grows in the Islands of Galatia over against Messalia, called ye Stoechades, from whence also it had its name, is an herb with slender twiggs, having ye haire like Tyme, but yet longer leaved, & sharp in ye taste, & somewhat bitterish, but ye decoction of it as the Hyssop is good for ye griefs in ye thorax. It is mingled also profitably with Antidots.

DIOSCORIDES, 60 A.D. (trans. John Goodyer, 1655)

Lavandula is an herbe men clepe lavendre. This herbe is moche lyk to ysope but it is mo lengger lewys thanne ysope and it hast a flour sumdel blew and also the stalke growith other-wyse. The vertu of this herbe is ef it be sothyn in water and dronke that water it wele hele the palsye and many other ewyls.

AGNUS CASTUS, 14th century

And first the Lavender hath the vertue of heating and drying, but profiteth not, unto the digestion of meate. And nowe if any applieth the Lavender often to the nose, in smelling thereto, it doth comforte and cleare the sight. And if any boyleth the Lavender in water, and that a shyrte wette in the same, and after dried againe (be worne) wyll suffer no Louse after to abyde in that shyrte, so long as the sherte keapeth the smell.

The Spykenarde groweth lyke unto the Lavender saving y the leaves be thicker and bygger and beareth also a longer stalke and bygger flowers whiche be purple of coloure, lyke unto the Lavender, and hath besydes, greater vertues.

THOMAS HYLL, *The Proffitable Arte of Gardening*, 1568

Smell often to it to comfort and cleare the sight. Boyle it in water and wett they shirt in it and dry it again and weare it ... Shred the herbe with the flowers and distill it and drinke two ounces of the water to helpe giddiness of the head and rub the head all over with it, and let it dry in by itselfe ... Seethe lavender in water and temper thy wine therewith and also make a syrop with the said water and use it against swooning and to comfort the heart.

WILLIAM LANGHAM, *The Garden of Health*, 1597

Lavender Spike hath many stiff branches of a woody substance, growing up in the manner of a shrub, set with many long hoarie leaves, by couples for the most part, of a strong smell, and yet pleasant enough to such as do love strong savors. The floures

grow at the top of the branches, spike fashion, of a blew colour.

The distilled water of Lavander smelt unto, or the temples and forehead bathed therewith, is a refreshing to them that have the Catalepsie, a light migram, and to them that have the falling sickness and that use to swoune much.

The floures of Lavander picked from the knaps, I meane the blew part and not the husk, mixed with Cinnamon, Nutmegs, and Cloves, made into pouder, and given to drinke in the distilled water thereof, doth helpe the panting and passion of the heart, prevaileth against giddinesse, turning, or swimming of the braine, and members subject to the palsie.

French Lavender hath a body like Lavender, short, and of a woodie substance, but slenderer, beset with long narrow leaves, of a whitish colour, lesser than those of Lavender; it hath in the top bushie or spikie heads, well compact or thrust togither; out of the which grow foorth small purple flowers, of a pleasant smell. The seede is small and blackish: the roote is harde and woodie.

JOHN GERARD, *The Herball*, 1597

French lavender being a herbe of very good smell, and very usual in Languedoc and Provence, doth crave to be diligently tilled in a fat ground and lying open to the sunne ...

The drie, stonie and sunne shining place is very fit for lavender. It is of swcct smcll, and very good when it is dried to put amongst linnens and woollen clothes, imparting of his sweetnes unto them, keeping of them from vermin.

It is very excellent to comfort weake and wearied sinewes, or otherwise ill affected through some cold cause: and by reason here of baths and fomentations made of lavender for palsies, convulsions, apoplexies, and other such like affects, are very soveraigne: the flowers with cinnamome, nutmeg, and cloves doe heale the beating of the hart: the distilled water of the flowers, taken in quantitie of two spoonfuls, restoreth the lost speech, healeth the swounings and disease of the hart: the conserve and distilled water thereof doe the like: the oile drieth up rheums ...

RICHARD SURFLET, *The Countrie Farme*, 1600

This flower is good for Bees, most comfortable for smelling except Roses: and kept dry is as strong after a year as when it was gathered. The water is comfortable.

WILLIAM LAWSON, *Country Housewifes Garden*, 1618

Lavendula (Lavender Spike)

After all these faire and sweet flowers before speci-fied, I must needes adde a few sweete herbes, both to accomplish this Garden, and to please your senses by placing them in your Nose-gayes, or else where, as you list. And although I bring them to the end or last place, yet are they not of the least account.

Lavendula Maier (Garden Lavender)

Our ordinary Garden Lavender riseth up with a hard wooddy stemme above the ground, parted into many small branches, whereon are set whitish, long, and narrow leaves, by couples one against another, from among which riseth up naked square stalkes, with two leaves at a ioynt, and at the toppe divers small huskes standing round about them, formed in long and round heads or spikes, with purple gaping flowers springing out of each of them: the roote is wooddy, and spreadeth in the ground: The whole plant is of a strong sweete sent, but the heads of flowers much more, and more piercing the senses, which are much used to bee put among linnen and apparrell.

There is a kinde thereof that beareth white flowers, and somewhat broader leaves, but it is very rare, and sene but in a few places with us, because it is more tender, and will not so well endure our cold Winters.

Lavendula Minor

(*Gen Spica*; Small Lavender or Spike)

The Spike or small Lavender is very like unto the former, but groweth not so high, neither is the head or spike so great and long, but shorter and smaller, and of a more purplish colour in the flower: the leaves also are a little harder, whiter, and shorter then the former, the sent also is somewhat sharper and stronger. This is not so frequent as the first, and is nourished but in some places that are warmer, where they delight in rare herbs and plants.

The Place

Lavender groweth in Spaine aboundantly, in many places so wilde, and little regarded, that many have gone, and abiden there to distill the oyle thereof whereof great quantity now commeth over from thence unto us: and also in Lanquedocke, and Provence in France.

The Names

It is called of some Nardus Italica, and Lavendula ... We doe call them generally Lavender, or Lavender Spike ...

Staechas or Cassidony (Italian lavender) from *Paradisus*, 1629

The Vertue

Lavender is little used in inward physicke, but outwardly, the oyle for cold and benumbed parts, and is almost wholly spent with us, for to perfume linnen, apparrell, gloves, leather, & c, and the dryed flowers to comfort and dry up the moisture of a cold braine.

Staechas

(Stickadove, Cassidony, or French Lavender)

Cassidony that groweth in the Gardens of our Countrey, may peradventure somewhat differ in colour, as well as in strength, from that which

83

groweth in hotter Countries; but as it is with us, it is more tender a great deale then Lavender, and groweth rather like an herbe then a bush or shrub, not above a foote and a halfe high, or thereabouts, having many narrow long greene leaves like Lavender, but softer and smaller, set at severall distances together about the stalkes, which spread abroad into branches: at the tops whereof stand long and round, and sometimes foure square heads, of a dark greenish purple colour, compact of many scales set together, from among which come forth the flowers, of a blewish colour, after which follow seede vessels, which are somewhat whitish when they are ripe, containing blackish browne seede within them: the roote is somewhat wooddy, and will hardly abide the injuries of our cold Winters, except in some places onely, or before it have flowred: The whole plant is somewhat sweete, but nothing so much as Lavender.

Cassidony groweth in the Islands Staechades, which are over against Marselles, and in Arabia also: We keep it with greate care in our Garden.

It is of much more use in physicke than Lavender, and is much used for old paines in the head. It is also held to be good for to open obstructions, to expell melancholy, to cleanse and strengthen the liver, and other inward parts, and to be a Pectorall also.

JOHN PARKINSON, *Paradisus*, 1629

An honest ale-house where we shall find a cleanly room, lavender in the windows, and twenty ballads stuck about the wall.

(Piscator), IZZAK WALTON, *The Compleat Angler*, 1653

> Lavender's blue, diddle, diddle,
>   Lavender's green;
> When I am king, diddle diddle,
>   You shall be queen.

English Nursery Rhyme, 1805

Who has not plucked up the sweet spikes of Lavender and laid them with the linen in the wardrobe? From this custom arises the saying, which used to be common in Sussex in my boyhood, when any one wished to pass a joke on another for his carefulness of a thing –
  'Do it up in Lavender!'
For a thing which was done up with Lavender would be regarded as choice and precious.

REV. HILDERIC FRIEND, *Flowers and Flower Lore*, 1884

It is generally known that the Queen (Victoria) is a great believer in Lavender as a disinfectant, and that she is not at all singular in her faith in this plant ... The royal residences are strongly impregnated with the refreshing odour of this old-fashioned flower, and there is no perfume that the Queen likes better than Lavender-water, which, together with the oil for disinfecting purpòses, Her Majesty has direct from a lady who distils it herself.

DONALD McDONALD, *Fragrant Flowers*, 1895

By the Greeks, the name Nardus is given to Lavender, from Naarda, a city of Syria near the Euphrates, and many persons call the plant 'Nard'. St Mark mentions this as Spikenard, a thing of great value.
  ... In Pliny's time, blossoms of the Nardus sold for a hundred Roman denarii ...

DR W.T. FERNIE, *Herbal Simples*, 1897

A bed or hedge of Lavender is pleasing in the same way that the dress of a Quaker lady is pleasing; it is respectful, refined. It has a soft effect at the edge of a garden, like a blue-gray haze, and always reminds me of doves. The power of association of some inherent qualities of the plant, makes Lavender always suggest freshness and cleanliness.

ALICE MORSE EARLE, *Old Time Gardens*, 1901

Lavender is one of the hardiest of herbaceous plants, and thrives under a wide range of conditions of both soil and climate – even poor, sandy or loamy soils are agreeable to it, and these conditions are recognised as resulting in the production of the finer classes of essential oil. One condition of soil is very necessary, and that is, it should be free from possibility of water-logging. Excessive moisture at the roots soon causes the plant to perish. Low, wet land should, therefore, be avoided, unless it is well drained.

JOSEPH KNIGHT, *Journal of Agriculture, Victoria*, 1912

Conserve of the Flowers of Lavender

Take the flowers being new so many as you please, and beat them with three times their weight of White Sugar, after the same manner as Rosemary flowers; they will keep one year.

W.M., Cook to Queen Henrietta Maria, *The Queen's Closet Opened*, 1655

For a Bath

Take Sage, Lavender flowers, Rose flowers of each two handfuls, a little salt, boil them in water or lye, and make a bath not too hot in which bathe the Body in a morning, or two hours before Meat.
JOHN MIDDLETON, *Five Hundred Receipts*, 1734

Lavender Sachet

Ground lavender flowers, 1 lb; gum benzoin in powder, $\frac{1}{2}$ lb; attar of lavender (essential oil), $\frac{1}{4}$ oz.
G.W.S. PIESSE, *The Art of Perfumery*, 1880

Lavender is the best-known 'nose-herb'. We grow it today for its fragrance, to use in sweet-smelling sachets and pot-pourri and to perfume linen, just as it was used 400 and more years ago.

The essential oil scents soaps, perfumes and powders, but lavender also has some medicinal and culinary uses which have been neglected.

With its fragrant blue-purple spikes and grey-green foliage, it is a shrub which brings beauty, aroma and colour to any garden. When we came to our house a huge bush of French lavender was waiting for us at the letterbox. Scores of bees clustered about the hazy blue sprays in the sunlight.

The thought of lavender usually evokes association with its pink-tinged mauve colour and with lavender water. It is 'clean', 'fresh', 'soft' and 'fragrant'. The word in fact is derived from the Latin, 'lavare', to wash.

Various types of lavender grow wild in the western Mediterranean in dry, sandy soil among rocks, mainly in the south of France, Spain, Italy, Corsica and Sicily. It is also native to parts of Yugoslavia, the Adriatic Islands and Crete.

There are some twenty-eight species of lavender, of which English lavender (*Lavandula vera*) is only one. It is one of those herbs of which the botanical titles have changed so many times that one species 'may have borne as many names as royalty, or a much-divorced woman', as Helen M. Fox remarked in *The Years in my Herb Garden* (1953). Mrs Fox herself preferred *L. officinalis* for English or True Lavender.

The hybridisation of both wild and cultivated lavenders has resulted in many pretty plants, but much confusion for nurserymen, botanists and herb lovers.

English Lavender (*L. vera*) has narrow, woolly, grey-green leaves, with one spike of soft mauve borne at the top of each erect stem. The spikes or lavender flowers are whorls of tiny blooms which resemble those of its relatives in the mint family. They bloom in summer.

Plants grow to about a metre in height, spreading out about the same distance. The roots are woody. *L. vera* yields the best quality oil for perfume.

Spike Lavender (*L. spica*) is a coarser, broader-leafed species than the true lavender, with thicker, shorter flower spikes. It yields more oil than *L. vera*, but it is of an inferior quality. Many variations of the tall lavenders differ mainly in the size and shape of their leaves.

The dwarf English lavenders are hardy in cool climates. Hidcote, Hidcote Blue, or Hidcote Purple (*L. atropurpurea nana*), is a compact bush with deep blue flowers, named for the garden of Hidcote Manor in Gloucestershire planted by Lawrence Johnston, an American.

Munstead grows to 30 cm in height, with

purplish blue blooms and grey, hairy foliage. It was developed by Gertrude Jekyll at Munstead in Surrey. Seeds germinate more quickly than other types. Among other dwarf lavenders is *L. alba*, which has white flowers when propagated from cuttings, but does not always come true from seed.

The English lavender types were probably taken to Britain in the 16th century by Huguenot exiles from France, though there is a possibility that they arrived earlier as a result of the Roman conquest.

Essential oil for perfuming and making aromatic waters became an important industry in the drier south of England, notably at Mitcham in Surrey (which is now built over), and later at Hitchin, Hertfordshire, and Maidenhead, Berkshire.

French lavender (*L. dentata*) is hardy and well suited to Australian conditions, especially along the coastline. The spikes are a true lavender hue, radiating out in dense clusters atop fringed, narrow, toothed leaves. It blooms in winter and for most of the year, reaching a height of a metre or more.

Italian lavender (*L. stoechas*) is the Sticka-dove or Cassidony of the early herbalists. The Romans named the Stoechades Islands off the south coast of France after this variety because it grew so abundantly there. The islands, not far from Marseilles, are now called the Iles de Hyeres.

This shrub grows to a metre, with clusters of small green lacy leaves. The flower spikes are distinctive, a deep purple, squared and tufted at the top. They look rather like the plumes of a guardsman's bearskin hat. *L. stoechas* blooms in spring.

Lavender has always been favoured by royalty. It was beloved by three British queens. Elizabeth I was fond of conserves of lavender and always kept them at her tables. Queen Henrietta Maria, the 'Cavalier Queen', had 'very great and large borders of Rosemary, Rue and White Lavender and great varieties of excellent herbs', according to a Parliamentary survey of 1649, the year her husband Charles I was beheaded.

John Parkinson dedicated his *Paradisus* to Henrietta Maria (daughter of Marie de Medici and Henri IV of France) asking her to accept

'this speaking Garden, that may informe you in all particulars of your store, as well as wants, when you cannot see any of them fresh upon the ground'.

Both John Tradescant the Elder and the Younger were gardeners to Charles and Henrietta Maria at Oatlands in Surrey. The queen's cook, 'W.M.', gave numerous recipes for the use of her 'store' of lavender in *The Queen's Closet Opened*, published in 1655.

The third English queen connected with lavender was Queen Victoria, who used lavender water as a deodorant and got it 'direct from a lady who distils it herself'. In the current era, Yardley & Co Ltd of London are suppliers of perfume and soap 'by appointment' to 'HM Queen Elizabeth, The Queen Mother' and of soap to 'HM Queen Elizabeth II'.

Charles VI of France (died 1420) is reported to have insisted that cushions stuffed with lavender be provided for his carriage. This may, or may not, have had something to do with the fact that the king suffered fits of madness and thought he was made of glass!

Louis XIV of France, the 'Sun King', was probably more sane. He carried sprigs of fresh lavender in his pocket and washed with lavender water.

In Elizabethan times, lavender was sewn into dresses and gloves and 'quilted in a cap' according to William Turner. Lavender drops were an ingredient in the 'smelling salts' used to revive fashionably swooning women in the 19th century.

Lavender was used in bath water — and still is — particularly in Turkey and Egypt. In Spain it remains a strewing herb in churches and women there use the essential oil as a hairdressing.

The oil is extracted by macerating the spikes and distilling them in water. A crude extraction method is to seal lavender flowers in a glass jar with a small amount of olive oil and place the jar in sunlight.

In the 1st century, Dioscorides recommended lavender for troubles of the thorax. It was used in the 16th century as a remedy for hoarse and sore throats. Externally, lavender oil may be used as a rubbing lotion to ease aches and pains.

It is also an antiseptic. The oil was used for swabbing wounds during World War I.

Because lavender culture is suited to the drier climate of many parts of Australia, high hopes were held at one stage that it would become a centre for the commercial production of essential oil.

A Government Scented Plant Farm was set up at Dunolly in Victoria to grow Spike lavender and *L. vera*. The Melbourne *Leader* reported in 1892:

This farm should be the subject of interest to every member of the community, and it is to be hoped will eventually become an object lesson which will bring home to the minds of a large section of the population the opportunities which await them of making profit out of what is now grown merely for ornamental purposes ...

As lavender enters largely into the composition of a good number of perfumes it will be extensively cultivated; the oil at present is worth about 10s per pound.

In 1912, the Victorian Government was still encouraging farmers to take on lavender cultivation as a small rural industry. Cuttings were available from the Labour Colony at Leongatha at 3s 9d per 1 000.

'The Governor of Pentridge, Mr Cody, planted out a small area, about half-an-acre or so, and returns given from this were highly satisfactory,' wrote Joseph Knight in the Journal of Agriculture, Victoria, for May 1912. 'Suffice it to say that, on his retirement from the Government Service, he is entering into lavender cultivation on a much larger scale.'

Cultivation

Lavender should be grown in a sunny, well-drained place. Feed with lime or dolomite to provide the alkaline conditions it needs. The seeds germinate slowly, so lavender is best propagated by cuttings 13 or 15 cm long, taken in autumn or spring. Remove leaves from the bottom 7 cm and poke the cuttings into moist sand or sandy soil.

Prune lavender bushes each year after the spikes have been gathered in autumn. This gives them time to grow before winter. Cut back old wood and generally thin out the plants to allow air and light to penetrate. Always gather lavender spikes for drying early in the morning, when they are dry. Dry in shade.

Lavender tea is aromatic, strong and green, good against headache and faintness, relieving tension. Pour 500 ml of boiling water over 30 g fresh tops (leaves and spikes, or leaves alone). Add lavender to other herbal teas.

Lavender sugar is made by bruising a few spikes to release their oil, then sealing them in a glass jar with sugar. This may be used for icing (remove the spikes) or in making ice-cream. A few leaves will add flavour to salads.

Lavender bath mix: Add a bunch of lavender and bunch of rosemary to a handful of Epsom salts for a refreshing bath. They may be placed in a muslin bag under the running tap or immersed in the bath water. A few drops of lavender oil has the same effect in a bath or footbath.

Lavender hair rinse: Infuse a handful of stalks and blossoms of lavender by boiling in a pint of cold water. Simmer for three minutes with top covered. When cool, use as a hair-conditioner.

Lavender water can be made at home by mixing 15 g of oil of lavender, 375 ml of spirits of wine and a drop of musk in a litre container.

Shake every few days. After a fortnight strain and store in perfume bottles. Use as a face wash and deodorant.

Lavender vinegar for toilet use is dabbed on cotton wool to rub over aching skin or across the forehead to relieve a headache. Steep lavender sprays in white vinegar, leave in sunshine and shake the container each day. Change flowers and repeat after a further week. Strain through muslin or blotting paper and bottle.

An insect repellent is made by absorbing a few drops of lavender on cotton wool and hanging it from the ceiling. One drop is said to be sufficient to kill any insect. The oil rubbed on the skin will repel flies, mosquitoes and ticks. A few sprigs of dry lavender will quickly deodorise a room if they are burnt on a fire.

Strew lavender leaves with stored fruit to deter pests.

Sachets & Sweet Bags

Lavender sachets are made from dried flowers, crushed and sewn up in muslin. Cut off long stems when the flowers spikes are out fully. Hang them upside down in loose bunches in a dry, shady place. They are dry in two weeks. The sachet is used to perfume linen, keep stored clothing fresh and to repel moths.

Another mix: Add to about 250 g dried lavender spikes, 10 g dried thyme and mint, 8 g ground cloves and 30 g cooking salt. Sew up in a small silk bag. A cheering present for someone ill, to place under their pillow.

Lavender Cotton

'to border knots with'

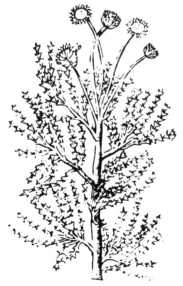

Lavender cotton from *Paradisus*, 1629

Lavender Cotton (*Santolina chamaecy-parissus*). Perennial.
   Santolina, Grey Santolina
   Old form: Lavender Cotten
Green Lavender Cotton (*S. virens*).
   Composite.

Lavender Cotten beside the beutie that it beareth in a garden is commonly given of women to young children for the wormes, being first punned & streined with milke & taken fasting warmed, which often it surely worketh (as I have prooved by often experience) which it doth through ye bitternes. For this is a general rule, ye all bitter things kill wormes, as Centory, wormwood & such like.
THOMAS COGHAN, *The Haven of Health*, 1584

Lavander Cotton bringeth foorth clustered buttons of a golden colour, and of a sweete smell, and is often used in garlands and decking up of gardens and houses. It hath a woodie storke, out of which grow foorth branches like little boughes, slender, very many, a cubite long, set about with little leaves, long, narrow, purled or crumpled on the tops of the branches stande up flowers, one alone on every branch, made up with short threds thrust close togither, like to the flowers of Tansie, and to the middle buttons of the flowers of Cammomil, but yet something broader, of colour yellow, which be changed in to seed of an obdure colour. The roote is of a woodie substance. The shrub it selfe is white both in branches and leaves, and hath a strong sweet smell.

Plinie saith, that the herbe *Chamacyparissum* being drunke in wine, is a good medicine against the poisons of all serpents and venemous beasts.

It killeth wormes either given greene or dry, and the seede hath the same vertue against wormes

88

... It is thought to be equall with the usual worme seede.

JOHN GERARD, *The Herball*, 1597

The whole plant is of a strong sweete sent, but not unpleasant, and it is planted in Gardens to border knots with, for which it will abide to be cut into what forme you think best, for it groweth thicke and bushy, very fit for such workes, besides the comely shew the plant it selfe thus wrought doth yeeld, being alwayes greene and of a sweet sent.

JOHN PARKINSON, *Paradisus*, 1629

Lavender Cotton, or Santolina, has knobby grey branches which make it look like coral out of water until the spikes thrust up with their flowers like tiny yellow buttons.

It was an obvious choice for border edgings and knots and mazes in the herbalists' gardens. Its growth is compact and the clippings were used for strewing on floors and as a moth repellent. It has a pungent smell.

The plant is not related to lavender. It grows as high as two feet, usually in a compact, round ball and is a hardy perennial.

Propagation is easiest from stem or root cuttings as the plant is difficult to raise from seed. There are no culinary uses.

Marigold

'the sunnes flour'

Double French or African marigold from *Paradisus*, 1629

Marigold (*Calendula officinalis*). Annual.
 Calendula, Pot Marigold.
 Old form: Golde, marigolde, marygold.
 Composite.

Golde is bitter in savour
Fayr and yelow is his flouwr
The golde flour is good to sene
It makyth the syth [sight] brythe and clene
Wyscely to lokyn on his flowris
Drawyth out of the heed wikked hirores [humors].

Macer's Herbal (trans. John Lelamoure, 1373)

Marigolds have not neede of any great ordering, for they grow in untilled fields and in any ground that a man will, neither doe they crave to be sowen everie yeere: for being once sowen, they afterwards grow of themselves; and beare flowers in the Calends of every moneth of the yeare, as well in sommer as in winter, for which cause the Italian cal them the flowre of al the moneths. To be short, the place where they have once been sowen can hardley be rid of them. If they be never so little husbanded, and cut manie times, they will beare most faire flowers and very great, but yet ever more in autumne than in the spring.

Some say that to eate oft of marigold leaves doth make a good countenance: the distilled water of marigold leaves being dropt into the eies, or linnen clothes wet therein and applied unto them, doth heale the rednes of the eies.

ANTHONY ASKHAM, *A Lytel Herball*, 1550

Marygoldes floures dronken, drawe downe wymens siknes: & so doth the iuice of the herbe: whyche is a present remedy for the toothe ake, if the mouthe be wasshed with it: summe use to make theyr here yelow with the floure of this herbe, not beyng content with the natural colour, which God hath geven them.

WILLIAM TURNER, *A New Herball*, 1551

Some terme it the Sunnes floure, or the follower of the Sunne, and it is of some named the Husbandman's Dyall, in that the same sheweth to them both the morning and evening tide. Other name it the Sunne's Bride, and Sunne's hearbe . . . This Marigold is a singular kind of Herbe, sowen in Gardens, as well for the potte as for the decking of Garlands bewtifying of Nosegayes, and to be worn in the bosom.

THOMAS HYLL, *A Most Briefe and pleasaunt treatyse*, 1563

The distilled water of Marigolds put into the eyes, cureth the rednesse, and inflammation of the same.

REMBERT DODOENS, *A niewe Herball*, (trans. Lyte, 1578)

The yellow leaves of the floures are dried and kept throughout Dutchland against winter, to put into brothes, in Physicall potions, and for divers other purposes, in such quantitie, that in some Grocers or Spice-sellers houses, are to be found barrels filled with them, and retailed by the pennie more or lesse, in so much that no brothes are well made without dried Marigolds.

JOHN GERARD, *The Herball*, 1597

The herbe and flowers are of great use with us among other pot-herbes and the flowers eyther greene or dryed, are often used in possets, broths, and drinkes, as a comforter of the heart and spirits,

John Parkinson from *Theatrum Botanicum*, 1640

and to expel any malignant or pestilential quality, gathered neere thereunto. The Syrup and Conserve made of the fresh flowers, are used for the same purposes to good effect.

JOHN PARKINSON, *Paradisus*, 1629

> The marigold observes the Sun
> More than my subjects me have done.

CHARLES I (in exile on the Isle of Wight)

These being so plentiful in every Garden, are so wel known that they need no Description.

They flower al the Summer long, and somtimes in Winter if it be mild.

It is an Herb of the *Sun*, and under *Leo*: They strengthen the Heart exceedingly, and are very expulsive, and a little less effectual in the smal Pox and Meazles than Saffron. The Juyce of Marigold Leavs mixed with Vinegar, and any hot swelling bathed with it, instantly giveth ease and asswageth it. The Flowers either green or dried are used much in Possets, Broths, and Drinks as a comforter of the Heart and Spirits, and to expel any malignant or pestilential quality which might annoy them. A Plaister made with the dry Flowers in Pouder, Hoge Grease, Turpentine and Rozin, and appled to the Breast, strengthens and succors the Heart infinitely in Feavers whether pestilential or not pestilential.

NICHOLAS CULPEPER, *The English Physician Enlarged*, 1653

The plant, especially its flowers, was used on a large scale by the American surgeons, to treat wounds and injuries sustained during the last Civil War; and obtained their warmest commendation. It quite prevented all exhaustive suppurative discharges and drainings. *Succus Calendula* (the fresh juice) is the best form, say the American surgeons, in which the Calendula is obtainable for ready practice.

W.T. FERNIE, *Herbal Simples*, 1895

Marigold Pudding

Take a pretty quantity of marygold flowers very well shred, mingle with a pint of cream on new milk and almost a pound of beef suet chopt very small, the gratings of a twopenny loaf and stirring all together put it into a bag flower'd and tie it fast. It will be boil'd within an hour – or bake in a pan.

JOHN EVELYN, *Acetaria*, 1699

The smaller double marigold from
Nicholas Culpeper's *The English Physician*, 1652

The old-fashioned pot marigold shown here is my favourite flower — as it has been the favourite in British cottage gardens since the Middle Ages.

This is the single, annual, *Calendula*, which blooms all summer, not the double, ruffled giant marigolds developed from it, nor the pungent French and African marigolds which deter nematodes.

The name comes from the Greek, *kalends*, the first days of the month, when it was said to be always in bloom. One Greek story says that the first marigolds were nymphs, turned into flowers by Artemis (Diana).

The vast amount of literature about marigolds shows how they have been loved for so long, yet, like most herbs, they also have a darker side. Geoffrey Chaucer in *The Knight's Tale* refers to them as a garland, worn by Jealousy. The flower is associated with death in Germany and Mexico and in ancient Greece it was a funeral offering.

Of course the marigold is more than just a pretty face. Petals are dried to use in flavouring soup, syrups and conserves and to colour butter and cheese. Or scatter the dried petals over custards, bread, cakes and salads.

A wound salve was formerly made by boiling marigold leaves in lard. Marigolds grow easily from seed. Their round heads range in colour

Pot marigold from *The Herball*, 1597

from pale yellow to deep orange, with contrasting centres. Leaves are dark, crinkly green and succulent.

Marigold tea is made from a teaspoon of dried petals and boiling water.

Marigold bath oil: Place a handful of dried petals (or fresh flower heads) in a glass jar and cover with about 60 g glycerine. Seal and allow to stand for a week. Strain off the glycerine and discard the petals and add 30 g olive oil. Shake well when adding to bath water.

Marjoram

'it hath a very good savour'

Sweet marjoram (left) and pot marjoram from *The Herball*, 1597

Marjorams

Sweet Marjoram (*Marjorana hortensis*). Annual.

Sweet or Knotted marjoram.

Old form: Merierum gentle, maioram, Marierum, Maiorana, Amaracum, Amaracus, Sampsuchum.

Pot Marjoram (*Origanum onites*). Perennial.

Winter Marjoram (*O. heracleoticum*). Annual.

Mint family.

Diocles the Physician, and the whole nation in manner of the Sicilians, have called that hearbe Amaracus, which in Aegypt and Syria is commonly named Sampsuchum. It commeth up both waies, as well of seed as of a slip and braunch. It liveth and continueth longer than the hearbes beforenamed, and hath a more pleasant and odoriferous sent. Marjoram is as plentiful in seed, as Southernwood . . .

PLINY, *Naturall Historie*, 77 A.D. (trans. Holland, 1601)

This herbe hast lewys lyk to organe and it hast sawour after cense and it hast a quyt flour and a quyt stalke.

AGNUS CASTUS, 14th century

Marierum is a thicke and busshy herbe creping by the ground with leves lyke small calaminte roughe and rounde. It hath lytle toppes in the hyest parte of the stalke much lyke scales one growinge over another as the fyr tree nuttes do appere. It hath a very good savour.

The drye leves layd to, with hony take away blew markes, whych come of beting. They are also good to be layd unto the styngyng of a scorpyone with salt & vinegre. The same receyed in to salve made of wex are good for the membres that are out of ioynte & after the same maner they are good for lose swellinges, and they are layd unto the eyes with the floure of barly, when they have an inflammation. The pouder of the drye herbe put in a mannes nose, maketh him to nese, & oyle that is made of merierum, warmeth and fasteneth the synoes.

WILLIAM TURNER, *A New Herball*, 1551

Maioram sweete, or Maioram gentle, tooke his name of a certaine Kinges wayting Boy, which in fetching his Lord certain oyntments at the Apothecaries, by chaunce (whilest he bare them) had a fall, and so by the spilling of everie eche of them (meeting togither by their flowing, and by such confusion) a marvellous sweete smell was made, which as they say, this Maioram representeth.

JOHN MAPLET, *A Green Forest*, 1567

And first the Maiorame, for the pleasaunt smel, as an herbe much esteamed of al persons, and may eyther bee sowen in the seedes, or set in slippes. And ioyeth also to be set in old dunge, the earth before well digged up, and to be rather set in moyste, and shadowie places, for so it groweth the fuller, and bigge, but set in an open and sunnye place, groweth the shorter, and cryspid. And it may eyther be sowen or set, in the springe tyme, and removed into Beddes, wel dressed with dry dunge, for so it prospereth the better.

THOMAS HYLL, *The Proffitable Arte of Gardening*, 1568

Lafeu: 'Twas a good lady, 'twas a good lady: we may pick a thousand salads ere we light on such another herb.

Clown: Indeed, sir, she was the sweet marjoram of the salad, or rather, the herb of grace.

Lafeu: They are not salad-herbs, you knave, they are nose herbs.

All's Well That Ends Well, Act IV, Scene 5

Sweete Marierome is a lowe and shrubbie plant, of a whitish colour and marvellous sweete smell, a foote or somewhat more high. The stalkes are slender, and parted into divers braunches: about which, grow foorth little leaves, soft, and hoarie. The flowers grow at the top in scalie or chaffie spiked eares, of a white colour like unto those of Candie Organie. The roote is compact of many small threds. The whole plant and every part thereof is of a most pleasant taste, and aromaticall smell, and perisheth at the first approach of winter.

Pot Marierome or winter Marierome, hath many threddie tough rootes, from which rise immediately divers small braunches, whereon are placed such leaves as the precedent, but not so hoarie, nor yet so sweete of smell bearing at the top of the braunches tufts of white flowers tending to purple. The whole plant is of long continuance, and keepeth greene all the winter, whereupon our English women have called it, and that very properly, winter Marierome.

The cause of the name of this most sweet and pleasant herbe is not determined except it came from the faining of the Poets, who report those of Cypres fawning upon their King *Cinara*, imagining to please his humor, said that his sonne in time of his youth, carried a boxe full of fragrant ointment, over the fieldes of most pleasant herbes, which by mischance he spilt upon the said herbes, which being moistioned therewith, yeelde unto this day that excellent savour, wherein we do so much delight. The boy mourning for the losse of his ointment, the gods (as the poets saith) in consideration of his parentage and excellent perfection, did change and transforme the boy into that hearbe, which is called *Amaracus*, after his owne name.

Sweete Marierome is a remedie against cold diseases of the braine and head, being taken any way to your best liking; put up into the nosthrils it provoketh sneesing, and draweth foorth much baggage flegme: it easeth the toothach being chawed in the mouth.

The leaves boiled in water, and the decoction drunke ... easeth such as are given to overmuch sighing and easeth the paines of the bellye. And given, dissolveth congealed or clotted bloud, and putteth away blacke and blew markes after stripes and bruses, being applied thereto.

The leaves are excellent good to be put into all odoriferous ointments, waters, pouders, broths and meates.

There is an excellent oile to be drawne forth of these herbes, good against the shrinking of sinewes, crampes, convulsions, and all aches proceeding of a colde cause.

JOHN GERARD, *The Herball*, 1597

The Sweet Marieromes are not onely much used to please the outward senses in nosegayes, and in the windowes of houses, as also in sweete powders, sweete bags, and sweete washing waters, but are also of much use in Physicke, both to comfort the outward members, or parts of the body, and the inward also.

The Use of Winter Marierome

The use of this Marierome is more frequent in our Land then in others, being put among other pot-herbes and sarsing (or sarseting herbes as they are called) and may to good profit bee applyed in inward as well as outward griefes for to comfort the parts, although weaker in effect then Sweet Marieromes.

JOHN PARKINSON, *Paradisus*, 1629

Sweet Marjoram is so wel known, being an Inhabitant in every Garden, that it is needless to write any Description thereof, neither of the Winter Sweet Marjoram, nor Pot Marjoram.

They grow commonly in Gardens; some sorts there are that grow wild in the Borders or Corn Fields, and Pastures in sundry places of this Land ...

Our common Sweet Marjoram is warming and comfortable in cold Diseases of the Head, Stomach, Sinews, and other parts, taken inwardly, or outwardly applied: The Decoction thereof being drank, helpeth al Diseases of the Chest which hinder the freeness of breathing, and it is also profitable for the Obstructions of the Liver and Spleen: It helpeth the cold griefs of the Womb, and the windiness thereof, and the loss of Speech, by resolution of the Tongue.

Being made into Pouder and mixed with Honey, it taketh away the black marks of blows and bruises, being thereto applied.

The Pouder thereof snuffed up into the Nose, provoketh sneezing, and thereby purgeth the Brain; and chewed in the Mouth draweth forth much Flegm ... Marjoram is much used in al odoriferous Waters, Pouders, & c. that are for ornament and delight.

NICHOLAS CULPEPER, *The English Physician Enlarged*, 1653

It is a chief Ingredient in most of those Powders that Barbers use, in whose Shops I have seen great store of this Herb hanged up.

WILLIAM COLES, *Adam in Eden*, 1657

A Conserve of Marjoram

Take the tops and tenderest parts of Sweet Marjoram, bruise it well in a wooden Mortar or Bowl; take double the weight of Fine Sugar, boil it with Marjoram Water till it is as thick as Syrup, then put in your beaten marjoram.

JOHN NOTT, *Receipts*, 1723

The sweet savour of marjoram is heady and distinctive. It was used in nosegays, as a strewing herb and in sweet bags in the Tudor and Stuart times when herbs were so much a part of daily life.

Sprigs of marjoram were used to scour wooden furniture and the sweet bags were stored with linen or placed under a pillow to bring peaceful sleep.

Today marjoram is one of the most useful kitchen herbs, to season roasts, stews and sausages and to flavour salads and soups. The essential oil was esteemed for medicine and used externally for sprains and bruises. A drop or so soaked in cotton wool helped to relieve the pain of toothache.

Sweet marjoram was a symbol of happiness which the Greeks planted on graves as a cheerful farewell to their relatives and friends.

All types are propagated by root division. The sweet marjoram is an annual, but a perennial in mild climates. It is slow to raise from seed.

Pot marjoram is native to Sicily and has small pink flowers. A perennial, it has hoary leaves, oval shaped, with purple-red stem and branches. It reaches 60 cm in height.

Winter marjoram is a native of Greece, not so commonly grown as the others.

Sweet marjoram was called knotted marjoram because of its squarish knobbed flower heads. It likes a sunny spot and also has purple-red stems and reaches 60 cm in height.

Marjoram tea is made by pouring 500 ml of boiling water over the tops and young leaves (about a handful). A good mixture is made with lemon balm and marjoram in the equal quantities. Good for headaches.

Pot marjoram from the *Juliana Anicia Codex*, 512 A.D.

Mazes

Here by the waye (gentle Reader) I doe place two proper Mazes... as proper adournments upon pleasure to a Garden, that who that listeth (having such rowme in their Garden) may place the one of them (which liketh them beste) in thatvoyde place of the Garden, that may best be spraed (for the onely purpose) to sporte them in at times, which Mazes being workmanly handled by the Gardiner, he shall bewtifie them much, in devising fowre sundrie fruites to be placed, in eche of the corners of the Maze, and in the mydle of it maye be a proper herber decked with Roses, or els some fayre tree of Rosemary, or other fruite, at the discretion of the Gardyner.

And here I also place the other Maze, whiche

may be lyke ordred & used, as I spake of before, and it may either be sette with Isope and Tyme, or with wynter Savery and Tyme. For these do well endure (all the Wynter through) grene. And there be some, whiche set their Mazes with Lavender Cottone, Spike, Maierome, and suche lyke.

THOMAS HYLL, *The Proffitable Arte of Gardening*, 1568

Mazes well framed a mans height may perhaps make your friend wander in gathering of Berries till he cannot recover himself without your helpe.
WILLIAM LAWSON, *A New Orchard and Garden*, 1618

Crispe Mynte, or Crispe Balme.

Crisp mint from *The Herball*, 1597

Spere Mynte, or right garden Mynte.

Spearmint from *The Herball*, 1597

Some Mints

Old form: Mynts, mintes, myntes.
Perennial.

Apple Mint (*Mentha rotundifolia*). Woolly mint.
Corn Mint (*M. arvensis*). Field mint, wild mint.
Corsican (*M. requienii*).
Curly Leafed (*M. crispa*).

Egyptian (*M. niliaca*).
Eau de Cologne (*M. pip citrata*).
Horse Mint (*M. longifolia*). Hairy mint.
Lemon (*M. citrata*). Orange mint, Bergamot mint.
Peppermint (*M. piperita*). English mint, Mitcham peppermint.

Curled Mynte.

Curled mint from *The Herball*, 1597

Red Mint (*M. gentilis*).
Spearmint (*M. spicata*). Garden, Lamb and Roman mint.
Variegated Apple (*M. rot variegata*). Pineapple mint.
Watermint (*M. aquatica*). Curled mint.

Mint

'seasoned with mints'

A pleasant hearb this is, and delectable to smell unto, insomuch as you shall not see a husbandmans bourd in the countrey, but all the meats from one end to the other be seasoned with Mints. If it be once set or sowne, and have taken to the ground, it will continue there a long time.

As touching garden Mint, as the very smell of it alone recovereth and refresheth the spirits: so the tast stirreth up the appetite to meat, which is the cause, that it is so ordinarie in our sharpe sauces wherein we use to dip our meats. Being put into milke, it will not suffer it to turn or soure; it keepeth it from quailing & curding: which is the reason, that they who use ordinarily to drinke milke, take Mints therewith, for feare it should coagulate or crudle in their stomacke, & put them in danger of suffocation.

It is singular to drie up the humors that mollifie the grisly wind pipe & the other instruments of the breath and voice, and when they are drie, knitteth and strengtheneth them. Taken in water and honied wine, it clenseth the corrupt and putrified flegmaticke humors which bee offensive to the throat and those parts. The juice of Mints is excellent for to scoure the pipes and clear the voice, being drunk a little before that a man is to straine himselfe either in the quier, or upon the stage, or at the bar; and not otherwise.

PLINY, *Naturall Historie*, 77 A.D. (trans. Holland, 1601)

Woe to you, scribes and Pharisees, hypocrites! for you tithe mint and dill and cummin, and have neglected the weightier matters of the law, justice and mercy and faith . . .
Matthew 23:23

I shall never lack a good supply of common mint, in all its many varieties, all its colours, all its virtues. But if any man can name the full list of all the kinds and all the properties of mint, he must know how many sparks Vulcan sees fly into the air from his vast furnace beneath Etna.
WALAFRID STRABO, *The Little Garden*, 840 A.D.

The vertue of this herbe is that yf it be ofte eaten, it wyll slee the wormes in a mans wombe. Also yf a man have botches or other rennynges or swellynges in his heade, take this herbe and stamp it, and lay it to the sore, and it wyll hele it. Also yf a mannes toth ake or stynke: take this herbe and seth it in whyte wyne and in eysel, and take that lycour and wasshe his mouthe therewith, and he shal have a swete smellynge mouth. Also take thou this herbe and eysell & make sauce, and it wyl make the to have a talent to thy mete.

Wyer's Herball, 1535

And first the Myntes may be planted near unto a well, or other running water, for that the herbe delighteth in a moyste place. And to be sette eyther in slippes, or in the whole rootes, and flourishinge in the Summer, but withered in the wynter.

All the sortes of the Myntes in the Garden, doe bothe comforte the stomacke, and helpe digestion. And nowe the Myntes broughte to pouder, and eaten in Mylke, doth slea the womes in the bodie. And the daily use of this herbe eaten, doth lose the belly, and the daily using of this herbe doth give a good colloure. And at any time eaten, is very healthful to the body.

THOMAS HYLL, *The Proffitable Arte of Gardening*, 1568

They lay it with good success unto the stingings of Bees and Waspes.

REMBERT DODOENS, *A Niewe Herball* (trans. Lyte), 1578

There be divers sorts of Mints, some of the garden, others wilde or of the field; and also some of the water.

The smell of Mint, saith *Pliny*, doth stir up the mind, and the taste to a greedy desire of meat. Mint is marvellous wholesome for the stomacke. It is good against watering eies. It is poured into the eares with honied water.

The savor or smell of the Water Mint rejoyceth the heart of man, for which cause they use to strew it in chambers and places of recreation, pleasure and repose, and where feasts and banquets are made.

JOHN GERARD, *The Herball*, 1597

All sorts of mints, whether garden or wild, doe nothing desire the ground dunged, fat or lying open upon the Sunne, but rather a moist ground neere unto Water, for want whereof they must be continually watered, for else they die.

RICHARD SURFLET, *The Countrie Farme*, 1600

Mintes are oftentimes used in baths with Baulme

and other herbes as a help to comfort and strengthen the nerves and sinewes. It is much used either outwardly applyed; or inwardly drunke, to strengthen and comfort weak stomackes.

It is used to be boyled with Mackarell, and other fish.

Being dryed, it is often and much used with Penniroyall, to bee put into puddings: as also among pease that are boyled for pottage.

JOHN PARKINSON, *Paradisus*, 1629

Garden mints were universally used for sauces in Pliny's time; and much commended for their singular Vertues, especially the young red buds in the Spring with a due proportion of Vinegar and Sugar, refresh the Spirits and stirreth up the appetite, and is one of the best Sallads the Garden affords. There are divers sorts of Mint but the red Garden Mint is the best.

JOHN WORLIDGE, *Systema Horti-culturae*, 1677

The common mint cultivated in our gardens is employed in different culinary processes, being sometimes boiled in certain dishes, and afterwards withdrawn. It has an agreeable aromatic flavour and forms an ingredient in soups, and sometimes is used in spring salads. It is valuable as a stomachio and anti-spasmodic; on which account it is generally served at table with pea soup.

MRS ISABELLA BEETON, *Household Management*, 1861

A Bag to Smell Unto for Melancholy, or to Cause One to Sleep

Take drie Rose leaves, keep them close in a glasse which will keep them sweet, then take powder of Mints, powder of Cloves in a grosse powder, and put the same to the Rose leaves, then put all these together in a bag, and take that to bed with you, and it will cause you to sleep, and it is good to smell unto at other times.

Ram's Little Dodoen, 1606

In Greek mythology, Minthe, a nymph beloved by Pluto, was changed by jealous Persephone into sweet-smelling mint. Now she waits by a cave at the edge of the dark underworld (Hades), Pluto's kingdom.

Ovid tells the story of an old couple, Philemon and Baucis, who welcomed strangers to their table which they 'rubbed o'er with newly gathered mint', unaware that they were entertaining Hermes and Zeus. Philemon is still the Greek word for hospitality.

Mint was a commonly used herb in ancient Greece, tied up with the daily lives of the people, who used it in baths and at funerals, with rosemary and myrtle, to offset the smell of decay. Demeter drank barley water flavoured with mint at Elefis and the water mint was sacred to Aphrodite.

Theophrastus, head of the Lyceum following Aristotle in the 4th century B.C., named the genus.

All the mints have their own character and each shares something of the features of the others, particularly their square stems, which spread so rapidly under the ground. This is because the mints hybridise each other and have produced such a wide diversity of types. For this reason it is best to plant them apart from each other, or they will cross-pollinate.

Oil of peppermint, or menthol, is derived from *M. piperita*, the peppermint, and was used long ago to mask the smell of tobacco. It is the most commonly used mint in medicine, as a mouthwash and for flavouring toothpaste and chewing gum and other sweets. It was used in the 14th century for whitening teeth. Spearmint is the mint used mostly in cooking, particularly the mint and vinegar sauce served with English style roast leg of lamb.

Mint tea is made by pouring 500 ml of water over a small handful of leaves and flavouring with lemon and honey; mint-flavoured tea is a popular drink in North Africa. The powdered, dried mint leaves are used in pea soup and seasonings.

In Tudor times, mints were grown along paths and around a sun-dial, so that their sweet smell would refresh those consulting it. Fresh sprigs of mint are boiled up with green peas and new potatoes. The powdered, dried mint leaves are used in pea soup and seasonings.

Apple and *lemon mint* chopped up with parsley and some cream cheese or cottage cheese added makes a delicious filling for a sandwich served with chicken salad.

Spearmint is said to deter mice, which will not go near stored food which has been scattered with its leaves. In the garden, peppermint protects cabbages from white butterfly and repels ants.

Corsican mint is a creeper with tiny round, vivid green leaves and minute flowers which makes a bright ground cover.

Mugwort

'it dissolves weariness'

Mugwort from *A Niewe Herball*, 1578

Mugwort (*Artemisia vulgaris*). Perennial.
  Mugwort.
  Old form: Mogworte, Muggurth, Muggons, Motherwort.
  Composite.

If any have ye herb Artemisia with him in ye way, it dissolves weariness & he that bears it on his feet, drives away venemous beasts & devils.
DIOSCORIDES, 60 A.D. (trans. Goodyer, 1655)

Eldest of worts
Thou hast might for three
And against thirty
For venom availest
For flying vile things,
Mighty against loathed ones
That through the land rove.

LACNUNGA (Saxon Herbal), 10th century

If this herbe be within a house there shall no wycked spyryte abyde.

The Grete Herball, 1526

Mugworte hath broad leaves, all iagged & torne like the leaves of Wormwood, but something smaller, & specially those which grow about ye stalke, they are of a browne greene colour above, and white hoare or gray underneath.

Mugworte as *Plinie* saith, had this name ·or *Artemisia* Queene of *Halicarnassus* and wife of *Mausolus* King of *Carie*, who chose this herbe & gave it her name, for, before that it was called *Parthenis*, that is to say, Virginal: Some say *Artemisia* was so called of the Goddesse *Diana* who was also called *Artemis* & for bycause this herbe is singular for womens diseases, who are all under the government of *Diana*, as the Heathen doe imagine and dreame.

. . . If it be hanged or cast into barrels or hogges-heads of Bier, it will preserve the same from sowring.

REMBERT DODOENS, *A Niewe Herball* (trans. Lyte), 1578

The first kinde of Mug wort hath broad leaves, very much cut or cloven like the leaves of common Wormewood, but larger, of a darke greene colour above, and hoarie underneath: the stalkes are long and straight, and full of branches, whereon do grow small round buttons, which are the floures, smelling like Merierome when they wax ripe: the root is great, and of a woodie substance.

Pliny saith, that the traveller of wayfaring man that hath the herbe tied about him feeleth no wearisomnesse at all; and that he who hath it about him can be hurt by no poysonsome medicines, nor by any wilde beast, neither yet by the Sun it selfe; and also that it is drunke against *Opium* or the iuyce of blacke Poppy. Many other fantasticall devices invented by Poets are to be seene in the Works of the antient Writers, tending to witchcraft and sorcerie, and the great dishonour of God; wherefore I do of purpose omit them, as things unworthie of my recording, or your reviewing.

JOHN GERARD, *The Herball*, 1597

And if a Footman take *Mugwort* and put it into his Shoes in the Morning, he may goe forty miles before Noon and not be weary.

WILLIAM COLES, *The Art of Simpling*, 1656

The leaves and tops of the young shoots and flowers in this plant are all full of virtue, they are aromatic to the taste with a little sharpness. The herb has been famous from the earliest times, and Providence has placed it everywhere about our doors so that reason, and authority, as well as the notice of our senses, point it out for use, but chemistry has banished natural medicines.

SIR JOHN HILL, *The British Herbal*, 1756

Mugwort was a white magic herb hung over doorways to keep away elves, devils, demons and other evil spirits. It was also relied on as a protection against thunder, lightning, and snakes and was used to relieve travel fatigue.

It was one of many herbs linked with St John the Baptist and was held over bonfires on St John's Eve (24 June) to purify it. An infusion of the dried leaves was added to beer (the leaves being discarded) instead of hops. This is thought to have given the herb its name, from *mug*, or 'cup' and *wort*, the old name for herb. However, some herbals associate the name with moughe (moth) because the dried leaves were stored with clothing to ward off attacks by moths.

The rather straggly mugwort grows wild beside paths and roads and on wasteland in most of Europe. The leaves are finely cut and pointed, bright green above and woolly white underneath. The plant grows to over a metre. Flowers are grey-white or pale yellow.

Mugwort is used to fatten geese, turkeys and other poultry and is used in stuffing for roast goose.

***Mugwort tea* is made by infusing 30 g of dried leaves in 500 ml of boiling water. The same liquid, cooled, may be sponged over the skin as a protection against insect bites.**

***A sleep pillow* of dried mugwort is supposed to bring on weird dreams!**

Nasturtium

'a delicate tussiemussie'

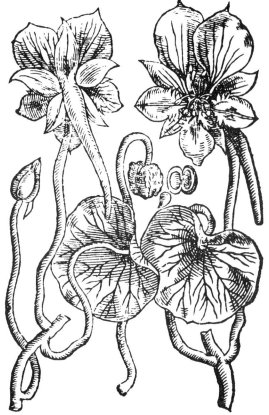

Nasturtium, or Indian cress from *The Herball*, 1597

Nasturtium (*Tropaeolum major*), Perennial.
  Old form: Indian cress, Cress of Peru, Larkes Heel.
Dwarf Nasturtium (*Tropaeolum minus*). Tom Thumb Nasturtium.
  Nasturtium family.

Cresses tooke the name in Latin Nasturtium, *a nasium tormento*, as a man would say, Nose-wring, because it will make one wryth and shrinke up his nosthrils: which is the reason that the word is grown into a proverb, when wee would signifie a thing which will put life into one that is dull and unlustie. In Arabia, the Cresses (by report) proove to a wonderfull bignesse.
PLINY, *Naturall Historie*, 77 A.D. (trans. Holland, 1601)

I sowed a seede thei brought me from the Peru, more to see his fairnesse than for any medicinall vertues that it hath . . . It is a flower very beautiful, which doeth adornate the gardens.
NICHOLAS MONARDES, *Joyfull Newes out of the New Founde Worlde* (trans. Frampton), 1577

The flours are dispersed throughout the whole plant, of colour yellow, with a crossed star over-thwart the inside, of a deepe Orange colour: unto the backe-part of the same doth hang a taile or spurre, such as hath the Larkes heele, called in Latine *Consolida Regalis*; but greater, and the spur or heele longer; which beeing past there succeed bunched and knobbed coddes or seed vessells, wherein is contained the seed, rough, browne of colour, and like unto the seeds of the beete, but smaller.
  The seeds of this rare and faire plant came from the Indies into Spaine, thence into France and Flanders, from whence I received seed that bore with mee both floures & seed, especially those I received from my loving friend John Robin of Paris.
JOHN GERARD, *The Herball*, 1597

The whole flower hath a fine small sent very pleas-ing, which being placed in the middle of some Carnations or Gilloflowers (for they are in flower at the same time) make a delicate Tussiemussie, as they call it, or Nosegay, both for sight and sent.
JOHN PARKINSON, *Paradisus*, 1629

The elegant nasturtium-plant, called by naturalists *Tropaeolum* and which sometimes goes by the name of Indian cress, came originally from Peru, but was easily made to grow in these islands. Its young leaves and flowers are of a slightly hot nature and many consider them a good adjunct to salads, to which they certainly add a pretty appearance.
MRS ISABELLA BEETON, *Household Manage-ment*, 1861

In the warm summer months the flowers have been observed about the time of sunset to give out sparks, as of an electrical kind, which were first noticed by a daughter of Linnaeus.
W.T. FERNIE, *Herbal Simples*, 1895

Pickled Nasturtium 'Capers'

Gather the buds before they open to flower; lay them in the shade three or four hours and, putting them into an earthen glazed vessel, pour good vinegar on them and cover it with a board. Thus let it stand for eight or ten days. Being taken out, and gently press'd, cast them into fresh vinegar, and let them so remain as long as before. Repeat this a third time, and barrel them up with vinegar and a little salt.

JOHN EVELYN, *Acetaria*, 1699

Nasturtium from *The Herball*, 1597

With the familiar nasturtium we can at last say with the early herbalists: here is a plant so well known in our gardens that we need not describe it! Everybody knows (and some dislike) this hardy plant, with its fast-spreading vines, saucer-shaped leaves and brilliant flowers of yellow, orange and red.

With its hot, peppery taste and smell it is indeed a nose-twister and so Pliny named it, from the Latin *nasus*, nose, and *tortus*, twisted.

We recall the spicy nasturtium sandwiches made in the backyard as children. We didn't know it was good for us then, but now we know the leaves contain vitamin C. The leaves and flowers are added to salads.

Pickling the seeds was an old Chinese delight long before John Evelyn gave his recipe for it. They may also be added to pickled cucumbers.

The nasturtium is a native of Peru and arrived in northern Europe only at the end of the 15th century, being given the name Indian Cress by John Gerard in 1597. Evidently it was known in Roman times as Pliny advised that 'a sluggish man should eat nasturtium, to arouse him from his torpidity'.

In the garden the nasturtium adds much colour and it is of great value as a 'trap' plant, attracting whitefly and aphis away from plants like beans, potatoes and broccoli and deterring the cucumber beetle. A circle of nasturtiums planted under apple and other fruit trees keeps away the woolly aphis.

The nasturtium can be protected from aphis itself by throwing soapy dishwater over the plants. Experiments at the Connecticut Experimental Station in the United States showed that aphis avoid the orange colour of nasturtiums or African and French marigolds. A nasturtium infusion can be used to benefit plants as a spray.

Ophelia's Garland

There's rosemary, that's for remembrance; pray, love, remember: and there is pansies, that's for thoughts . . .

There's fennel for you, and columbines: – there's rue for you; and here's some for me: – we may call it herb-grace o' Sundays:

. . . O, you must wear your rue with a difference. – There's a daisy:
. . . I would give you some violets, but they withered all when my father died . . .

Hamlet, Act IV, Scene 5

Ophelia, woodcut by Camille Pisarro

"OPHELIA"

Oregano

'against the bitings and stingings'

Oregano from *The Herball*, 1597

Oregano (*Origanum vulgare*). Perennial.
Oregano or Wild Marjoram.
Old form: Organie, Joy of the Mountains, Bastard marierome.
Mint family.

There be many kinds of Cunila (marjorams) known in Physicke: and first, that which is called Bubula

(oregano) and hath seed like unto Pennyroiall, being either chewed in the mouth or applied outwardly, it is a good wound-hearb, so that it be not remooved but every five daies. Taken in wine, it is singular against the poisonous sting of Serpents, in case the hearbe it selfe be stamped, and laid withall upon the sore place: and verely it is an ordinarie thing, to rub therewith well and thoroughly, the wounds that they make.

PLINY, *Naturall History*, 77 A.D. (trans. Holland, 1601)

And first the *Organie*, delighteth to be sette in roughe and stonie places, and to be dunged and watered, untyll the same be well fastened in the earth.

And it ought to be gathered when the same beareth flowers and to be dried in the shadowe, for so the leaves and flowers, will continue for a yere, if (they before) be sripped away from the stalkes, and the stalkes cut away.

... All the kyndes of the *Organie*, nave the vertue of cutting asunder, drying, drawing, and consuming, yet the roote of any of theym, hath no vertue in medicine.

... And the flowers and leaves put into a litle linnen bagge, and the same boyled in wine, applye hot to the heade, the pacient then covered with clothes to sweate, and this doth so drive furth, and put away many grieffes of the heade, and breaste, and healpeth also the strayghtnes of fetching breath.

THOMAS HYLL, *The Proffitable Arte of Gardening*, 1568

Bastard Marierome groweth straight up with little round stalkes of a reddish colour, full of branches, a foote high and sometimes higher. The leaves be broad, more long than round, of a whitish greene colour: on the top of the branches stand long spikie eares, out of which shoote foorth little white flowers, like the flowring of wheate. The whole plant is of a sweete smell, and sharpe biting taste.

Organie given in wine is a remedie against the bitings and stingings of venemous beasts, and cureth them that have drunk *Opium*, or the iuce of blacke Poppie, or Hemlocke, especially if it be given with wine and raisons of the sunne.

It is profitable used in a loach, or a medicine to be licked against an old cough, and the stuffing of the lungs.

It healeth scabs, itchings, and scurvinesse being used in bathes, and it taketh away the bad colour which commeth of the yellow iaunders.

JOHN GERARD, *The Herball*, 1597

104

Wild or Field Marjoram hath a Root which creepeth much under ground, which continueth a long time, sending up sundry brownish hard square stalks with smal dark green Leavs very like those of sweet Marjoram, but harder, and somwhat broader, at the tops of the stalks stand tufts of Flowers of a deep purplish red color; the Seed is smal and somthing blacker than that of sweet Marjoram.

It strengthens the stomach and Head much, there being scarce a better remedy growing for such as are troubled with sowr humor in their stomachs; it restores Appetite being lost, helps the Cough and Consumption of the Lungs, it clenseth the Body of Choller expelleth poyson, and remedieth the infirmities of the spleen, helps the bitings of Venemous Beasts, and helps such as have poysoned themselves by eating Hemlock, Henbane, or Opium ... And thus much for this Herb, between which and Adders there is a deadly Antipathy.

NICHOLAS CULPEPER, *The English Physician Enlarged*, 1653

Theophrastus bestowed the beautiful name 'Joy of the Mountains' on this plant about 300 B.C. It was derived from *oros*, joy and *ganos*, mountains. John Gerard's title of *Bastard Marierome* seems inappropriate, though his alternative of *Oraganie* seems more apt.

The modern Greeks are just as enthusiastic about this herb, which they call *rigani*. I have eaten it with them in tomato salads and lamb grilled on the spit.

This name covers about ten different species of *oreganium* which dot the hillsides of the Aegean and Mediterranean and includes the Italian oregano prized by Italian cooks in pasta and pizza.

It has a pungent smell, more like thyme than marjoram and a very spicy taste. Use it wherever marjoram is called for in a recipe.

The original seal of the famous Faculty of Paris showed three storks with twigs of oregano in their beaks.

Oregano grows to about 45 cm in height with reddish woody stems carrying rosy-white flowers. Divide roots to increase. The oil is a stimulant.

Oregano tea is made by pouring 250 ml of boiling water over 15 g of the fresh tops or dried herb.

Parsley

'a swete smelling breath'

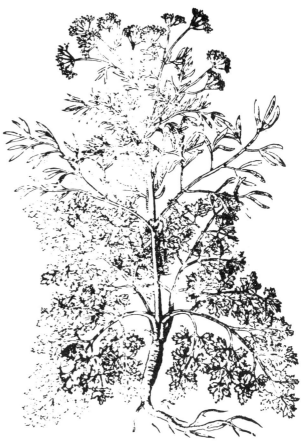

Parsley from Mattioli, 1583

Parsley (*Petroselinum hortense, Hoff., Apium petroselinum, L.*) Biennial. Parsley.
   Old form: Parcely, persely, parcelye, perslie.
Curled (*P. crispum*).
Italian (*P. crisp. neapolitanum*).
Fern-Leaf (*P. crisp. filicinum*).
Hamburg Parsley (*Carum petroselinum*). Turnip-rooted parsley.
   Umbelliferae – parsley family.

Isthmian victory with horses
Poseidon granted to Xenokrates,
sending a wreath of Dorian parsley
to bind on his hair in token of triumph.

PINDAR, *Second Isthmian Ode*, 470 B.C.

At Sparta's Palace twenty beauteous mayds,
The pride of Greece, fresh garlands crowned
    their heads
With hyacinths and twining parsley drest,
Graced joyful Menelaus' marriage feast.

THEOCRITUS, 300 B.C., quoted by Gerard, 1597

Now as touching Ach or Parsley, the manner is to soe it immediately after the Spring Aequinox in March, but the seed would be first brused and beaten a little in a mortar: for some are persuaded, that by this means it groweth thicker and more crispe or curled: which it will doe likewise, in case after a bed be sowed therewith, it be troden upon with mens feet, or beaten downe with a roller or cylindre. This peculiar propertie hath Persley, That it will chaunge the colour. It was an auncient custome in Achaia, to doe honour unto this hearb, by crowning those that went away with victorie and wan the prize in the solemne tourneys and sacred games Nemei, with a chaplet of Persley.

Parsley is in great request, and no man lightly there is but loveth it: for nothing is there more ordinary, than to see large branches of Parsley good store, swimming in their potage: and commonly you have not a salad or sawce served to the bourd, you see not a peece of meat sarced or seasoned, but Parsley carrieth therein a great stroke, and contenteth everybodie. Over and besides, if it be applied as liniment, togither with hony unto the eyes, so that they be fomented also ever and anon with the hot juice or Parsley boiled, it is a singular remedie for the humors distilling thither.

Moreover, if a man perceive that the fish in any pond or stew do mislike and grow sickly, it is a common practice to give them green Parsley for to scoure and refresh them.

PLINY, *Naturall Historie*, 77 A.D. (trans. Holland, 1601)

Grynde perslie with vynegre and oyle of roses and with this oynement oynte the frounte of the heed that akyth, and this wole destroie the hede-ache.

The smoke of perslie dryveth a-wey alle serpentis and alle other bestes that casten veneme out at her mouth, and ther-fore it is the manere to rypmen (reapers) for to medle perslie in here metes, for-they that suche venemous bestis shulde fle fro hem and do hem no harm, yf it be-tyde hem for to falle on slepe whan they were werye.

Macer's Herbal, 12th century

And if you will have the leaves of the *Parcely* grow crysped, then before the sowing of them stuffe a

Tennis ball with the seedes, & beat the same well agaynst the ground, whereby the seeds may be a lytle brused, & then sowe them in the ground, or when the Parcelye is well come up goe over the bedde with a wayghty roller, whereby it may so presse the leaves downe, or elles treade the same downe with thy feete.

And the chawinge of the freshe and grene Parcelye, doth cause a swete smelling breath, so that the chawing of this herbe doth amende a fowle stinkinge breathe.

THOMAS HYLL, *The Proffitable Arte of Gardening*, 1568

The chief vertue of Perslie is in the roote, the next in the seede, the leaves are of least force, yet of a moost use in the kitchin. And manie use to eate them not onely with flesh or fish, but also with butter in the morning, and that for good cause, for by the judgement of later writers, Perslie is verie convenient for the stomacke, and stirreth up appetite and maketh the breath sweete.

THOMAS COGHAN, *The Haven of Health*, 1584

The leaves of garden Parsley are of a beautiful greene, consisting of many little ones fastened togither, divided most commonly into three parts ... the stalke is above one cubite high, slender, something chamfered, on the top whereof stande spoked rundles, bringing foorth very fine little flowers, and afterwards small seedes somewhat of a flierie taste: the rootes long and white, and good to be eaten.

The leaves are pleasant in sauces, with broth ... they be also singular good to take away stoppings, and to promote urine: which thing rootes likewise do notablie performe if they be boiled in broth: they be also delightfull to the taste, and agreeable to the stomacke.

The seeds are more profitable for medicine, they make thinne, they open, they provoke urine, they dissolve the stone: they be commended also against the cough if they be mixed or boiled with medicines made for that purpose: lastly they resist poisons, and therefore they be mixed with treacle.

JOHN GERARD, *The Herball*, 1597

Parslie craveth no great labour, but loveth a stonie and sandie ground, for which cause it is called parslie; againe it craveth not any store of manure: whereof it will be good to sow it under arbours: it desireth above all things to be well watered, and if it so fall out as that it be sowen or planted neere unto any fountaine or river, it groweth very faire, and in great quantitie.

The often use of parsley taketh away the stinking of the breath, especially from such as have drunke much wine or eaten garlike: and therefore such as use to keepe company much, and have an ill breath, must not goe unprovided of good store of fresh parsley to chaw or hold in their mouthes . . . The leaves of parsley cast upon the water of fish ponds, doe recreate and reioice the sicke and diseased fish.

RICHARD SURFLET, *The Countrie Farme*, 1600

Parsley, sow the first yeare, and use the next yeare, it seeds plentifully, an herbe of much use, as sweet Siccily is. The seed and rootes are good against the stone.

WILLIAM LAWSON, *The Countrie Housewifes Garden*, 1617

This parsley is much used in meate and broths, &c. in all countries . . . being of so mild a taste, and so comfortable to the stomacke. They use also to caste the herbe into their Fish ponds if there be any sicke among them to clense them. The distilled water of the herbe is a familiar medicine with nurses, to give their children when they are wrung in the stomacke or belly with wind, which they call the frets . . .

JOHN PARKINSON, *Theatrum Botanicum*, 1640

If there be nothing new under the sun, there are, at any rate, different uses found for the same thing; for this pretty aromatic herb was used in ancient times, as we learn from mythological narrative, to adorn the head of a hero no less than Hercules; and now – was ever fall so great? – we moderns use it in connection with the head of – a calf. According to Homer's 'Illiad', warriors fed their chariot steeds on parsley; and Pliny acquaints us with the fact that, as a symbol of mourning, it was admitted to furnish the funeral tables of the Romans.

MRS ISABELLA BEETON, *Household Management*, 1861

To Preserve Parsley through the Winter

Use freshly gathered parsley for keeping, and wash it perfectly free from grit and dirt; put it into boiling water which has been slightly salted and well skimmed, and then let it boil for 2 or 3 minutes; take it out, let it drain, and lay it on a sieve in front

Lady gathering parsley from *Tacuinum Sanitatis in Medicina*, 14th century

of the fire, when it should be dried as expeditiously as possible. Store it away in a very dry place in bottles, and when wanted for use, pour over it a little warm water, and let it stand for about 5 minutes.

MRS ISABELLA BEETON, *Household Management*, 1861

Parsley Soup (Soupe a la Bonne Femme)

500 ml milk, 250 ml water, 5 ml salt, 40 ml butter, 40 ml flour, 1 medium sized onion.

Melt butter, add flour and salt, and the liquids and onion. Boil for one hour. Remove the onion, add 125 ml of cream mixed with the yolk of two eggs. Do not boil. Cook until thickened. Just before serving add 125 ml of finely chopped parsley. Stir well, and serve at once.

Traditional French Recipe

In our time, parsley is perhaps both the most familiar and the most underrated of all the garden herbs. Too often it is used merely as a garnish and tossed aside after food has been served.

A handful of parsley contains more vitamin C than one orange. The herb also contains vitamin A, some vitamin G, protein, phosphorus and calcium.

Parsley is a natural deodoriser. Eaten after garlic, onions, or other strong-smelling foods, it subdues their strong odour. The same effect comes from drinking parsley juice, liquefied in a blender.

Chop up parsley finely, or tear it apart with the hands to use in salads, green soups, sauces, stuffing, rissoles, minces and stews. It is used to stop bleeding gums, to build up the blood and to preserve the eyesight.

In legend and folklore, parsley has an unexpectedly dark side. It was always considered unlucky in some way, especially to transplant it from one house to another. It had a reputation for causing abortion and the saying 'parsley grows rank in a cuckold's garden' pointed up another aspect of its bad reputation. It was an ingredient in the witches' 'flying ointment' (with many more grisly components). All these bad influences could be overcome, it was believed, if parsley was planted on Good Friday (at least in the northern hemisphere).

Some of this superstiton may have been caused by parsley's erratic and slow germination. It was said to go 'seven times to the devil and back again' before the seeds shoot.

In ancient Greece, parsley was used for victors' crowns in the Nemean Games after the Persian war, when it replaced the olive as a token of mourning. Chaplets of parsley were worn at Greek and Roman banquets in the belief that they would absorb the fumes of wine. It was also a Greek funeral wreath.

Propagate from seed, or buy plants from a nursery. The bright green, tightly curled leaves are aromatic. Parsley does best in shade or semi-shade and makes a good garden border.

Hamburg, or turnip-rooted parsley is grown for its swollen parsnip-like root which is cooked in soup or served with sauce.

Pennyroyal

'for swimming of the head'

Pennyroyal from *The Herball*, 1597

Pennyroyal (*Mentha pulegium*). Perennial. English pennyroyal.

Old form: Pennie royall, peniriall, penny-ryall, penny-royall, piliall royall, penyroiall, Pudding Grasse.

Mint family.

The braunches of Mint and Penyroiall both, are usually put into glasse viols with vinegre, for to be infused therein: and a man would not thinke how good this vinegre is for faintings of the heart; so great is the societie that these two hearbs have one with the other in this behalfe. For which cause, I remember upon a time when divers learned Physicians were met togither to confer in my chamber, they resolved and concluded definitely, That a chaplet of Penyroiall was without comparison far better for the giddinesse and swimming of the head, than one of roses; for a garland of Penyroiall, if it be worne onely upon the head, allayeth (by report) the ach thereof. More than that, it is said, That the very sent of Penyroiall preserveth the brain from the offence that may come by the distemperature either of heat or cold, yea and from the inconvenience of thirstinesse: insomuch as whosoever have two braunches or sprigs of Penyroiall put into his ears, shall feel no excessive heat though they continue in the Sun all the day long.

The seed of Penyroiall if it be smelled unto, is singular good to recover their tongue againe who be speechlesse: for the falling sicknesse also, it is given in a cyath of vinegre. If it fortune that one must drinke unholesome waters, the seed thereof reduced into powder and strewed thereupon, correcteth all the malice thereof.

The floures of Penyroiall that be fresh and new gathered, if they be burnt make a singular perfume to kill fleas.

PLINY, *Naturall Historie*, 77 A.D. (trans. Holland, 1601)

They say that Eastern doctors will pay as much for it as we pay here for a load of Indian pepper. If you cook some pennyroyal and use it as a potion or a poultice, it will cure a heavy stomach. When the sun is blazing down on you in the open, to prevent the heat from harming your head, put a sprig of pennyroyal behind your ear.

WALAFRID STRABO, *The Little Garden*, 840 A.D.

It crepeth much upon the ground and hath many lytle round leves not unlyke unto the leves of merierum gentil but that they are a little longer and sharper and also litle indented rounde about, and grener than the leves of meriurum are. The leves grow in litle branches even from the roote of certayn ioyntes by equall spaces one devyded from an other. Where as the leves grow in litle tuftes upon the over partes of the braunches.

WILLIAM TURNER, *A New Herball*, 1551

Peniriall is to print your love
So deep within my heart.

CLEMENT ROBINSON, *A Nosegaie*, 1584

In all your Gardens, Banks and Seats of Camomile, Pennyroyal, Daisies and Violets are seemly and comfortable.

THOMAS HYLL, *The Gardeners Labyrinth*, 1577

Pennyroyal from the *Juliana Anicia Codex*, 512 A.D.

The first and common Pennie royall, groweth naturallie wilde in moist and overflowen places, as in the Common neere London called Miles ende, about the holes and pondes thereof in sundrie places, from whence poore women bring plentie to sell in London markets, and it groweth in sundrie other commons neere London likewise.

Pennie royall taken with honie, clenseth the

lungs, and cleereth the breast from all gross and thicke humours.

If you have when you are at the Sea Pennie royall in great quantitie drie, and cast into corrupt water, it helpeth it much, neither will it hurt them that drinke thereof.

A Garland of Pennie roiall made and worne about the head is of great force against the swimming in the head, the paines and giddines thereof.
JOHN GERARD, *The Herball*, 1597

Let them that unto choller much incline,
Drinke *Penny-royall* steeped in their wine.
And some affirm that they have found by tryall,
The paine of Gowt is cur'd by Penny-royall.
SIR JOHN HARINGTON, *The Englishmans Doctor*, 1607

Penniroyall chopped & put into a bag-pudding giveth it a savoury relish.
WILLIAM COLES, *The Art of Simpling*, 1656

'Tis used to provoke the Courses, and to help Delivery. 'Tis good for Coughs, for the Gripes, the Stone, Jaundice and Dropsie. A spoonful of the juice given to Children is an excellent remedy for the Chin-cough (whooping cough) ... The fresh Herb wrap't in a Cloth, and laid in a Bed, drives away Fleas; but it must be renewed once a week.
JOHN PECHEY, *The Compleat Herbal of Physical Plants*, 1694

Pennyroyal, famed as flea repellent, is named from the Latin word for a flea – (*pulex*). It has a pungent, peppermint smell and a sharp taste.

The leaves are tiny, lying on the ground, but the blossoms stand out higher. It is very easy to start from cuttings or root divisions and likes a moist soil. It makes an ideal ground cover for the front of a border or bank and for the traditional garden seat of earth. The flowers are blue.

Pennyroyal is also said to deter lice, flies, mosquitoes, moths and ants. Squash the leaves and rub them on exposed skin. Sew up the dried leaves in sachets to use as 'sleep pillows' or for storing with linen. In Italy, the herb is hung on trees to prevent figs falling before they are ripe.

Pennyroyal tea is made by pouring 500 ml of water over 30 g of leaves. Drink in small cupfuls, or use pennyroyal mixed with other minty herbs such as catnip and lemon balm.

Rosemary

'rosemary for rememberance'

Rosemary from *The Herball*, 1597

Rosemary (*Rosmarinus officinalis*). Perennial shrub. Rosemary.

Old form: Rosemarine, Rosemarin, Rosemarie, Libanotis.
White-Flowered (*R. albus*).
Prostrate (*R. prostratus*).
Mint family.

Libanotis which ye Romans call Rosmarinus, & they which plait crowns use it: the shoots are slender, about which are leaves small, thick somewhat long, thin, on ye inside white, but on ye outside green, of a strong scent.
DIOSCORIDES, 60 A.D. (trans. Goodyer 1655)

Libanotis commeth naturally of seed in rotten grounds, lean and subject to deawes: it hath a root like to Alisanders, differing little or nothing in smell from Frankincense. The use of it, after it be one yeare old, is most wholesome for the stomack.

PLINY, *Naturall Historie*, 77 A.D. (trans. Holland, 1601)

Take the flowres and put them in a chest amonge youre clothes or amonge bokes and moughtes shall not hurte them . . .

Also boyle the leves in whyte wyne and wasshe thy face therewith and thy browes and thou shall have a fayre face.

Take the timber thereof and burn it to coales and make powder thereof and rubbe thy teeth thereof and it shall keep they teeth from all evils. Smell it oft and it shall keep thee youngly.

Also make thee a box of the wood and smell to it and it shall preserve thy youthe.

Banckes' Herbal, 1525

For weyknesse of ye brayne. Agaynst weyknesse of the brayne and coldenesse thereof, seth rosmarin in wyne and lete the pacyent receye the smoke at his nose and kepe his heed warme.

The Grete Herball, 1526

As for Rosmarine, I lett it runne all over my garden walls, not onlie because my bees love it, but because it is the herb sacred to rememberance, and, therefore, to friendship; whence a sprig of it hath a dumb language that maketh it the chosen emblem of our funeral wakes and in our buriall grounds.

SIR THOMAS MORE, early 16th century

Rosemary is a plante of a pleasaunt savoure, whyche for the Bewtie and smell of it; is set (at thys day) in Gardens. And the Gardeners also in our time, do make dyvers seates, and lyke to benches, and other proper formes (as lyketh them best, to be dilighted at) in their beddes running of lengthe and of heyghte.

And the same plant also in medicine hath a marvelouse efficacie. And Dioscorides nameth it the Garlande Rosemarie, for that (in tymes past) they made Garlandes thereof.

THOMAS HYLL, *The Proffitable Arte of Gardening*, 1568

Rosemary is as it were a little tree or woddish shrubbe, with many small branches and slender boughes, of harde and woodie substance, covered and set full of little, smal, long, and tender leaves,

white on the side next the ground, and greene above. The floures are whitishe, and mixte with a little blewe . . .

The Arrabians and their successours Physitions, do say that Rosmarie comfortheth the brayne, the memory, and the inward sences, & that it restoreth speach, especially the confertue made of the floures thereof with sugar, to be receyed dayly fasting.

The ashes of Rosemarie burnte, doth fasten loose teeth, and beautifieth the same if they be rubbed therewith.

REMBERT DODOENS, *A Niewe Herball* (trans. Lyte), 1578

The use of Rosmarine in kitchine is well knowen to all men. I would the herbe were as plentifull among us in Englande, as it is in that part of Fraunce which is named Provance, where it groweth of it selfe without setting; and is used for a common fuell.

Take Rosmarie with the flowers, or without a hand full or more, seeth it in white wine a good space, and put thereto if you may a little cinomon, then drinke it and wash your mouth therewith. The same wine without cinomon is good to wash the face, and handes, for it maketh a verie cleare skinne.

THOMAS COGHAN, *The Haven of Health*, 1584

> Rosemary is for remembrance
> Between us daie and night;
> Wishing that I might alwaies have
> You present in my sight.

CLEMENT ROBINSON, *A Nosegaie*, 1584

The distilled water of the floures of Rosemary being drunke at morning and evening first and last, taketh away the stench of the mouth and breath, and maketh it very sweet, if there be added thereto, to steep or infuse for certaine daies, a few Cloves, Mace, Cinnamon, and a little Annise seed.

The floures made up into plates with Sugar after the manner of Sugar Roset and eaten, comfort the heart, and make it merry, quicken the spirits, and make them more lively.

JOHN GERARD, *The Herball*, 1597

Seethe much Rosemary, and bathe therein to make thee lusty, lively, joyfull, likeing and youngly.

WILLIAM LANGHAM, *The Garden of Health*, 1597

One of the goatherds perceiving the wound, bad him give himself no trouble about it, for he would

apply a remedy that would heal it in a trice; so saying, he took some leaves of rosemary, which grew in great plenty round the hut, and having chewed and mixed them with a little salt, applied the poultice to his ear, and binding it up carefully, assured him, as it actually happened, that it would need no other plaister.

MIGUEL DE CERVANTES, *Don Quixote*, 1605 (trans. Smollett, 1761)

Rosemarie the grace of hearbes in England, in other Countries common . . . It becomes a Window well. The use is much in meates, more in Physicks, most for Bees.

WILLIAM LAWSON, *The Countrie Housewifes Garden*, 1617

Take a quantity of the flowers of Rosemary, according to your own will either more or lesse, put them into a strong glasse close stopped, set them in hot horse dung to digest for fourteen dayes, which then being taken forth of the dung, and unstopped, tye a fine linnen cloth over the mouth, and turn down the mouth thereof into the mouth of another strong glasse, which being set in the hot sun, an oyle will distil down into the lower glasse; which preserves as precious for the uses before recited, and many more, as experience by practice may informe divers.

JOHN PARKINSON, *Paradisus*, 1629

The cry of 'Rosemary and Briar' once resounded through the thoroughfares; and every alley smelt 'like Bucklersbury in simple time', when the whole street was a mart for odoriferous herbs. Cries like these are rare enough now, yet we do hear them occasionally, when crossing some bye-street, and have then smelt an unwonted fragrance in the air; and as someone has truly said that scents call up the most vivid associations, we have visions of a fair garden afar off, and the sports of childhood.

CHARLES HINDLEY, *A History of the Cries of London*, 1885

Hungary Water

1 gallon brandy or clean spirits
1 handful of rosemary
1 handful of lavender
1 handful myrtle

Buy Rosemary! Buy Sweetbriar!
Rosemary and Sweetbriar, O!
From Charles Hindley's *A History of the Cries of London*, 1885

Handfuls are measured by cutting branches of the herbs 12 inches long. A handful is the number of such branches that can be held in the hand. After measuring, the branches should be cut up into one-inch pieces, and put to infuse in the brandy. You will then have the finest 'Hungary Water' that can be made.

QUEEN ELIZABETH OF HUNGARY, 1235 (MS in Vienna State Library)

To Make Rosemarie Water

Take the Rosemarie, and the flowers in the middess of May, before sunne arise, and strippe the leaves and the flowers from the stalke, take foure or five Alicompagne (elecampane) rootes, and a handfull or two of Sage, then beat the Rosemarie, the Sage and rootes together, till they be verie small, and take three ounces of cloves, three ounces of mace, halfe a pound of Anniseedes and beat these spices everie one by it selfe. Then take all the Hearbes and the Spices, and put therein foure or five gallons of good white wine, then put in all these Hearbes and Spices, and Wine, into an earthern Pot, and put the same Pot in the ground the space of thirteen dayes, then take it up and still in a Still with a verie soft fire.

THOMAS DAWSON, *The good huswife's Jewell*, 1587

Moth Destroyer

Take of dried rosemary and mint half a pound each, of tansy and thyme four ounces each, of fresh ground cloves two tablespoonsfull. Mix these all well together and store in a well-closed box. If this powder is lavishly scattered among furs, blankets and clothing as they are stored, no moth will go near them.

MARIAN CRAN, *The Garden of Ignorance*, 1917

Rosemary is the emblem of love and the symbol of remembrance. In every way it is a herb of great virtue, much loved and spoken of by gardeners and writers.

It was always thought to bring good luck and to be a powerful force against magic, witchcraft and the evil eye. As a protection against infection it was strewn at funerals and burned in sick-rooms and hospitals.

113

In Australia and New Zealand, a sprig of rosemary is often worn by returned soldiers on Anzac Day, 25 April, to remember comrades who died at Gallipoli and other battles.

An evergreen shrub, rosemary grows slowly from seed and is best propagated from cuttings or divided root clumps. It bushes out to a height of one and a half metres, with erect, branching stems clustered about with curved slivers of spiky leaves, green on top and grey underneath. The whole plant is fragrant and spicy.

Its sea-blue flowers appear at the tips of the branches, small and fragrant. The prostrate type (*R. prostratus*) reaches only 20 cm in height and has spreading branches which make it ideal for hanging baskets or pots. The white-flowering variety (*R. albus*) reaches only one metre.

In the kitchen, rosemary is often stuck, green or dried, into the skin of a roasting chicken. It also flavours pork, lamb and beef, tomatoes and omelettes and makes herb butters and vinegars. The dried leaves are often chopped or powdered to add to biscuits, scones or pickles.

Rosemary tea is made by infusing 500 ml of water with 30 g of fresh tips or a teaspoon of dried leaves. Add lemon juice and honey to taste.

Rosemary wine is made by chopping up sprigs of green rosemary, pouring white wine over them, and straining for use after four or five days. It is said to be a good remedy for headache, stimulating the brain, nervous system and the heart.

To make *rosemary water*, simmer a large bunch of rosemary, stalks and all, preferably in rainwater, for about an hour. Use as a hair rinse or conditioner. Borax is often added.

Rosemary oil is obtained by distilling the leafy tips and leaves, either fresh or dried. This is used in eau-de-cologne, perfumes and soap and added to baths.

A *culinary oil* is made by soaking tops and sprigs in vegetable oil for a week in the sun, then straining for use in cooking.

Rosemary conserve is used as a relish with meat or game, or eaten as a snack. Beat to a pulp young green tips and flowers; then add three times their weight of honey, or sugar. Beat all together until it makes a smooth paste.

Rosemary sachet – Stuff a small pillow with a mixture of hops and rosemary.

Rosemary or Libanotis from the *Juliana Anicia Codex*, 512 A.D.

When Anne of Cleves arrived in England to marry King Henry VIII she wore a coronet of gold and precious stones in her hair, set full of branches of rosemary. Its 'civil' uses (as John Parkinson described them) were at weddings, both for bride and groom, as an omen of a happy marriage. It was made into a wreath, sometimes gilded, for Christmas and New Year.

Rosemary was worn as a garland or chaplet in both ancient Greece and Rome. In churches it was burned as incense – 'insensier' is its old French name. Rosemary oil is still used today in the Greek Orthodox Church.

Rue

'herb of grace'

Rue from Mattioli, 1583

Rue (Ruta graveolens). Perennial.
Rue, Herb of Grace.
Old form: Rew, ruwe.
Rue family

And of the garden kinde, that is fittest for eating which grows near fig trees.

DIOSCORIDES, 60 A.D. (trans. Goodyer, 1655)

Rue also is sowed usually in Februarie when the Western wind Favonious bloweth, and soone after the Aequinox in Autumne. It cannot away with winter, for it brooketh not cold or rain, nor moist ground, neither will it abide mucke: it liketh well to grow in drie places, and such as lie faire upon the Sun-shine; but a clay ground which is good for bricke and tile, that is alone for it and best of all

other: it delighteth in ashes, and therewith is it fed and nourished; insomuch as they use to blend ashes and the seed togither, for to keep away the cankerworme and such like.

The Figtree and Rue are in great league and amitie, insomuch as this hearb, sow and set it when and where you will, in no place prospere h better than under that tree: for planted it may be of slip or sprig.

When Rue is come to bee of any strength, there is untoward sarcling and weeding of it; for if it be handled, it will raise blisters upon a mans fingers, unlesse the hands be well gloved, or defended with oil. The leaves also of Rue are kept and preserved, being made up into little knitches or bunches.

PLINY, *Naturall Historie*, 77 A.D. (trans. Holland, 1601)

She doth mekyl good to the stomak if she be ofte drunke. For the hede-ache. Medle the jus of rue with the oil of roses and vynegre and the oynment wole cese hede-aches.

Macer's Herbal, 12th century

Behind the turf plot let there be a great diversity of medicinal and aromatic herbs which not only please by the odor of their scents; but by their variety of flowers refresh the sight, among which rue should be mingled in many places for its beauty and greenness, and its bitterness will drive away poisonous animals from the garden.

PETRUS DE CRESCENTIIS, *Opus Ruralium Commodorum*, 13th century

Also to make a mannes sigh cleer tak the dew in the morweynyng that is up-on the ruwe and kepe hit in a vessel and a noynt thyne eysen ther-with ofte and hit schal clere they sigh.

AGNUS CASTUS, 14th century

Yea, both curious Painters, and fine Gravers, do often eate of this herbe with their meate, for the clearing and amending of their sight.

Also the herbe mixed with Rose water, and that layde on bleared eies, or bloudshotte eyes, doth marveilously clense, and heale them.

THOMAS HYLL, *The Proffitable Arte of Gardening*, 1568

> Here did she fall a tear; here in this place,
> I'll set a bank of rue, sour herb of grace:
> Rue, even for ruth, here shortly shall be seen,
> In the remembrance of a weeping queen.

(Gardener), *King Richard II*, Act III, Scene 4

The leaves of Rue eaten with the kernels of Walnuts or figs stamped together and made into a masse or paste, is good against all evill aires, the pestilence or plague, resists poison and all venome.

JOHN GERARD, *The Herball*, 1597

Rew is a noble hearbe to give it right,
To chew it fasting, it will purge the sight.
One quality thereof yet blame I must
It makes men chaste, and women fils with lust.

SIR JOHN HARINGTON, *The Englishmans Doctor*, 1607

Rue, or Hearbe of Grace, continually greene, the slips are set. It lasts long as Rosemary, Southernwood & c, to strong for mine Housewifes pot, unlesse she wil brue Ale therewith, against the plague: let him not seed, if you will have him last.

WILLIAM LAWSON, *The Countrie Housewifes Garden*, 1617

It is set down by divers of the Ancients that Rew doth prosper much and becometh stronger if it be set by a Fig tree; which (we conceive) is not caused by reason of Friendship but by extraction of a contrary juyce, the one drawing juyce fit to result sweet, the other bitter.

FRANCIS BACON, *Sylva Sylvarum*, 1627

The Weasell when she is to encounter the serpent arms herselfe with eating of Rue.

It hast been found by wofull experience, that Toades doe oftentimes lye amongst *Sage*; it would therefore be good to Plant one slip of *Sage*, and another of *Rue*, for Toades will by no meanes come nigh unto *Rue*.

WILLIAM COLES, *The Art of Simpling*, 1656

Garden Rue is so well known by this name, and the name Herb of Grace, that I shall not need to write any further description of it.

The seed thereof taken in wine, is an antidote against all dangerous medicines or deadly poisons. The leaves taken either by themselves, or with figs and walnuts, is called *Mithridate's* counter-poison against the plague, and causes all venemous things to become harmless; being often taken in meat and drink, it abates venery. A decoction thereof with some dried dill leaves and flowers, eases all pains and torments, inwardly to be drank, and outwardly to be applied warm to the place grieved.

NICHOLAS CULPEPER, *The English Physician*, 1652

I like the pungent clean and acrid perfume of rue; many people do not know that a few sprigs of it hung in a room will keep flies away. Also it has a charming way with gin; a sprig put in a bottle gives this spirit a curious vague and almost pleasant taste.

...Rue likes shade, and a chalky soil for preference.

MARIAN CRAN, *The Garden of Ignorance*, 1917

Vinegar of the Four Thieves

Take the tops of common wormwood, Roman wormwood, rosemary, sage, mint and rue of each $\frac{3}{4}$ ounce, lavender flowers 1 ounce, garlic, calamus aromaticus, cinnamon, cloves and nutmeg each 1 drachm, camphor $\frac{1}{2}$ ounce, alcohol or brandy 1 ounce, strong vinegar 4 pints. Digest all the materials except the camphor and spirit in a closely covered vessel for fourteen days at summer heat; then express and filter the vinegar produced and add camphor previously dissolved in brandy or spirit.

G.W. SEPTIMUS PIESSE, *The Art of Perfumery*, 1880

Its scent is strong and its taste is bitter. From the earliest times, rue has had a reputation as an effective antidote against poison. It is said to be 'moly' (wild rue) which protected Ulysses from the charm used by Circe to turn his men into swine.

It was the chief ingredient in an antidote concocted by Mithridates, Emperor of Pontus (136–63 B.C.) which he used to test many fatal poisons. John Parkinson in his *Theatrum Botanicum* (1640) says this included rue, salt, walnuts and figs stamped together in a mass.

Another story relates that when Mithridates tried to commit suicide by poisoning himself, he found the antidote had made him immune. Finally, he persuaded a slave to stab him to death.

Stories of rue's power are many in folklore and superstition. Both the Romans and Greeks believed that the plant would prosper most if it were stolen from a neighbour's garden. The Romans believed rue gave second sight and their priests wore chaplets of rue. Once it was thought that arrows rubbed with rue would always find their mark. When gunpowder was introduced, shot was boiled in rue water for the same effect. Like sage and balm, it has entered the English language: to 'rue the day', meaning to repent.

The first Duke of Saxony was allowed by Frederick Barbarossa in 1181 to use a chaplet of rue as a mark of heraldry. The design made by the leaves passed from this to become the symbol for the suit of clubs in playing cards.

In the 18th century, *Vinegar of the Four Thieves* was used as an antiseptic to wash the face and hands and was sprinkled on clothing and in rooms against the plague.

The name came from four villains who were supposed to have robbed the homes of the sick during the great plague of 1722 at Marseilles without being infected themselves. It contained rosemary, sage, mint, rue, lavender, cloves, cinnamon, nutmeg, garlic and Roman wormwood, most of them germicides of some sort.

In 1760 a rumour which later proved false spread through London that plague had broken out. The price of rue and wormwood at Covent Garden market the next day rose by forty per cent!

In Britain judges at the Assizes were presented with sprigs of rue and other herbs as a defence against the 'jail fever' and other illnesses of prisoners brought before them.

Some people are allergic to rue and come out in a rash if they brush against it with their hands or bare skin. The cure is to rub oil over the affected part.

Rue will start well from seed, and will self-seed if allowed to do so. Cuttings and root slips grow readily. The blue-green colour of the foliage is outstanding and lasts through winter in mild areas. The deeply-cut leaves are club-shaped and occur in groups of four or five on the woody stems, the whole plant reaching about 75 cm in height. Flowers are flat, greenish-yellow with spreading petals.

The ancient writers said rue has a special affinity for figs. Modern gardeners recommend that rue be kept away from basil. These days we find rue too bitter for eating, though the leaves may be chopped for sparing use in salads, or eating with bread-and-butter.

Rue water is sprinkled to deter fleas and the plants repel flies.

Rue tea is a tonic for indigestion and stomach troubles. Infuse some chopped leaves with 500 ml of boiling water. Drink two small glasses a day. Eaten to excess, rue is a poison. A few leaves may be added to mixed herbal teas.

Sage

'sage for age'

Sage from *A Niewe Herball*, 1578

Sage (*Salvia officinalis*). Perennial.
Common sage.
Old form: Sawge, salgia, sauge.
Mint family.

Amongst my herbs, sage holds place of honour; of good scent it is and full virtue for many ills.

WALAFRID STRABO, *The Little Garden*, 840 A.D.

> Why of seknesse dyeth man
> Whill sawge in gardeyn he may han.

Macer's Herbal, 12th century

Salgia ys an herbe that men clepyth sauge. The vertu of thys herbe ys that how that ever a man use hure yn etyng or drynkyng or yn powder he ys goud for the palsy. Also he ys good to hele a man of the tothe-ache. Also yf a man have a raw wond that bledythe moche take the powder of hure and ley to thee wond ... Also yf a man wyl have blak here tak the juys of thys herbe and whessh well yn the hot sonne thyne hed ther-wyth.

AGNUS CASTUS, 14th century

> *Cur moriatur homo cui Salvia crescit in horto?*
> Why should a man die while sage is in his garden?

Latin Proverb, early Middle Ages

Of all garden herbes, none is of greater vertue than Sage ... such is the virtue of Sage that if it were possible, it would make a man immortall.

Nowe because it is good against palsies and comforteth the sinewes and braine, it must needes be good for studentes, who are commonly cumbered with diseases of the heade. It may be used in way of meate ·as in the spring time with breade and butter, especially in May. As I my selfe have knowen a man of 80 yeares and upwarde, who for his breakfast in summer, used to eate 6 or 7 Sage leaves minced small with a little Salt, and in winter as many blades of unset leekes, drinking alwaies a draught of good ale after it by which meanes hee preserves himselfe long in a healthfull state.

Sage is used commonly in sawces, as to stuffe veal, porke, rosting pigges, and that for good cause: for it dryeth up superfluous moysture, and stirreth up appetite.

... Moreover Sage is used otherwise to put in a drinke over night close covered, or two or three houres before wee drinke it, for so it is good against infection, especially if rewe be added thereto.

THOMAS COGHAN, *The Haven of Health*, 1584

Sage is singular good for the head and braine; it quickeneth the sences and memory, strengthneth the sinewes, restoreth health to those that have the palsie, takes away shaking or trembling of the members; and being put into the nosthrils, it draweth thin flegme out of the head.

It is likewise commended against the spitting of bloud, the cough, and paines of the sides, and bitings of Serpents.

No man needs to doubt the wholesomnesse of Sage Ale, being brewed as it should be, with Sage, Scabious, Betony, Spikenard, Squinanth, and Fennell seeds.

JOHN GERARD, *The Herball*, 1597

> He that would live for aye,
> Must eat Sage in May.

Old English Saying

> But who can write thy worth (O soveraigne *Sage*).
> Some aske how man can die, where thou dost
>   grow,
> Oh that there were a medicine curing age,
> Death comes at last, though death comes ne're
>   so slow:
> *Sage* strengths the sinewes, fevers heat doth
>   swage,
> The Palsy helpes, and rids of mickle woe.
> In Lattin (*Salvia*) takes the name of safety,
> In English (*Sage*) is rather wise than crafty.
> Sith then the name betokens wise and saving,
> We count it nature's friend and worth the having.

SIR JOHN HARINGTON, *The Englishmans Doctor*, 1607

Sage hath been of good use in the time of the plague at all times, and the small Sage more especially (which therefore I think our people called Sage of Vertue) the juyce thereof drunke with vinegar. The use of Sage in the moneth of May, with butter, Parsley and some salt, is very frequent in our Country to continue health to the body: as also Sage ale made with it, Rosemary and other good hearbes for the same purpose ... Gargles likewise are made with Sage, Rosemary, Honisuckles, and Plantaine boyled in water or with some Honey and Allome put thereto to wash cankers, sore mouthes, and throates ...

JOHN PARKINSON, *Theatrum Botanicum*, 1640

This was originally a native of the south of Europe, but it has long been cultivated in the English gardens. There are several kinds of it, known as the green, the red, the small-leaved, and the broad-leaved balsamic. In cookery, its principal use is for stuffings and sauces, for which purpose the red is the most agreeable, and the green the next. The others are used for medicinal purposes.

MRS ISABELLA BEETON, *Household Management*, 1861

Sage and Onion Sauce

Chop very fine an ounce of onion and half an ounce of green sage leaves, put them in a stamper with four spoonsful of water, simmer gently for 10 minutes, then put in a teaspoon of pepper and salt and one ounce of fine bread-crumbs. Mix well together, then pour to it ¼ pint of Broth, Gravy or Melted Butter, stir well together and simmer a few minutes longer. This is a relishing sauce for Roast Pork, Geese or Duck, or with Green Pease on Maigre (meatless) Days.

The Cook's Oracle, 1821

Sage Cheese

Bruise the tops of young red sage in a mortar with some leaves of spinach and squeeze the juice; mix it with the rennet in the milk, more or less, according to the preferred colour and taste. When the curd is come, break it gently and put it in with the skimmer till it is pressed 2 ins above the vat. Press it eight to 10 hours. Salt it and turn every day.

Walsh's Manual of Domestic Economy, 1857

Common sage is a perennial bushy plant, with grey-green, veined leaves, square stems and purplish flowers. There are several hundreds of sages in many colours — red, blue, purple and pink — including the sage bushes of the North American deserts.

Sage was once used as a tobacco substitute after being dried and powdered. The Chinese used to barter with the Dutch, giving three times the quantity of tea in exchange for sage tea. The fresh leaves brewed as tea calm the nerves and are good for the liver and against fevers.

Sage grows wild in many places about the Aegean and in Yugoslavia and the Adriatic Islands, where sage honey is a speciality.

In cooking, sage is chiefly used in stuffings for pork, turkey, sausages, ducks and geese. It blends well with the flavour of rosemary. Sage breaks down the oils and fats in meat, which aids the digestion.

Garden sages will grow from seed or cuttings and should be renewed every four years. The leaves have a strong taste and aroma. As a companion plant, sage repels carrot fly and cabbage butterfly.

Sage gargle — Sage tea, cooled, is used as a gargle to whiten teeth and strengthen the gums.

Sage tooth-powder is made by mixing sage leaves and sea salt well together. Bake until hard and pound into a fine powder. This removes yellow stains from teeth. Leaves rubbed on the teeth have the same effect.

Sage hair tonic (for dark hair) — Sage will darken brunette hair and made it shiny. Make an infusion of a teaspoon of powdered, dried sage leaves to 500 ml of boiling water. Use as a rinse after your shampoo.

Another hair tonic is made by cutting up a handful each of sage and rosemary (leaves and tops). Bring to boil in 500 ml of cold water. Simmer for three minutes with top covered. Allow to cool and steep for three hours, then strain out the herbs. Rub the tonic into your hair once or twice a week to keep it free from dandruff.

Savory

'sauce to meat'

Winter savory (top) and summer savory from *The Herball*, 1597

Summer Savory (*Satureia hortensis*). Annual.
Winter Savory (*S. montana*). Perennial.
  Old form: Saverie, Savorie.
  Mint family.

Winter Savorie, garden Savorie, which among us has another name in Latine, to wit, Satureia, much used in sauces and seasoning of our meats.

  This Savorie is commonly sowne in the month of Februarie, and hath no small resemblance of Origan, insomuch, as they are never both used at once in sauce or sallads, their vertues & operations be so like. And yet the Aegyptian Origanum is preferred before the said Savorie.

PLINY, *Naturall Historie*, 77 A.D. (trans. Holland, 1601)

Thys herbe hath levys y-lyche to ysope. The vertu of this herbe is yf he use hire moche he shal be lykyng to wymmen. Also he wol distroye rebellyng in a mannys wombe yf he drynke it with wyne warmly. Also yf ther be eny maner of medesyn that a man shuld use Tyme he may take that oon for that other for they acordith moche yn vertu.

AGNUS CASTUS, 14th century

And now this herbe eaten wythe creame, doth amende a cold stomacke by purging it.

  And *Dioscorides* writteth, that the use of Saverie in meates; dothe long preserve the boddye in healthe.

THOMAS HYLL, *The Proffitable Arte of Gardening*, 1568

There be two kinds of Savorie, the one that endureth winter & is of long continuance: the other is an annual or yearly plant, that perisheth at the time when it hath perfected his seede, and must be sowen againe the next yeare, which we call Sommer Savorie, or Savorie of a yeare.

  Winter Savorie is of temperature hot and drie in the third degree, it maketh thinne, cureth and clenseth the passages, to be brief, it is altogether of like vertu with Time.

  Sommer Savorie is not full so hot as Winter Savorie, and therefore saith *Dioscorides*, more fit to be used in medicine: it maketh thin, and doth marvellously prevail against winde: therefore it is with good success boiled and eaten with beanes, peason, and other windie pulses, yea if it be applied to the belly in fomentation, it foorthwith helpeth the mother, proceeding of winde.

JOHN GERARD, *The Herball*, 1597

Sommer savorie doth delight in an open sunne shining place, and therefore must be set or sowen in such a one, not in a fat or manured ground: for it is often seene growe of it selfe in leane groundes and neere unto the sea. It groweth more delightfully and of a better taste; if it be sowen amongst onions.

120

It is very good for sauce to meat. The leaves and flowers applied unto the head in forme of a cappe or garland, doth awake the drowsily inclined.

Both thyme and winter savorie are good for the nourishing of bees, and for the preserving and seasoning of meates.

RICHARD SURFLET, *The Countrie Farme*, 1600

Saverie seedes and dyes the first yeare, good for my Huswifes pot and pye.

WILLIAM LAWSON, *The Countrie Housewifes Garden*, 1617

This we find described by Columella, a voluminous Roman writer on agriculture, as an odoriferous herb, which 'in the brave days of old,' entered into the seasoning of nearly every dish. We possess two varieties of this aromatic herb, known to naturalists as *Satureja*. They are called summer and winter savory, according to the time of year when they are fit for gathering. Both sorts are in general cultivation throughout England.

MRS ISABELLA BEETON, *Household Management*, 1861

Winter Savory will grow either from seed or slips. It is a woodier and more bushy plant than the Summer Savory, and flowers contentedly among the stones of a rockery. Thus have I seen it in the Old Physic Garden, Chelsea. Gardeners still have faith in the virtue of its leaves and sprigs to cure wasp and bee stings.

FRANCES A. BARDSWELL, *The Herb Garden*, 1911

Savory from the *Juliana Anicia Codex*, 512 A.D.

Summer savory (*Satureia hortensis*) and Winter savory (*Satureia montana*) are the two types among a dozen savories which have traditionally been used in cooking.

At first glance they look like an upright type of thyme. Looking closer, the perennial winter savory is much branched, with a profusion of neat, dark green leaves, dotted with scent glands emitting an aroma also similar to thyme. The flowers are pale white or pinkish, very small, on spikes. .

Growing to about 45 cm high, winter savory makes a good border edging, staying green all winter (though it benefits by being cut back). Seed propagation is slow, so it might be best to start with a nursery plant and increase later by cuttings from the side shoots, or by root divisions. The flavour is peppery.

Summer savory has more slender stems and grows to about one foot high, with fragrant leaves 13 mm long in bunches and white-spiked flowers. It grows easily from seed. Its flavour is sweeter and more delicate than the winter variety, something akin to marjoram.

The leaves and tops of both savories are used in stuffings for turkey, veal, pork pies and sausages, also with fish and in herb vinegar. Fresh sprigs are boiled with broad beans and peas in France and Germany, where the name for savory is *Bohnenkraut*, or bean herb. It is also used in lentil and pea soups.

In the garden, summer savory is a good growing companion for peas. Traditionally, it has been grown with onions, but recent research suggests these plants may not be mutually beneficial.

A leaf of either type of savory rubbed on bee stings gives quick relief from pain.

Strawberry

'Strawbery Rype'

Strawberry from Heironymus Bock's *Kreuter Buch*, 1546

Strawberry (*Fragaria vesca*). Perennial.
Alpine Strawberry.
Old form: Steawberie, Strawberrie, Strawberies, Strabery, O.E. Streawberidge, Fraise du Bois (Fr.).
Rose family.

Then unto London I did me hye
   Of all the land it beareth the pryse
'Hot pescodes' one began to crye
   'Strawbery rype' and 'cherryes in the ryse'.
JOHN LYDGATE, *London Lyckpeny*, 14th century

The vertue of this herbe is good for blered men. Also it is good to destroy the webbe in a mannes eyes. Also the ioyce of it medled with hony, and drunken helpeth the milte.
ANTHONY ASKHAM, *A Lytel Herball*, 1550

And firste the Strawberie, is accounted amonge those herbes which growe in the fields, of the own accorde. And the beries be muche eaten at mens tables in the Summer, for the pleasantnes of them, which for a more delight in the eatinge, they dresse with wyne and sugar.

And now it aptly groweth in shadowie places, and rather ioyeth under the shadowe of other herbes, than by growynge alone. And yet the plants sette in Gardens, wyll growe unto the bignes of the Mulberie, if the earth before (in the beddes) be well dressed and trymmed, and diligently tended of the Gardener. But the herbe (of it selfe) continueth above a yeare.

And the strawberie leaves used in a bath, doe greatlye helpe the stone.
THOMAS HYLL, *The Proffitable Arte of Gardening*, 1568

Wife unto the garden and set me a plot
With strawberry rootes of the best to be got;
Such growing abroade, among thornes in the wood
Wel chosen and picked proove excellent good.
THOMAS TUSSER, *Five hundred points*, 1573

The leaves boyled & applied in maner of a pultis taketh away the burning heate in wounds: the decoction thereof strengthneth the gums, fastneth the teeth, and is good to be helde in the mouth, both against the inflammation or burning heate thereof, and also of the almonds of the throat.

The berries quench thirst, and do alaie the inflammation and heate of the stomacke.

The distilled water drunke with white wine is good against the passion of the hart, reviving the spirits, and maketh the heart merrie.

The distilled water is reported to scower the face, to take away spots, and to make the face faire and smooth; and is likewise drunke with good success against the stone in the kidneies.
JOHN GERARD, *The Herball*, 1597

Strawberries have no need of great toile or tilling, so that they be planted in some good ground not manured, notwithstanding, but well shaded howsoever: because they delight in the shadow of other herbes, so also they are found growing amongst great tall trees, without any manner of husbanding or tillage.

They must be removed every three yeeres, to make them beare faire berries, and their earth raised about them once every yeere . . . and to weed them by hand when as weeds do overgrow them: in the ground whither you remove them, you must first put horse-dung well rotted, or cowes dung, a scuttle full to everie border that is three foot broad.

RICHARD SURFLET, *The Countrie Farme*, 1600

Strawberies long lasting, set rootes at Michael-tide or the spring, they be redd, white and greene, and ripe, when they be great and soft, some by Mid-sommer with us. The use is: they will coole any Housewife well, if they be put in Wine or creame with Sugar.

WILLIAM LAWSON, *The Countrie Housewifes Garden*, 1617

The leaves of Strawberries are alwaies used among other herbes in cooling drinkes, as also in lotions, and gargles for the mouth and throate . . .

The berries themselves are often brought to the Table as a reare service, whereunto claret wine, creame or milke is added with sugar, as every one liketh; as also at other times, both with the better and meaner sort, and are a good cooling and pleasant dish in the hot Summer season.

The water distilled of the berries, is good for the passions of the heart, caused by the pertubation of the spirits, being eyther drunke alone, or in wine; and maketh the heart merry.

Some doe hold that the water helpeth to clense the face from spots, and to adde some cleerenesse to the skinne.

JOHN PARKINSON, *Paradisus*, 1629

The wild, wood or Alpine strawberry may still be classed as a herb, though we usually think of the fat, lush strawberry as a fruit. The modern strawberry was developed in the last century as a result of many crosses, including the wild strawberry and the Virginian strawberry from North America.

But the wild strawberry yields tiny fruit the size of your little fingertip, bright red and delicious. It looks like a cultivated strawberry in miniature, the leaves very delicate and finely cut.

There is some doubt about how the name strawberry evolved. The most likely explanation is that it got its Old English name, *streawbridge,* or 'strawed berry' from its appearance of having been strewn on the ground.

Wild strawberries were brought in from the woods and transplanted into gardens in the way Thomas Tusser describes.

The strawberry symbolised the fruit of right-eousness and was depicted in paintings as a fruit of Venus or the Virgin Mary, as in Botticelli.

The leaves were added to cooling drinks, the fruit made into jam and a wine which was Sir Walter Raleigh's favourite tipple. Teeth were cleaned with strawberry juice, which dissolves the tartar coating, and the distilled water was used as a face wash to clear the skin.

Strawberry leaf tea is medicinal and cooling, astringent and used for fevers. Pour 500 ml of boiling water over a handful of young leaves, or a mixture of strawberry and woodruff leaves. The leaves contain iron.

If you do obtain wild strawberries, grow them apart from the commercial types or they will cross. Culture is the same. See *Borage* for notes on companion planting.

Fragaria elatior is the old-fashioned straw-berry from France called '*haught boys*' in the London street cries.

Strewing Herbs

Their chambers and parlours strawed over with sweet herbes refreshed mee; their nosegays finely intermingled with sundry sorts of fragraunte flowers, in their bedchambers and privy rooms, with comfortable smell cheered me up, and entirely delighted all my senses.

LEVINUS LEMNIUS, *Dutch visitor to England,* 1560

Ladies strewing herbs

123

Strewing Hearbs of Al Sorts

1. Basil fine and bush, sowe in maie.
2. Baulme in March.
3. Camomill.
4. Costmarie.
5. Cowslips & pagles.
6. Daisies of all sorts.
7. Sweet fenell.
8. Germander.
9. Hop set in february.
10. Lavender.
11. Lavender Spike.
12. Lavender Cotton.
13. Mariorum knotted, sowe or set at the Spring.
14. Maudeline.
15. Penallraiall.
16. Roses of all sorts in Januarie and September.
17. Red mints.
18. Sage.
19. Tansie.
20. Violets.
21. Winter savorie.

THOMAS TUSSER, *Five hundred points*, 1573

Queen Elizabeth of famous memorie did more desire meadowsweet than any other sweete herbe to strewe her chambers withall.

JOHN PARKINSON, *Theatrum Botanicum*, 1640

Tansy

'good for the Stomacke'

Tansy from Mattioli, 1583

Tansy (*Tanacetum vulgare*). Perennial.
Bachelor's Buttons.
Old form: Tansie.
Composite.

I have heard that if maids will take wild Tansy and lay it to soake in Buttermilk for the space of nine days and wash their faces therewith, it will make them look very faire.

JHEROM BRUYNSWYKE, *The vertuouse boke Of Distyllacyon*, 1527

The seede of Tansie is a singular and proved medicine against wormes: for in what sorte soever it be taken, it killeth and bringeth forth wormes.
    The same pounde and afterwards mengled with oyle; is very good against the payne and swelling of sinewes.

REMBERT DODOENS, *A Niewe Herball* (trans. Lyte), 1578

In the Spring time are made with the leaves hereof newly sproong up, and with egs, cakes or tansies, which be pleasant in taste, and good for the stomacke. For if any bad humours cleave thereunto, it doth perfectly concoct them and scowre them downwards.

JOHN GERARD, *The Herball*, 1597

It is much used both in Lent and in the beginning of the Spring, while the hearbe is young and tender, to make cakes thereof with eggs fried, which are called Tansies and are very profitable for those stomackes that are troubled with bad humours cleaving thereunto ...

JOHN PARKINSON, *Theatrum Botanicum*, 1640

Dame Venus was minded to pleasure Women with child by this Herb, for there grows not an Herb, fitter for their use than this; it is just as though it were cut out for the purpose. This herb bruised and applied to the Navel, stays miscarriages; I know no herb like it for that use: Boiled in ordinary Beer, and the decoction drank, doth the like, and if her Womb be not as she would have it, this decoction will make it so. Let those Women that desire Children love this herb, it is their best companion, their husbands excepted.

It consumes phlegmatic humours which the cold and moist constitution of Winter usually affects the body with, and that was the first reason for eating Tansies in the spring . . . the herb fried with eggs, helps to digest and carry downwards those bad humours that trouble the Stomach.

NICHOLAS CULPEPER, *The English Physician Enlarged*, 1653

Tansy; hot and cleansing; but in regard to its domineering relish, sparingly mixt with our cold sallet, and much fitter (tho' in very small quantity) for the pan, being qualified with the juices of other fresh herbs, spinach, green corn, violet, primrose-leaves, & c at entrance of the spring, and then fried brownish, is eaten hot, with the juice of orange and sugar, as one of the most agreeable of all the boil'd herbaceous dishes.

JOHN EVELYN, *Acetaria*, 1699

John Evelyn's Tansie

Take the gratings or slices of three Naples-biscuits, put them into half a pint of cream, with twelve fresh eggs, four of the whites cast out, strain the rest, and break them with two spoonsfull of rose-water, a little salt and sugar, half a grated nutmeg. And when ready for the pan, put almost a pint of the juice of spinach, cleaver, beets, corn-sallet, green corn, violet, or primrose tender leaves (for of any of these you may take your choice), with a very small sprig of tansie, and let it be fried so as to look green in the dish, with a strew of sugar, and store of the juice of orange. Some affect to have it fryed a little brown and crisp.

JOHN EVELYN, *Acetaria*, 1699

Apple Tansy

Pare your apples, cut them in thin round Slices, fry them in Sweet Butter; then beat half a score of eggs with a quart of cream, the juice of spinach and Tansy of each a quarter of a pint, and a little Rose-water; when these are beaten together pour them on your apples.

JOHN NOTT, *Receipt Book*, 1723

The bright clusters of rounded Tansy flowers really do look just like golden buttons. Tansy is a spreader and had captured the bank and part of a paddock at an 1870 stone railway house in the country where we once lived.

The downy, lacy fernlike blooms in the paddock had been cropped by cows and sheep, but the stalky, woody plants in the bank were growing so densely that some had pushed up to one and a half metres high seeking sunlight.

Tansy has a strong scent like camphor, rather lemony — some say it smells like ginger. It was terribly bitter to the taste, which is too sharp for our modern palates. In fact, it is an irritant narcotic and should be used very sparingly, say *just a piece of a leaf* to herb teas, pottage and puddings.

Our ancestors, who had no refrigerators or coolers, kept tansy in the meat safe or basement and rubbed it over flesh to keep away flies and ants. The powdered, dried leaves seem to be the best insect deterrent.

Tansy leaves were strewn, mixed with elder leaves, on floors in houses and stables and it was used as a garnish to meats. It once was used in embalming and for a green dye.

The custom of eating a Tansy, or tansy pudding of milk, eggs, flour and a tansy leaf, developed as a practical purging of the system following the Lenten fast. Tansies eaten on Palm Sunday and Easter Sunday were symbolic of the bitter herbs eaten by the Jews during Passover.

In Ireland, tansy leaves were added to sheep's blood and milk to make a kind of sausage called a *drisheen*, a local specialty in Cork.

The plant grows slowly from seed but readily from root division, reaching about a metre high in gardens usually. Leaves are a deep green, finely cut, very pretty. The buttons last a long time and make a lovely picture.

Tansy contains volatile oil, wax, stearine, bitter resin, gallic acid and tanacetic acid.

Tansy tea is medicinal, made from an infusion of a chopped leaf to 500 ml of boiling water. Take sparingly in wineglass doses for gout and fevers.

Tarragon

'the sallade herbe'

Tarragon from *The Herball*, 1597

Tarragon   (*Artemisia dracunculus*). Perennial.
  French tarragon.
  Old form: Dragons, Little Dragons, Dragance.
  Fr: Herbe au Dragon.
Russian Tarragon   (*A. redowski*).
  Composite.

Tarragon, the sallade herbe, hath long and nar-rowe leaves, of a deepe greene colour, greater and longer than those of common Hyssope, with slender brittle rounde stalkes, two cubites high: about the branches whereof, hang little rounde flowers, never perfectly opened, of a yellowe colour mixed with blacke, like those of common Wormewoode. The roote is long and fibrous, creeping farre abroad under the earth, as doe the rootes of Couch-grasse, by which sprouting foorth it increaseth, yeelding no seede at all, but as it were a certaine chaffie or dustie matter that flieth away with the winde.

Tarragon is cherished in gardens, and is en-creased by the yoong shootes: *Ruellius* and such others have reported many strange tales heerof,

scarse worth the noting, saying that the seede of flaxe put into a radish roote or sea Onion, and so set, doth bring foorth that herbe Tarragon.

It is greene all summer long, and a great part of Autumne, and flowreth in Iulie.

It is named in Latine *Draco*: of the Italians *Dragontellium*: of French *Dragon*: in English Tar-ragon.

Tarragon is not to be eaten alone in sallades, but ioyned with other hearbes, as lettuce, purslaine, and such like, that it may also temper the coldnes of them, like as Rocket doth, neither do we knowe what other use this herbe hath.

JOHN GERARD, *The Herball*, 1597

Tarragon hath long and narrow darke greene leaves, growing on slender and brittle round stalkes, two or three foot high, at the tops whereof grow forth long slender spikes of small yellowie flowes, which seldome give any good seede, but a dustie or chaffie matter, which flieth away with the winde: the roote is white, and creepeth under ground, whereby it much encreaseth. The whole herbe is of a hot and biting taste.

It is altogether used among other cold herbes, to temper the coldnesse, and they to temper its heate, so to give the better rellish unto the sallet; but many doe not like the taste thereof, and so refuse it.

There are some Authors that have held Tarragon not to be an herbe of it owne kinde, but that it was first produced by putting the seed of Lin or Flaxe into the roote of an Onion, being opened and so set into the ground, which when it hath sprung hath brought forth this herb Tarragon, which absurd and idle opinion, Matthiolus by certaine experi-ence saith, hath been found false.

JOHN PARKINSON, *Paradisus*, 1629

They are so well known to every one that plants them in their Gardens, they need no Description; if not, let them look down towards the lower end of the stalk, and see how like a snake they look.

Pliny and *Dioscorides* affirm that no serpent will meddle with him that carried this Herb about him.

NICHOLAS CULPEPER, *The English Physician Enlarged*, 1653

Tarragon, of Spanish extraction, hot and spicy; the tops and young shoots, like those of *rochet*, never to be secluded our composition, especially where there is much lettuce. 'Tis highly cordial and friendly to the head, heart, liver, correcting the weakness of the ventricle, & c.

JOHN EVELYN, *Acetaria*, 1699

126

The French or 'true' tarragon is a sterile plant, cultivated so long by root divisions that it has lost the power to set seed. It was originally a native of central Asia and did not become well-known in Europe until Tudor times.

The aromatic leaves are used in seasoning and salads, in pickles and mustard and in Tartare sauce for fish dishes.

The name is derived from the Latin *dracunculus*, meaning a little dragon, through the French, *esdragon*. It has smooth, dark green leaves, which really only release their perfume when crushed. The flavour is strong. The herb was used to cure the pain of toothache or to deaden pain in the mouth by Arab physicians.

Inferior in taste is Russian tarragon, which is ranker, a brighter green, with rougher leaves. This sets seed and is often sold in seed packets as tarragon.

French tarragon needs care in cultivation, though it requires only poor, sandy soil. Set in semi-shade and allow good drainage as it easily catches mildew. Lift and divide the roots (after untangling them) every three years.

The plant reaches about 60 cm in height. Space about 60 cm apart and keep well weeded. Yellowish green blossoms form at times, but a chaffy substance takes the place of the eagerly expected seeds, so don't be fooled. Pick leaves fresh for use, or dry in bundles in a sunny room.

Tarragon vinegar is a great delicacy. Gather dry leaves before the plant flowers. Discard stalk and place leaves in a bottle, pouring over vinegar. Allow 250 g herb to two litres vinegar. Cork and leave for two weeks. Strain and repeat. Leave a sprig of tarragon in the jar. Use in salad dressing and mayonnaise.

Thyme from *Mrs Beeton's Book of Household Management*, 1861

Thyme

'sweet to ye smell'

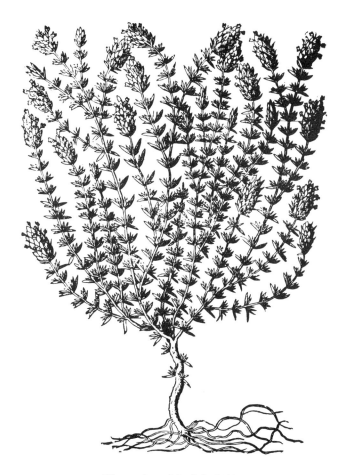

Thyme from Mattioli, 1583

Wild Thyme (*Thymus serpyllum*). Mother-of-Thyme, Horse thyme, Shakespeare's thyme.
Garden Thyme (*T. vulgaris*). Common thyme. Old form: Tyme, Time.
Lemon-Scented (*T. citriodorus*).
Golden Lemon Thyme (*T. cit. variegata*).
Carraway-Scented (*T. herba-barona*).
Crimson-Flowered (*T. coccineus*).
Woolly (*T. serpylium lanuginosus*).
White-Flowering (*T. serp. albus*).

And many others . . . such as Magic Carpet, *T. nitidus*, *T. micans*, Silver Posie etc.

Shrubs of the mint family.

127

There is a black and a white thyme, and it flowers very freely: it is in bloom about the summer solstice. It is from this flower that the bee gets the honey, and by it beekeepers say that it is made known whether they have a good yield of honey or not, for if the thyme flowers abundantly, they have a good yield, but the bloom is injured or even destroyed if it is rained upon.

THEOPHRASTUS, *Enquiry into Plants*, 300 B.C. (trans. Hort, 1916)

And *Thestylis* stamps wilde thyme and garlicke too,
Strong smelling herbs, for mowers wearied in scorching sunne.

VIRGIL, *Bucolics*, 30 B.C. (trans. A.F., 1589)

Two kinds there by of Thyme, to wit, the white and the blacke: this hearbe doth flourish about the Summer Solstice, at what time as Bees also begin to gather honey from it; and according to the flouring of it more or lesse, a man may guesse full well what season there will be for honey: for honey-mistresses and such as keep Bees, hope to have a good yeere of honey, when they see the Thyme to bloume abundantly.

Thyme cannot well away with raine, and therefore it taketh harme by showres and sheddeth the floure.

The honey of Athens carrieth the name for the best honey in the world, by reason of the Thyme growing thereabout.

In this our age verely, we are advertised and know for certain, That in Languedoc and the province of Narbon, the very stonie places are all overgrowne and covered with Thyme, upon which there are fed thousands of sheepe and other cattaile: in such sort, as this kind of herbage and pasturage, yeeldeth a great revenue to the inhabitants and paisants of that countrey . . .

The garden Serpyllum, which commeth of seed, creepeth not but groweth to the height of foure fingers breadth. The wild Thyme which commeth up of the owne accord, liketh and thriveth better, having whiter leaves and branches than the other: this (I say) is thought to have a speciall vertue against serpents . . . If the same be burned, it yeeldeth a perfume, which with the very sent chaseth them all away.

PLINY, *Naturall Historie*, 77 A.D. (trans. Holland, 1601)

Thyme boyled in water & hony and dronken is good against a hard and painfull cough and short-nesse of breath . . .

Thyme eaten in the morning fasting, and in the evening before supper is good for bleared and watering eyes, & the paine in the same and it is also good for the same purpose to be often used in meates.

REMBERT DODOENS, *A Niewe Herball* (trans. Lyte), 1578

The first is our common creeping Time, which is so well knowne, that it needeth no description; yet this ye shall understand that it beareth floures of a purple colour, as every body knoweth. Of which kinde I found another sort, with floures as white as snow, and have planted it in my garden, where it becommeth an herbe of great beauty . . . The white kinde I found at South fleet in Kent. They floure from May to the end of Summer.

JOHN GERARD, *The Herball*, 1597

I know a bank whereon the wild thyme blows,
Where oxlips and the nodding violet grows.

(Oberon), *A Midsummer Night's Dream*, Act II, Scene 2

Thyme craveth a place upon the Sunne neare unto the sea . . . and also that it may grow the fairer and fuller leafe, it will be good to water the ground oft with water wherein hath been steeped for the space of one whole day drie Thyme somewhat bruised.

RICHARD SURFLET, *The Countrie Farme*, 1600

Time both seedes, slips and rootes are good. If it seede not, it will last three or foure years at most, it smelleth comfortably. It hath much use: namely, in all cold meates, it is good for Bees.

WILLIAM LAWSON, *The Countrie Housewifes Garden*, 1618

The ordinary Garden Thyme is a small woody plant with brittle branches, and small hard greene leaves, as every one knoweth having small white purplish flowers, standing round about the tops of the stalkes: the seed are small and browne, darker than Maieirome seed: the root is woody and abideth well divers Winters.

JOHN PARKINSON, *Paradisus*, 1629

Lemon Thyme (T. citriodorus)

The wild Thyme that smelleth like unto Pome-citron or Lemon, hath many weake branches trayling on the ground . . . with small darke greene leaves, thinly or sparsedly set on them, and smell-

Lemon Thyme from Paradisus, 1629

ing like unto a Lemon, with whitish flowers at the Toppes in roudels or spikes.

Variegated Lemon Thyme (*T. cit variegata*)

This kinde of wilde Thyme hath small hard branches lying or leaning to the ground, with small party coloured leaves upon them, divided into stripes or edges, of a gold yellow colour, the rest of the leafe abiding grene, which for the variable mixture or placing of the yellow, that caused it to be called embroydered or guilded Thyme.
JOHN PARKINSON, *Paradisus*, 1629

These fragrant turfy plants tempt one to make edgings of them, and they charm so used on warm or calcareous soils, not so good on cold soils except on raised banks or rock garden. *T. micans* I use as a modest green edge.
WILLIAM ROBINSON, *The English Flower Garden*, 1883

Two or three tufts of the species *Thymus Citrodorus*, usually find a place in the herb compartment of the kitchen garden. It is a trailing evergreen, is of smaller growth than the ordinary common kind, and is remarkable for its smell, which closely resembles that of the rind of a lemon. Hence its distinctive name. It is used for some particular dishes, in which the fragrance of the lemon is desired to slightly predominate.
MRS ISABELLA BEETON, *Household Management*, 1861

There are so many different types of thyme — about sixty varieties according to botanists. You could have a garden made of nothing but different kinds of thyme.

They are small, woody sub-shrubs. Some hug the ground, others are upright. Some we grow for ground cover, others for their refreshing scent, some for seasoning, all for the joy and beauty of their leaves and flowers massed in a colourful carpet.

Today we can easily have the white flowering thyme (*Thymus serpyllum albus*) which John Gerard was so proud to have in his garden. There are thymes with leaves of variegated silver or gold at the edges, green leaves, and a grey woolly type. Flower colours include white, pink, lavender, mauve, purple and crimson.

They have a range of scents which include carraway, lemon, mint, pepper, pineapple, nutmeg and some more pungent odours.

The common thyme of our gardens is *Thymus vulgaris*, a woody perennial. Usually it stays at about 15 cm in height but may rise up to 30 cm high and spread 45 cm. Its leaves are grey-green, tiny, set in pairs and dotted with scent glands. The vivid little flowers grow in whorls at the end of the spikes.

Thyme is increased by seed, cuttings, root division, or by replanting stems with a piece of root attached. Lemon thyme retains its perfume better if it is not grown from seed.

The wild thyme (*Thymus serpyllum*) or Mother-of-Thyme is more thickset. It is the source of many of the vari-scented and vari-coloured plants and makes a pretty ground cover. It was also called Shepherd's thyme and Shakespeare's thyme.

Caraway thyme (*Thymus herba-barona*), also called seedcake thyme, got its name because it was rubbed on a baron of beef in the Middle Ages.

The ancient Greeks used thyme as the emblem for courage, the Romans said it livened the spirits. It is antiseptic – the Greek name is derived from a word meaning to fumigate.

The Scots also thought wild thyme gave them courage and made it into a tea to stop nightmares.

Wild thyme was the badge of the Drummond clan. During the Wars of the Roses in England, Lancastrian ladies embroidered a bee hovering over a sprig of thyme on scarves they gave to their knights.

The Swiss boil thyme with milk to cure a cough and today Thymol is the active ingredient in cough medicines. Use the leaves fresh, dried or powdered in soups, stews and stuffings (particularly poultry), meatloaf, fish and cheese and egg dishes.

Grown in the sun in rockeries and in paved paths, thyme should flourish as it does on the rocky shores of the Aegean. It is a good complement to lavender.

The classic garden seat is a raised earth mound covered with thyme, for which the grey woolly thyme (*Thymus serp. lanuginosus*), which looks and smells like grey velvet and has pink flowers, would be ideal.

Violet

'sweet violets'

The black or purple violet from *A Niewe Herball*, 1578

Violet (*Viola odorata*). Perennial.
  Sweet violet.
  Old form: Vyolette, Blacke or Purple Violet, March violet (N. Hemisphere),
  Violet family.

Neither the rose colour ne the lylie may over-passe the violet, neither in beaute, neither in strenghe or vertue, neither in odour.
Macer's Herbal, 12th century

Violet is a lytyll herbe in substaunce and is better fresshe and newe than whan it is olde. And the floure thereof smelleth moost, and so the smell thereof abateth heate of the braine, and refreshyf and comfortyth the spirites of feeling and maketh sleepe, for it cooleth and tempereth and moysteneth the braine. And the more vertuous the floure thereof is, the more it bendyth the heed thereof downwarde. Also floures of spryngnge tyme spryngeth fyrste and sheweth somer. The lytlynes thereof in substance is nobly rewarded in gretnesse of savour and vertue.
BATHOLOMAEUS ANGLICUS, *De proprietatibus rerum*, 1260 (printed 1495)

Syrope of vyolettes i mach in this maner – Sethe vyolettes in water and let it lye all nyght in ye same water, than poure and streyne out the water and in the same put sugre and make your syrope.
Grete Herball, 1526

For them that may not slepe for sickness, seeth this herb in water and at even let him soke well hys feete in the water to the ancles, and when he goeth to bed, bind of this herbe to his temples and he shall slepe wel, by the grace of god.
ANTHONY ASKHAM, *A Lytel Herball*, 1550

The sweete violet (as the Emperor Constantine wryteth) was called in Greek Ion, after the name of that sweete guirle or pleasant damosell to, which Jupiter, after that he had gotte her with childe, turned her into a trim Heafer or gallant Cowe, bycause that his wife Juno (being bothe an angry and Jelous Goddesse) should not suspect that he loved Ion. In the honour of which his Io, as also for her most delicate and holsome feeding, the earth at the commaundement of Jupiter, brought foorth violettes... Nicander wryteth that the name of Ion was given unto Violettes, bycause of the Nymphes of Ionia, who firste of all presented Jupiter with these kindes of floures.

The Decoction of Violets is good against hoate fevers, and the inflammation of the liver, and all other inwarde partes, driving forth by siege the hoate and cholerique humors. The like propertie hath the iuyce, & syrupe, or confertue of the same.

REMBERT DODOENS, *A Niewe Herball* (trans. Lyte), 1578

The Violets called the blacke or purple violets, or March Violets of the garden, have a great prerogative about others, not only because the mind conceiveth a certain pleasure and recreation by smelling and handling those most odoriferous floures, but also for that very many of these violets receive ornament and comely grace: for there be made of them garlands for the head, nosegaies and poesies, which are delightful to looke on and pleasant to smel to, speaking nothing of their appropriat vertues: yea gardens themselves receive by these the greatest ornament of all, chiefest beauty, and most excellent grace, and the recreation of the minde which is taken hereby cannot be but very good and honest; for they admonish and stir up a man to that which is comely and honest; for floures through their beauty, variety of colour, and exquisit forme, do bring to a liberall and gentle manly minde, the remembrance of honestie, comlinesse, and all kindes of vertues: for it would be an unseemly and filthy thing (as a certain wise man saith) for him that doth looke upon and handle faire and beautiful things, to have his mind not faire, but filthy and deformed.

The floures are good for all inflammations, especially of the sides and lungs; they take away the hoarsenesse of the chest, the ruggednesse of the winde-pipe and jawes, and take away thirst.

JOHN GERARD, *The Herball*, 1597

> Violets dim,
> But sweeter than the lips of Juno's eyes,
> Or Cytherea's breath.

(Perdita), *The Winter's Tale*, Act IV, Scene 3

He that shall have taken a blow upon the head, so that it hath astonished him, shall not have anie greater hurt, if presently after such a blow he drinke Violet flowers stampt, and continue the same drinke for a certaine time...

The flowers of March Violets applied unto the brows, doe assuage the headach, which commeth of too much drinking and procure sleepe.

RICHARD SURFLET, *The Countrie Farme*, 1600

...That which, above all others, yields the sweetest smell in the air, is the violet; especially the white double violet, which comes twice a-year – about the middle of April, and about Bartholomew-tide.

FRANCIS BACON, *Of Gardens*, 1625

Conserva of Violettes

Take the flowers of Violettes, & picke them cleane from the stalke, and cut off all that which is greene. Punde them small, and put to them double the weight of Sugar, to the weight of violet flowers. But to all other flowers, put three partes of Sugar to the weight of the flowers, incorporate wel together the violets & sugar, and keepe it in a glasse or gallipot, it will last one yeare, it is verie good to be used of such as have hoate stomackes, or hoat livers. Also it cooleth the heade and procureth sleepe, it tempereth the heart and all other parts of the body.

THOMAS COGHAN, *The Haven of Health*, 1584

131

To Make Sirrop of Violets

First gather a great quantity of violet flowers and pick them clean from the stalkes and set them on the fire and put to them so much rose-water as you think good. Then let them boil all together until the colour be forth of them. Than take them off the fire and strain them through a fine cloth, then put so much suger to them as you thinke good, then set it againe to the fire until it be somewhat thick and put it into a violet glasse.

THOMAS DAWSON, *The Good Huswifes Jewel*, 1587

A Way to Make Suger-plate Both of Colour and Taste of Any Flower

Take violets, and beat them in a mortar with a little hard sugar; then put into it a sufficient quantitie of Rose-water; then lay your gum arabic to steep in the water, and so work it into paste; and so will your paste be both the colour of the violet and of the smell of the violet. In like sort you may worke with Marigolds, Cowslips or any other flowers.

SIR HUGH PLAT, *Delightes for Ladies*, 1594

Many poems and songs have been written about the sweet violet, the emblem of love, constancy and faithfulness. Shakespeare referred to violets many times in his plays and sonnets – notably in Hamlet and Pericles.

In ancient Greece the tiny violet was the flower of Aphrodite and of Priapus, the child of Apollo, who was depicted as a gardener carrying a pruning knife. The violet was a flower used in garlands. The Romans and Persians made violet wine and in the Middle Ages in Europe the first violet of spring caused rejoicing.

There are 600 known kinds of violets. The familiar type has dark green, heart-shaped leaves, with the flowers growing on stems from the roots, deep in colour and in scent. Violet was once used as a commercial perfume, but this has largely been replaced by powdered orris root because of the cost of extraction.

Sow seeds in autumn in shade or semi-shade, or take root cuttings or runners in winter. Violet makes a beautiful ground cover or border and can be massed under trees or in a rockery.

Violet from the *Morgan Codex* 652, 10th century

The leaves are mainly used in salads, pottage and conserves and contain vitamin C. Add to mixed green salads, wines and jellies or use the leaves for fritters.

Violet vinegar is made by steeping the flowers in white wine vinegar. The dried leaves made into tea, or added to other herbal teas, are said to be good for the kidneys.

Violet conserve: Beat the flowers and leaves to a pulp and add three times their weight of honey or raw sugar and mash into a smooth paste.

Syrup of Flowers – Violets, Poppies etc.

To 250 g of flower heads allow 750 g sugar and 100 ml of water. Crush the flowers in a mortar. Boil the sugar and water to a syrup and add the flowers when boiling. Allow to come to the boil five or six times over a very slow fire. Stir with a wooden spoon. Strain and pour into pot or bottle while hot.

Another method is to add 30 g of glycerine to the syrup and seal in fruit bottles. Pour over ice-cream and puddings for dessert.

132

Wormwood

'bitter as wormwood'

Wormwood from *The Herball*, 1597

Wormwood (*Artemisia absinthium*). Perennial.
  Common wormwood, absinth.
  Old form: Wermode, wormewoode.
Roman Wormwood (*A. pontica*).
  Old form: Pontick wormwood.
  Composite.

For the lips of a loose woman drip honey,
  and her speech is smoother than oil;
but in the end she is bitter as wormwood,
  sharp as a two-edged sword.

Proverbs, 5.3–4

What can equal this for fever and gout, for head-ache use an infusion of it and plaster your head with a crown of the wet leaves.
WALAFRID STRABO, *The Little Garden*, 840 A.D.

This herbe comfortith and strenghith the stomak in what-so-evere wyse a man take it. But betere is it thereto, if thou sette it in rayn-water and lay it a-colde thereoute and oft drinke it in this wise.
  The smel of wermode wole make the sike to slepe and so it wol, if it be leide under his hede him unwittyng.
  . . . For to make faire her (hair).
  The asshen of wermode blekkyth her, if it be medelid with oile and wex and if thou will anonite thi her with this oynement. Ley wermode in thy cheste, and there shall no motth come there-in.
Macer's Herbal, 12th century

This herbe is called wormewood. The vertue of this herbe is good to comforte the herte, and clenseth the stomake . . . If this herbe be drunke with Spy-knarde, it swageth the stomake and wombe that are infected of wycked windes. Also if this herbe be tempered with hony, it will ease the swellyng in a mannes mouthe.
ANTHONY ASKHAM, *A Lytel Herball*, 1550

Pontick wormwode . . . hath much less floures and leaves than other wormwodes, and the smell of thys is not onely not unpleasant, but resembleth a certyne spicines or pleasant savor, all other have a verye foull smell.
  Wormwood hath astringent or binding together, bitter and bitinge qualities, heatinge and scouringe awaye, strengthing and driyng.
WILLIAM TURNER, *A New Herball*, 1551

While Wormwood hath seed, get a handful of
  twaine,
To save against March, to make flea to refrain:
When chamber is sweep'd, and Wormwood is
  strown,
No flea, for his life, dare abide to be known.
What savour is better, if Physic be true,
For places infected than Wormwood or Rue?
It is a comfort for heart and the brain,
And therefore to have it, it is not in vain.
THOMAS TUSSER, *Five hundred points*, 1573

And while it is young, it is eaten in salades with other herbes to the great comoditie of the stomack and liver for it strengtheneth a weake stomacke & openeth the liver & spleene.

For which purpose there is to be had in the stilliarde at London a kinde of wine named wormewood wine which I would wish to be much used of all such students as be weake of stomack. They may easily have a rundlet of three or foure galons or lesse, which they may draw within their owne chambers as neede requireth. I was wont when appetite failed, to steepe a branch or two of common wormwood in halfe a pynte of good white wine, close covered in somme potte all night, and in the morning to streine it through a cleane lynnen, and to put in a little suger and warme it, and so drinke it. Or sometime to burne the like quantitie of wine with sugar and a branch or two or wormewoode put into it. Wherein I have founde many times marveilous commoditie, and shall be sure of a good stomacke to meate, and be free from wormes.

THOMAS COGHAN, *Haven of Health*, 1584

It is very profitable to a weak stomacke that is troubled with choler, for it clenseth it thorough his bitternes, purgeth by siege and urine: by reason of the binding qualities, it strengtheneth and comforteth the stomacke, but helpeth noting at all to remoove flegme contained in the stomacke as *Galen* addeth.

JOHN GERARD, *The Herball*, 1597

Two sorts of wormwood are wel knowen to many, that is our common wormwood and that which is called *Ponticum*, now sowen in many gardens, and commonly called french wormwood. And while it is young, it is eaten in salades with other herbes to the great commodite of the stomack and liver, for it strengtheneth a weake stomacke and openeth the liver and splene.

NICHOLAS CULPEPER, *The English Physician*, 1652

'Tis good in long putrid Fevers, it carries off the vitious Humours by Urine, it expels Worms from the Bowels, and preserves Clothes from Moths. The Juice, the distill'd Water, the Syrup, the fixed Salt, and the Oyl of it are used; but the Wine or Beer seems to be the best.

JOHN PECHEY, *The Compleat Herbal*, 1694

The leaves have been commonly used, but the flowery tops are the right part. These, made into a light infusion, strengthen digestion, correct acidities, and supply the place of gall, where, as in many constitutions, that is deficient. One ounce of the Flowers and Buds should be put into an earthern vessel, and a pint and a half of boiling water poured on them, and thus to stand all night. In the morning the clear liquor with two spoonfuls of wine should be taken at three draughts, an hour and a half distance from one another. Whoever will do this regularly for a week, will have no sickness after meals, will feel none of that fulness so frequent from indigestion, and wind will be no more troublesome; if afterwards, he will take but a fourth part of this each day, the benefit will be lasting.

SIR JOHN HILL, *The British Herbalist*, 1772

A. asbsinthium is the common Wormwood found wild in many parts; both the flowers and leaves of this variety possess a peculiar aromatic scent, somewhat resembling peppermint.

DONALD McDONALD, *Fragrant Flowers and Leaves*, 1895

Common wormwood is a bitter herb, but an aromatic, pretty silver-grey bush which makes a highlight in the herb garden.

It was used in absinthe, the French liqueur, and also in vermouth. It still adds strength and flavour to home-brewed beer.

Its strong odour repels moths and fleas where it is strewn. Brush over clothing in cupboards and wardrobes two or three times a year with a whisk made of wormwood tops. Spread in stored grains and fruit to keep away weevils, or spray with a weak tea solution, which will also repel slugs, plant lice and cabbage butterfly in the garden. It is a companion plant for radish.

Medicinally, wormwood should be used with caution. A strong tea may cause hallucinations and it is a poison in concentrated form. Habitual drinking of absinthe in earlier days caused death through paralysis and a law was passed in France in 1915 prohibiting its manufacture. It is antiseptic.

There are few culinary uses, though leafy tops have been placed on roast goose in the oven to cut the grease.

Wormwood is an erect sub-shrub, growing to a metre in height, with woolly, grey-silver leaves. Seeds are slow to germinate, so it is best to start from cuttings or divisions. Roman wormwood (*A. pontica*), grows to 60 cm and has a soft silvery foliage and a more delicate aroma.

Yarrow

'achilles' herb'

Yarrow from Mattioli, 1583

Yarrow   (*Achillea millefolium*). Perennial.
  Yarrow, Milfoil.
  Old form: Yarowe, Yarroway, Milfoil, Milfoile, Mylfoile, Knight's Milfoil, Nosebleed, Carpenter's Weed, Achillea, Achilles Yarrow.
Cloth of Gold   (*A. filipendulina*).
Pearl   (*A. ptarmica*).
Red-Flowering   (*A. mil. rosea*).
  Composite.

Of this wort which is named *millefolium* and in our language yarrow, it is said that Achilles the alderman (chieftan) found it out; and he, with the same wort, healed them who were struck and wounded with iron. Also, for that reason, it is named of some men Achillea. With this wort it is said that he also healed a man named Telephos.

For toothache, take a root of this wort, which we named millefolium; give it to eat fasting. For wounds which are made of iron, take this same wort, pounded with grease; lay it to the wounds; it purgeth and healeth the wounds.
HERBARIUM APULEIUS, 1050 A.D. (trans. Cockyane, 1866)

Ach of womb. Take yarowe that is noseblede and stamp and temp hitt wt gode stale ale and giffe the syke to drynke iij sponfull and aft this take piliall royall and bynd it to the wombe as hote as he may suffre it.
MS. 136, MEDICAL SOCIETY OF LONDON, 1444

Kynge Achyllis founde this herbe, and with it he heled his men that were wounded with yron. For Woundes stampe this herbe with Swynes grece, and playster it to the wounde and it shall hele it. And the same is good for an ache in the back or in the side.
  Take the ioyce of this herbe and vynegre and drynke it, and merveylously it helpeth a wounde that hath taken colde. Stampe this herbe in butter and laye it to the wounde and it wyll hele it well.
  Also for the heedache stampe this herbe and playster it to the heed. Also for bytynge of a wode Dogge, stampe this herbe with the Graynes of wheat, and it heleth it.
Banckes' Herbal, 1525

Mylfoile of some Yarrow or Nosebleede, is a small and short set or shrub. It hath his leaf like to the Birdes feathers. They are devided by cuttes and are sharpe also like the Cummin. Dioscorides saith, it is profitable to stay eruption of bloud.
JOHN MAPLET, *A greene Forest*, 1567

Achilles Yarrow or noble Milfoile, hath a thicke rough roote, with strings fastened thereto; from which immediately rise up divers stalkes, very greene and crested, whereupon do growe long leaves composed of many small jagges, cut even to the middle rib: the flowers stand at the top of the stalkes in spokie umbles or tufts, of a yellowish colour, and pleasant smell.
  It is a principall herbe for all kinde of bleedings, and to heale up new and old ulcers and greene wounds.
  The plant *Achilles* is thought to be the very same, wherewith *Achilles* cured the wounds of his soldiers.
JOHN GERARD, *The Herball*, 1597

Yarroway, yarroway, bear a white blow
If my love love me, my nose will bleed now.
East Anglian Saying

A common plant in pastures, hedgerows, and wastes, with a peculiarly scented leaf, and flowers generally of a white or pinkish tinge of colour. In some parts of the country it used to be largely employed in bridal wreaths.
DONALD McDONALD, *Fragrant Flowers and Leaves*, 1895

Milfoil is always the greatest boon, wherever it grows wild in the country – at the edges of the field or roads, where cereals or potatoes or any other crops are growing. It should on no account be weeded out. Like sympathetic people in human society, who have a favourable influence by their mere presence and not by anything they say, so milfoil, in a district where it is plentiful, works beneficially by its mere presence.
DR RUDOLF STEINER (1861–1925)

Yarrow or milfoil is a weedy herb once used commonly fresh and in ointments to heal wounds. Soldiers took it to the Crusades and carpenters used it to cure chisel cuts in their hands.

The earliest account of its use as a wound-wort stretches back to Greek mythology. Golden-haired Achilles cured his comrade Telephus of a spear wound during the Trojan wars. Warned by Apollo that the wound could only be cured by its cause, Achilles dressed it with rust from an iron spear and the herb Achilleos, which we take to be yarrow.

Achilles was one of the many pupils of the wise Centaur, Chiron, who reared him at Mount Pelion, instructing him in riding, hunting, pipe-playing and healing and no doubt in the traditional maxim that 'like cures like'.

Put into the nostrils, yarrow was supposed to stop bleeding; also to cause bleeding as in the verse about 'yarroway', its name in the eastern English counties.

Added to beer in place of hops, it made the beer more intoxicating. Yarrow was also a tobacco substitute and used as snuff. A few young leaves or flowering tops may be cut up and added to salads.

Yarrow is a hardy perennial, growing to about 30 cm high. It does best in sunlight. The green leaves are feathery and finely serrated (milfoil= thousand-leaved). Flowers are pinkish-white in flat clusters, though there are red and yellow forms.

Propagate yarrow at first by root cuttings. After that it will spread rapidly by self-seeding and root growth. It does well as a ground cover or garden border.

Yarrow is a dynamic herb, used in Bio-dynamic preparations. It gives vigour to nearby plants and also to crops and pastures. It repels ants, flies and other insects. A few sprigs should be added to the compost occasionally.

Yarrow tea is made by pouring 500 ml of boiling water over 5 ml of dried leaves and flowers (which dry well). It promotes perspiration and opens the skin pores and is recommended against fevers, cold, flu, hay fever and malaria.

Externally, the tea is used in hot foments for sores or wounds. A stronger infusion, cooled, is said to stop hair falling out after the scalp has been bathed with it.

The Zodiac

'a time to plant'

For everything there is a season, and a time for every purpose under heaven:
a time to be born, and a time to die;
a time to plant and a time to pluck up
that which is planted.
ECCLESIASTES 3, 1–2

The Auncient Romaines . . . learned the apte tymes, whiche were most conveniente, to sowe or plante in, according to the increase and decrease of the Moone, with the Aspectes of the Moone unto such Planettes, as moost aptely serve unto the same.
THOMAS HYLL, *The proffitable Arte of Gardening*, 1568

'The nature and qualitie of the xij. signes, after the principles of Phisik' from Thomas Hyll's *Prognostications for the Year 1572*

Sow peason and beans in the wane of the moon,
Who soweth them sooner he soweth too soon,
And they with the planet may rest and arise,
And flourish with beauty most plentiful wise.
THOMAS TUSSER, *Five Hundred Points*, 1573

Who would looke dangerously up at Planets that
might safely loke down at Plants?
JOHN GERARD, *The Herball*, 1597

The admirable Harmony of the Creation is herein
seen, in the influence of Stars up on Herbs, and the
Body of Man, how one part of the Creation is
subservient to another, and all for the use of Man.
   This indeed is true, God hath stamped his Image
upon every Creature . . .
NICHOLAS CULPEPER, *The English Physician
Enlarged*, 1653

It is a subject as antient as the Creation, yea more
antient than the Sunne or the Moon, or Starres,
they being created on the fourth day whereas Plants
were the third. Thus did God even at first confute
the folly of those Astrologers who goe about to
maintaine that all vegetables in their growth are
enslaved to a necessary and unavoidable depen-
dence on the influences of the starres; whereas
Plants were even when Planets were not.
WILLIAM COLES, *The Art of Simpling*, 1656

Some General Guides:

Sow when the moon is waxing.
Reap when the moon is waning.
Sow root crops (like potatoes) when moon
   is waning.
Don't plant in the barren signs.
Plant in the moist and fruitful signs.
Don't transplant in Aries and Leo.

In the 15th century (and later), men of wisdom
believed that the planets ruled all human con-
duct. In the herbals, the signs of the Zodiac had
a dual purpose: they influenced the operations
of growing and collecting plants and were also
identified with the various parts of the human
body they governed.

Each herb came under a particular Zodiacal
sign which showed its virtues. The list here is
based on Nicholas Culpeper's, *The English
Physician Enlarged* (1653) and certainly helps
to make that work more intelligible!

The illustration showing the signs and their
relations with the body is taken from Thomas
Hyll's, *Prognostications for the year 1572*.

Planting and growing 'by the signs' is hinged
on the relationship of the moon to the 12
Zodiacal signs. You will need to consult an
almanac to figure this out for the current year.

Herbs and their Planets

Agrimony – Jupiter
Balm – Jupiter
Basil – Mars
Bay – Sun
Borage – Jupiter
Burnet – Sun
Caraway – Mercury
Catnip – Venus
Chamomile – Sun
Chives – Mars
Dill – Mercury
Fennel – Mercury
Hyssop – Jupiter
Lad's Love – Mercury
Lavender – Mercury
Marigold – Sun
Marjorams – Mercury
Mints – Venus

Mugwort – Venus
Oregano – Mercury
Parsley – Mercury
Pennyroyal – Venus
Rosemary – Sun
Rue – Sun
Sage – Jupiter
Savory – Mercury
Tansy – Venus
Tarragon – Mars
Violet – Venus
Wormwood – Mars
Yarrow – Venus

The Signs

Sign	Planet	Symbol	Part of Body	Element	Operation
Aries	Mars	Ram	Head	Fire	Barren/dry (plough, cultivate)
Taurus	Venus	Bull	Neck, throat	Earth	Fruitful
Gemini	Mercury	Twins	Arms, lungs	Air	Barren/dry
Cancer	Moon	Crab	Breast, stomach	Water	Fruitful
Leo	Sun	Lion	Heart, spine	Fire	Barren (harvest roots)
Virgo	Mercury	Virgin	Stomach, bowels	Earth	Barren
Libra	Venus	Balance	Kidneys, lower back	Air	Fruitful (plant flowers)
Scorpio	Mars	Scorpion	Pelvis, sex organs	Water	Fruitful
Sagittarius	Jupiter	Archer	Thighs, liver	Fire	Barren/dry
Capricorn	Saturn	Goat	Bones, knees	Earth	Fruitful
Aquarius	Saturn	Watercarrier	Shin, ankles	Air	Barren/dry (harvest roots)
Pisces	Neptune	Fish	Feet	Water	Fruitful

7
BIBLIOGRAPHY

The bibliography lists in abridged title form the authorities and sources from which this herbal has been compiled. It is divided into sections covering manuscripts and the printed herbals (in chronological order) consulted either in the original or on microfilm, then farm and garden books, books about herbals and later sources.

Manuscripts

* The asterisks mark printed works or translations of the originals, or works about them.

300 B.C. – *Enquiry into Plants*, Theophrastus.
* See: *Theophrastus*, Enquiry into Plants, With an English Translation, Sir Arthur Hort, 1916 (Two volumes).

30 B.C. – *Bucolics*, Publius Vergilus Maro (Virgil).
* 1589 – *The Bucoliks* of Publius Virgilius Maro, Prince of all Latine Poets, otherwise called his Pastoralls, or shepeherds meetings. All newly translated into English by A.F. London.

60 A.D. – *De Materia Medica*, Pedacius Dioscorides.
* See: *The Greek Herball of Dioscorides*, Illustrated by a Byzantine A.D. 512, Englished by John Goodyer, Edited and first published A.D. 1933, by Robert T. Gunther. With 396 plant figures in line drawings by Miss F.A. Boustead after the Juliana Anicia Codex of 512 A.D. (701 pages). Recent reprint by Hafner Publishing Co., New York.

512 A.D. – *Cod. med. gr. 1*, known as the Juliana Codex or Codex Vindobonesis. Original in the Austrian National Library, Vienna.
* Facsimile edition: *Codex Aniciae Iuliane* Picturis Illustratus nunc Vindobonesis Med. Gr. I. Phototypice editus Moderante Iosepho de Karabacek. Bibliothecae Palatinae Vindobonesis Praefecto. Prefuel A.V. Premerstein, Carolus Wessely, Joseph Mantuani. Lugduni Batavarin. A.W. Sijthoff, 1906 (491 pages). Published in Leiden, Holland, this is in two large tomes, with black and white photographs of the original.
* See the works of Kurt Weitzmann, *Ancient Book Illumination* (1959) *and Studies in Classical and*

Byzantine Manuscript Illumination (1971), for further information on the Codex.

77 A.D. – *The Natural History*, Caius Plinius Secundus (Pliny the Elder).
* 1601 – The Historie of the World, Commonly called, *The Naturall Historie* of C. Plinius Secondus, Translated into English by Philemon Holland Doctor in Physicke. London. Printed by Adam Islip (Two tomes, total 1,438 pages).

812 A.D. – *Capitulare de Villis Imperialibus*, Emperor Charlemagne.
* Facsimile of *Cod. Guelf. 254* published by Verlag Muller, Stuttgart.

840 A.D. – *Hortulus, or The Little Garden*, Walafrid Strabo.
* 1512 – *Hortulus*, Norinberge, Officinas Dni, Johannis Weysenburger (first printed version).
* See: *Hortulus or the Little Garden*, A ninth century poem by Walafrid Strabo, trans. Richard S. Lambert, 1924 (limited edition of 132 copies).
* Facsimile: *Hortulus*, Walahfrid Strabo, trans. Raef Payne, Hunt Botanical Library, Pittsburgh, 1966 (limited edition, 1500 copies – 91 pages).

900–950 A.D. – *Leech Book of Bald*, Anglo Saxon.

10th Century – *Lacnunga*, Anglo Saxon.

1050 A.D. – *Herbarium Apuleius*, Anglo Saxon, Latin original.

* For Leech Book of Bald, Lacnunga and Herbarium Apuleius, see: *Leechdom, Wortcunning and Starcraft of Early England*, collected and edited by Rev. Thomas Oswald Cockayne (3 vols, total 1,004 pages), 1864–6.
Recently reissued by The Holland Press, London.
* Also: *English Medicine in the Anglo Saxon Times*, The Fitzpatrick Lectures, 1903, Joseph Frank Payne, Oxford, 1914 (162 pages).
* Also: *Anglo-Saxon Magic and Medicine*, J.H.G. Grattan & Charles Singer, Oxford University Press, 1952 (234 pages).

12th century – *Macer's Herbal*.
* See: A Middle English Translation of Macer Floridus de Viribus Herbarum, ed. Gösta Frisk, English Institute of Uppsala, Sweden, 1949 (338 pages).
1260 – *De proprietatibus rerum*, Bartholomaeus Anglicus.

* Printed in English by Wynken de Worde, 1495.

14th century – *Agnus Castus*.
* See: A Middle English Herbal, Reconstructed from Various Manuscripts, ed. Gösta Brodin, English Institute, University of Uppsala, Sweden, 1959 (329 pages).

1444 – *MS. 136 Medical Society of London*.
* See: *A Leechbook* or Collection of Medical Recipes of the Fifteenth Century, ed. Warren R. Dawson, Macmillan & Co., 1934.

Printed Herbals

1495 – *Bartholomeus de proprietatibus* (Bartholomeus Anglicus, de Proprietatibus Rerum). London. Imprint initials of Wynken de Worde. Liber XVII, on trees, lists several herbs.

1525 – *Banckes' Herball:* Here begynnyth a new mater, the which sheweth and treateth of ye herbes, the which is called an Herball. Imprynted by me Rycharde Banckes, dwelling in London a lytel from ye Stockes in ye Pultry.

1526 – *The Grete Herball*, which is translated out of ye Frensshe into Englysshe. Peter Treveris. First edition thought to be 1516.

1535 – *Macers Herbal Practysyd by Doctor Lynacro* Translated out of laten into Englysshe … Imprynted by me Robert wyer … besyde Charynge Crosse.

1541 – *The Castel of Helth*, corrected and in some places augmented by the fyrste authour thereof. Syr Thomas Elyot Knight. London. Thomas Bertheleti.

1550 – *A Lytel Herball* of the properties of Herbes, newely amended & corrected … made & gathered … by Anthonye Askham Phisycyon. Imprinted at London.

1551 – *A new Herball*, wherein are conteyned the names of Herbes in Greke, Latin, Englysh, Duch, Frenche, and in the Potecaries and Herbaries Latin, with the properties degrees and naturall places of the same, gathered & made by Wylliam Turner, Phisicion unto the Duke of Somersettes Grace. Imprinted at London by Steven Meirdman (184 pages).

1562 – *The Seconde Parte of William Turners Herball* . . . wyth the vertues of the same herbes with diverse confutations of no small errours, that men of no small learning have committed in the intreatinge of herbes of late yeares. Imprinted at Collen by Arnold Birckman.

1568 – *The first and seconde partes* of the Herbal of William Turner Doctor in Physick lately oversene corrected and enlarged with the Thirde parte lately gathered . . . God save the Quene. Imprinted at Collen by Arnold Birckman.

1567 – *A green Forest*, or a naturall Historie . . . Compiled by John Maplet, M. of Arte and Student in Cambridge. Imprinted at London, by Henry Denham.

1578 – *A Niewe Herball*, or Historie of Plantes: wherein is contayned the whole discourse and perfect description of all sortes of Herbes and Plantes: their divers and sundry kindes: their straunge Figures, Fashions, and Shapes . . . First set foorth in the Doutche or Almaigne tongue, by that learned D. Rembert Dodoens Physition to the Emperour: And nowe first translated out of French into English, by Henry Lyte Esquyer. Imprinted at Antwerpe, by me Henry Loe Bookeprinter (779 pages, 870 figures).

1584 – *The Haven of Health:* Chiefely gathered for the comfort of Students, and consequently of all those that have a care of their health . . . By Thomas Coghan, master of Artes, & Bacheler of Phisicke. Hereunto is added a Preservation from the Pestilence, With a short Censure of the late sicknes at Oxford. At London. Printed by Henrie Midleton, for William Norton.

1597 – *The Garden of Health:* containing the sundry rare and hidden vertues and properties of all kindes of Simples and Plants . . . Gathered by the long experience and industry of William Langham, Practioner in Physicke, London (Dated 1579, a printer's error).

1597 – *The Herball* or Generall Historie of Plantes. Gathered by John Gerarde of London Master in Chirurgerie. Imprinted at London by John Norton 1,392 pages, 1,800 figures).

1633 – *The Herball* or Generall Historie of Plantes. Gathered by John Gerard of London Master in Chirurgerie. Very much Enlarged and Amended by Thomas Johnson Citizen and Apothecarye of London. Printed by Adam Islip, Joice Norton and Richard Whitakers (1,630 pages, 2,705 figures).

1607 – *The Englishmans Doctor* or, The Schoole of Salerne. Or Physicall Observations for the perfect Preserving of the Body of Man in continuall health. Sir John Harington, London.

1629 – *Paradisi in Sole Paradisus Terrestris*, A Garden of all Sorts of Pleasant Flowers Which Our English Ayre will Permitt to be noursed up: with a Kitchen garden of all manner of herbes, rootes & fruites, for meat or sause used with us . . . Collected by John Parkinson Apothecary of London (612 pages).

1640 – *Theatrum Botanicum:* The Theatre of Plants or a Herball of a large extent . . . Collected by the many yeares travaile, industry and experience in the subject, by John Parkinson, Apothecary of London, and the King's Herbarist. Printed by Tho. Cotes (1,755 pages).

1652 – *The English Physician* Or an Astro-physical Discourse of the Vulgar Herbs of this Nation Being a Compleat Method of Physick whereby a man may preserve this Body in health; or cure himself, being sick, for three pence charge, with such things one-ly as grow in England, they being most fit for English Bodies. By N. Culpeper, Student in Physick and Astrology.

1653 – *The English Physician Enlarged* by Nich. Culpeper, Gent. Student in Physick and Astrologie. Living in Spittle Fields. London, Printed by Peter Cole.

1656 – *The Art of SIMPLING*, an Introduction to the Knowledge and Gathering of Plants. Wherein the Definitions, Divisions, Places, Descriptions, Differences, Names, Vertues, Time of flourishing and gathering, Uses, Temperatures, Signatures and Appropriations of Plants, are methodically laid down . . . By W. Coles. London (175 pages).

1657 – *Adam in Eden* or Natures Paradise. The History of Plants, Fruits, Herbe and Flowers etc. By William Coles, Herbarist. London. Printed by J. Streater (629 pages).

1694 – *The Compleat Herbal of Physical Plants*. Containing All such English and Foreign Herbs, Shrubs and Trees, as are used in Physick and Surgery . . . by John Pechey, Of the College of Physicians, in London. Printed for Henry Bonwicke . . .

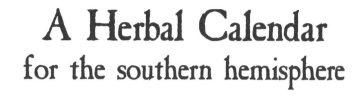

A Herbal Calendar
for the southern hemisphere

Many herbs originated in the rocky, dry shores around the Aegean and Mediterranean and are quite at home in the Antipodes. The European herb garden migrated south with the early settlers. In general, herbs dislike extremes of heat, so plant them in semi-shade except in cool places. They hate wet feet, so use raised beds or provide drainage.

Spring

September to November is the time to sow seeds of annual herbs, except in cold areas. Sow anise, basil, borage, dill, fennel, marigolds, summer savory. Take cuttings from balm, chives, comfrey, hyssop, marjoram, mints, tansy, thyme, violet, wormwood, yarrow.

Wait until the frost has gone before sowing. Water regularly, especially on windy days, to stop seedlings and transplants drying out. Pick fresh herbs for use as needed.

Summer

December is the time for hot, dry weather. Give the plants a good soaking and hoe to loosen the soil, or mulch with straw, lucerne hay, compost or well-rotted manure. Use garlic and herbal sprays against insects, which are most active in heat. Cut marjoram, sage, mint for drying.

January is the best time to cut angelica stems for candying. Collect and dry thyme, summer savory, hyssop, lavender spikes.

In *February* cut and dry clary sage flowering top, mints and sage.

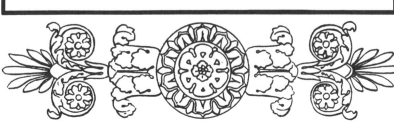

Autumn

Early autumn – hot and dry inland, humid near the coast. Collect seeds in *March* from angelica, dill, caraway and plant angelica seeds immediately. Strike cuttings of lavender, rosemary, lad's love.

Divide and replant yarrow in *April*. Cut marjoram and sage for drying. Late autumn is often balmy weather. Harvest herbs for drying.

Winter

Perennials become dormant. Many annuals can't stand the frost. *June* and *July* are the coldest months, with cold winds and frosty nights. Prepare soil for next year's garden, plan garden layout and order seeds. In mild areas, start sowing seeds in pots and flats for later transplanting.

When consulting the old herbals for sowing or harvesting times, remember that our winters are milder and shorter than in the northern hemisphere.

This chart converts the northern seasons and months for use south of the Equator:

The Four Seasons

	Spring	Summer
NORTH	March, April, May	June, July, August
SOUTH	September, October, November	December, January, February

	Autumn	Winter
NORTH	September, October, November	December, January, February
SOUTH	March, April, May	June, July, August

1756 – *The British Herbal*: an History of Plants and Trees, Natives of Britain, cultivated for use, or Raised for Beauty. By John Hill. M.D. London. (532 pages, coloured plates).

Farm & Garden

1563 – *A most briefe and pleasaunt treatyse*, teachynge howe to dress, sowe and set a Garden, and what propertyes also these few herbes heare spoken of, have to our comodyte . . . Gathered out of the principallest Authors in this art by Thomas Hyll Londyner.

1568 – *The proffitable Arte of Gardening*, now the third tyme set fourth . . . Englished by Thomas Hyll, Londyner. Imprinted at London by Thomas Marshe (166 pages).

1573 – *Five hundred points of good husbandry* united to as many of good huswiferie . . . Set forth by Thomas Tusser gentleman. Imprinted at London by Rychard Tottell.

1577 – *The Gardeners Labyrinth*: Containing a discourse of the Gardeners life in the yearly travels to be bestowed on his plot of earth . . . Gathered out of the best approved writers of Gardening, Husbandrie, and Physike: by Dydymus Mountaine. Printed at London by Henry Bynneman.

1600 – *Maison Rustique*, or *The Countrie Farme*, Compiled in the French tongue by Charles Stevens and Iohn Liebault Doctors of Physicke. And translated into English by Richard Surflet Practicioner in Physicke.

1617 – *The Countrie Housewifes Garden*. Containing Rules for Hearbes of common use. Together With the Husbandry of Bees, Published with secrets, very necessary for every Housewife. Together with divers new knots for Gardens (William Lawson). London.

1618 – *A New Orchard & Garden* or The best way for planting, grafting, and to make any ground good, for a rich Orchard: Particularly in the North parts of England . . . With the Country Housewifes Garden for hearbes of common use, their vertues, seasons, profites, ornaments, variety of knots . . .

being the Labours of forty eight yeares of William Lawson. London.

1625 – The Essays or Councels, Civil and Morall, of Francis Lo. Verulam Viscount St. Albans (Francis Bacon – includes essay *Of Gardens*).

Stillroom & Cookery

1527 – *The Vertuose boke of Distyllacyon* of the waters of all maner of Herbes with the figures of the styllatoryes. Fyrst made and compyled by the thyrte yeres study and labour of the most conynge and famous mayster of phisyke Master Jherom brunswyke And now newly Translate out of Duyche into Englysshe . . . Imprinted at London in the flete strete by me Laurens Andrewe.

1587 – *The good huswifes Jewell*, Wherein is to be found most excellent and rare Devises for Conceits in Cookerie, found out by the practise of Thomas Dawson. London.

1594 – *The Jewell House of Art and Nature*, Sir Hugh Plat.

1608 – *A Closet for Ladies and Gentlewomen*, or, The Art of Preserving, Conserving, and Candying. With the manner howe to make divers kinds of Syrups: and all kinds of banqueting stuffes . . . At London. Printed by Arthur Johnson.

1654 – *The Art of Cookery*, Joseph Cooper (Cook to Charles I).

1655 – *The Queen's Closet Opened*, W.M. (Cook to Queen Henrietta Maria).

1699 – *Acetaria*: A Discourse of Sallets. By JESRS Author of the Kalendarium Hortense (John Evelyn). Printed for B. Tooke.

Later Works

1861 – *The Book of Household Management*, by Mrs Isabella Beeton, Ward, Lock and Co., London (1,644 pages). Facsimile edition Thomas Nelson Australia 1977.

1884 – *Flowers and Flower Lore*, Rev. Hilderic Friend Swan Sonnenschein & Co. Ltd, (704 pages).

1885 – *A History of the Cries of London*, Charles Hindley, London (390 pages).

1887 – *The Australian Botanic Guide*, John Broadbent, Melbourne (189 pages).

1895 – *Fragrant Flowers and Leaves*, Donald McDonald. F. Warne & Co. London, (136 pages).

1895 – *Herbal Simples*, Approved for Modern Uses of Cure, Dr. W.T. Fernie, John Wright & Sons, Bristol, 1897 (596 pages). *Meals Medicinal*, 1899.

1911 – *The Garden of Ignorance*, Mrs George Cran (Marian Cran), Herbert Jenkins Ltd. (273 pages).

Books about Herbals

Herbals, Their Origins and Evolution, A Chapter in the History of Botany, 1470–1670, Agnes Arber, Cambridge University Press, 1912, 253 pages.

The Art of Botanical Illustration, Wilfrid Blunt, Collins, London, 1950, 304 pages, plates.

Men with Green Pens, Lives of the Great Writers on Plants in Early Times, Louise Bush-Brown, Dorrance & Co., Philadelphia, 1964, 161 pages.

Herbs and Savory Seeds, Culinaries, Simples, Sachets, Decoratives, Rosetta E. Clarkson, Dover Publications, Inc., New York, 1972, 369 pages. First published as *Magic Gardens: A Modern Chronicle* of Herbs and Savory Seeds, The Macmillan Co., 1939.

The Golden Age of Herbs and Herbalists, Rosetta E. Clarkson, Dover Publications, Inc., New York, 1972, 328 pages. First published as *Green Enchantment: The Magic Spell of Gardens*, The Macmillan Co., 1940.

Books by E.S. Rohde

The Old English Herbals, Dover Publications, Inc., New York, 1971, 326 pages. First published by Longmans, Green & Co., 1922.

The Old English Gardening Books, The New Aldine Library, Martin Hopkinson and Co. Ltd, London, 1924, 144 pages.

The Scented Garden, Medici Society, London, 1931, 311 pages.

The Story of the Garden, The Medici Society, London, 1932, 326 pages.

Shakespeare's Wild Flowers, Fairy Lore, Herbs, Gatherers of Simples and Bee Lore, The Medici Society, London, 1935, 236 pages.

A Garden of Herbs, Dover Publications, Inc., New York, 1969, 300 pages. First published by Hale, Cushman & Flint, 1936.

Herbs and Herb Gardening, The Medici Society, London, 1936, 205 pages.

8
GLOSSARY of ARCHAIC WORDS

The modern meanings of the archaic words are given as closely as possible to fit the context in which they are quoted. Where the meaning of words is obvious by their spelling e.g. aboute (about), ete (eat), pretie (pretty), they have not been included.

a

abiden, stayed
abroade, wild
abyde, live
acordith, agree
adaies, nowadays
Adonis garden, potplants
Aequinox, equinox
affecteth, inhabits
aft, after
a-gen, again
ague, fever
akinge, aching
akyng(e), aching
akyth, aches
al, all
alaieth, allays
alchymist, chemist
alderman, chief (old man)
allayeth, allays
alleis, alleys, walks
alyes, alleys, walks
amitie, friendship
an, a
ancles, ankles
anie, any
anon, soon

anonite, anoint
antient, ancient
antidot, antidote
antipathy, dislike
apothecary, herbal chemist
apparrell, clothing
appell, apple
apte, apt
asshen, ashes
as(s)wage, assuage, sooth
astonished, stunned
at, in
attenuate, make thin
auctours, authors
auncient, ancient
avouch, avow
a-wey, away
awn, own
ayl, ever

b

bad, asked
baggage, excess
bagge, bag
bare, carried
barely, barley
batled, ploughed
bawle, ball

beareth, carries
becomyn, become
bee, be are
bellye, belly
ben(e), been, is
berest, carries
bereth, carries
beryst, carries
beryth, carries
beset, covered
beste, beast
betere, better
betokeneth, indicates
betyde, happen
beutie, beauty
bid, ask
bier, beer
bignes, largeness
bignesse, largeness
bin, been
blackishe, dark
blak, black
bleared, dim
bledyth, bleeds
blek, black
blekkyth, darkens
blered, dim
blethely, easily
blew(e), blue

bloud, blood
bloume, bloom
boccles, blotches
boddye, body
bokes, books
bonys, bones
botches, blotches
boughes, boughs
bourd(e), board, table
boyl'd, boiled
braunch, branch
brawnches, branches
bray, beat (pound small)
braynes, brains
brede, breed
bressed, bruised, burst
brod, broad
brodest, broadest
brokyn, broken
bru(e), brew
bruis, crush, bruise
bruite, brute
bryhteth, brightens
bryteth, brightens
brythe, bright
burres, burs
buttons, flowers
bytinges, bites
bytynge, biting

c

cattaile, cattle
cattis, cats
caus, cause
cense, incense
cese, cease
chaffie, chaffy
chamfered, grooved
chaplet, crown of flowers
chaunce, chance
chaunge, change
chaunting, singing
chawing, chewing
chymical, chemical
civill, everyday
cleave, stick to
clensynge, cleansing
clepen, call, name
clepid, call(ed)
clepit, call(ed)
clepyn, call(ed)
clerks, scholars
close, closed, enclosed
cloven, split
clypped, clipped
coales, coals
coddes, balls, seeds
cole, cool
colys, coals
colloure, colour
comfit(t), sweet, confection
comfort(e), relieve
comfortable, contented
comly, pretty
composition, mixture
comyn, coming
conceyed, conceived (give birth)
conceyve, imagine
condite, conserve
conduceth, tends to
confect, sweet
confected, prepared
confertue, conserve
confute, refute
convenient, suitable
cordial, heart stimulant
coronet, crown of flowers
corrupt, rotten
couge, cough
cownted, counted
crake, crackle
crested, plumed
crispe, curled
croppes, umbels
crown, plaited flowers
crudle, curdle
cryspid, curled
cubyte, cubit (18 inches)
cumbered, hindered

cumfits, confections
curding, curdling
cuttes, cuts
cyath, Roman measure

d

daie, day
damosell, lady
deaw(e), dew
decoccion, decoction
decoction, essence from boiling
decks, bedecks, arrays
dich, ditch
dight, prepare
discuss, change
distichon, couplet
diureticall, promoting urine
doe, do
dores, doors
dost, do
draught, dose
drawn, picked
drey(e), dry
drincke, drink
driying, drying
dro(u)nken, drunk
druncke, drunk
dryveth, drives
dulce, sweet
dunge, manure
dunged, manured
dyars, dyers

e

eche, each
eek, also
ef, if
egs, eggs
eies, eyes
eine, eyes
electuary, powder
els, else, otherwise
elles, else
ellys, else
embanked, banked
enterposed, interposed
entertained, maintained, admitted
environed, surrounded
ere, before
ere, ear
esyle, vinegar
etyng, eating
evyl(l), evil, illness
ewelys, evils
expectoration, spitting
eyen, eyes
eysyght, eyesight
eysell, vinegar

f

fall, autumn
farre, far
farre, fare (get on)
fat(te), rich
fayre, pretty, fine
filisofres, philosophers
fle, escape
fleagme, phlegm, humour
flegmatike, sluggish
flouer, flower
flour, flower
flourryth, flowering
flouwr, flower
flower, flour
flowred, flowers
flures, flowers
fluxes, discharge
flye, fly, flee
foment, warm cloth
fond(e), found
force, power
fouer, four
foure, four
fower, four
fowle, foul
fowre, four
frounte, front
ful, very
furmenty, frumenty (hulled wheat boiled in milk)
furth, forth
fyndes, finder
fyr, fir

g

gallant, fine
gardaynes, gardens
gare, vinegar
garland, crown of flowers
gederid, gathered
geven, given
gif(f), give
gode, good
goon, go
goth, goes
goud, good
govn, given
graffing, grafting
grateful, pleasing
gravers, engravers
graynes, grains
greace, fat
greefs, pains
greene, green, fresh
greke, Greek
grete(e), great
grosse, coarse

gude, good
guirland, garland
guirle, girl

h

hackt, cut
han, have, has
heare, hair
heed, head
hegges, hedges
helt, held
hcm, him, it
her, hair
herber, arbour
here, her, it
here, hair
herte, heart
heyghte, height
hicket, hiccup
hicock(e), hiccup
hir(e), her
hirores, humours
his, its
hit, it
hoare, grey
hoarie, grey
hoat, hot
hol(e), whole, heal(ed)
holden, considered
holsum, healed
hond, hand
honie, honey
hony(e), honey
hoom, homeward
hors, hoarse
hose, whose
ho-so, who-so
hote, hot
hous, house
humures, humours
hure, here, it
hye, go

i j

i, in
iagged, jagged
iaunders, jaundice
iewels, jewels *
imposthumes, sores
in, on, of
inflation, puffing
insession, insertion
intermedled, intertwined
inunction, salve
ioyce, juice
ioyeth, revels
ioyfull, joyfull
ioyned, joined
ioynt, joint

ioyntie, branched
itt, it
iuice, juice
ius, juice
iust, just
iuus, juice
iuyce, juice
jawndees, jaundice

k

King's evil, scrofula (gland
   swelling)
knaps, buds (knobs)
knops, buds
knitches, bunches
kytlyngis, kittens (kitlings)

l

latitudes, boredom
launces, lances
laxatyf, loosening
leane, poor
leechcraft, spells
leechdom, herb knowledge
lef(e), leaf
lengere, longer
lengger, longer
lewys, leaves
list(e), will, desire
listeth, likes
loach, medicinal lick
lokyn, look
lose, loose
lowe, low
lykyng, liking, attractive
lymmes, limbs

m

mach, make
makynge, making
mannes, person's
mannys, person's
mart, market
matere, matter
mawe, gullet
mayds, maids
meane, middle
medele, mixed
medelid, mixed
medesyn, medicine
medle, mix
meet, proper
megrim, migrane, headache
membres, limbs
menely, meanly
mengled, mixed
merveye, marvel
mete, meat

mikel, much
mo, more
moats, dust
moch(e), much, many
modre, womb (mother)
mollifie, ease
moost, most
morweynyng, morning
mother, womb
moughes, moths
mowe, more
mowers, reapers
mucke, manure
mundifie, modify
myn, my

n

nat, not
ne, nor
neddre, adder
nephriticall, kidney sufferers
nese, sneeze
neesing, sneezing
nicked, indented
non, no
noo, no
noon, none
noryce, nurse
nosethrill, nostril
noteth, notes
nosth, not
noyous, noxious,
   troublesome
noysome, noxious

o

obdure, hard obstructions,
   blockages
obfuscated, darkened
odoriferous, perfumed
of, to, by
on, a
oon, one
oynt(e), anoint

p

pale, fence, boundary
pacient, patient
pacyent, patient
paisants, peasants
pappes, breasts
parboile, scald
parboyle, scald
pare, cut
passe, pass
paties, potatoes
peason, peas
peble, pebbly
peece, piece
peradventure, perhaps
perfit, perfect

pescodes, peas
phrenticke, frantic
physicall, medicinal
physick(e), doctor
picke, pick
pipes, throat, windpipe
pipkin, earthenware pot
placis, places
plaister, plaster
playster, plaster
playstyr, plaster
pleached, entwined
polled, cropped
posset, hot drink
pothearb(e), vegetable
pot(t)age, soup
prise, prize
punde, pounde, beat
punned, cooked (panned)
purled, looped
purpure, purple

q

quailing, curdling
quier, choir
quyche, which
quyete, quiet
quyt, white
qwyt(e), white
qwyth, white

r

rariefie, lessen
raynes, bladder
reed, red
recreate, refresh
reioice, rejoice
rel(l)ish, flavour
renued, renewed
rennynges, running
rewes, rows
rheum, watery discharge
rhewms, discharge
rhums, discharge
rinde, bark
rote, root
roste, roast
roudels, spikes
rowme, room
rundles, umbels
rundlet, cask
rusticall, common
ruth, compassion
rypmen, reapers (reap-men)
rysyth, rises

s

sarced, cooked

sarsing, cooking
savor(e), taste, smell
sawour, savour
scalie, scaly
schal, shall
scharp, sharp
sciences, sections
scower, scour, rub
seaye, sea, salt
seethe, boil
seid, said
seignorie, lordship
seething, boiling
sekness, sickness
seme, seem
sent, scent
set, plant
seyn, say, said
shrubbie, shrubby
shynynge, shining
sigh, sight
sightes, views
sike, sick
sikerley, surely
simple, herb
sith, since
skalded, scalded
skinne, skin
slee, slay
slepe, sleep
slippes, slips, cuttings
smelles, smells
sod, boil
sod(d)en, boiled
sodder, solder, join
som(m)er, summer
soort, sort
sorys, illnesses
sothen, boiled
soveraigne, powerful
sowring, souring
spechly, speckled
specis, species
spedde, hurried
spoakie, spiky
spokie, spiky
spoked, spiked
sporte, relax
sprong, sprung
sprouts, slips
spyces, species
stamped, beaten in mortar
stancheth, staunches
stew, fishpond
stilled, distilled
stilliard, still, distillery
stiptick, gummy
stok, stalk
stomager, poultice
stoppeth, blocks, prevents
straw, strew, scatter

strawed, strewn
strengest, strongest
stroke, portion
strown, strewn
stusseth, smells
stryepe, bruise
styreth, stirs
stynge, sting
sugre, sugar
sumdel, somewhat
swage, soothe
swiche, such
swounings, fainting
synge, sing
syth, sight

t

tak, take
tarie, delay
tast, taste
temp, blend, combine
tempre, blend
tempered, blended
terme, call
than, then
the(i), they, them, their
then, than
they, thy
theyr, their
thi, thy
thre, three
threddie, thready

thro(o)te, throat
throwe, through
thyn, thine, yours
toon, one
topp(e), top
tormina, fever
toth, tooth
tothe, tooth
tother, other
tournoy, tourney
tre, tree
treacles, antidote
tretyn, treat
triacles, antidote
troden, trodden
turves, grass pieces

U V

umbels, seed heads, spikes
unbyndyth, unbinds
unlustie, weak
unsodden, uncooked
upbraidings, belching
ureticall, bringing urine
urin, urine
us'd, used
valewe, value
vawting, arches
venery, lust
venym(e), venom
verie, very
veryue, virtue

veyne, vein
viols, phials
voyde, empty
vulnerary, of wounds

W

waies, ways
wan, won
wasshe, wash
watrie, watery
wayghty, weighty
waxe, become
werye, weary
weyke, weak
whan, when
whesshe, wash
whiles(t), while
whill, while
widdered, withered
windines, windy
with, by
wode, wood
woful, bitter
wole, will
wollen, will, wish
woon, won
wond, wound
woormes, worms
wort, herb
wodys, woods
wrought, mixed
wt, with
wurts, herbs

wil(l), will
wyscely, wisely

y z

y, that
y-benched, with seats
yeald, yield
yealowe, yellow
yeeld, yield
yeere, year
yeeldeth, yields
yelow evil, jaundice
yel(l)owe, yellow
yere, year
y-grave, dug, cut
y-lyche, like
y-nowe, enough
yeoking, hiccup
yest, yeast
yf, if
yong, young
yoong, young
yn, in
yryn, iron
ys, is
yunglise, young

Numerals
ij, two
lld, second
iii, three
iij, three

9
INDEX
of PLANTS

Agrimony, 6, 34, 35, 138
Alexander, 9
Alpine strawberry, 123
Anise, 5, 7, 9, 38, 39, 40, 56, 68, 74, 111, 113
Apple, 125
Apple mint, 96, 99
Artemisias, 41, 79, 80, 100
Asparagus, 68

Balm (Melissa), 5, 7, 41, 42, 43, 58, 68, 123, 138
Basil, 5, 7, 10, 14, 43, 44, 45, 46, 66, 67, 68, 79, 123, 138
Basil, bush, 10, 46
Bay laurel, 3, 6, 17, 37, 46, 47, 48, 75, 138
Bean, 67, 68, 102
Betony, 22, 118
Bohnenkraut (see savory)
Borage, 6, 9, 49, 51, 52, 64, 67, 68, 138
Broccoli, 68, 102
Bugloss, 9, 64
Burnet, 6, 10, 14, 53, 54, 138
Buttercup, 9

Cabbage, 68
Camphor, 116
Caraway, 5, 7, 54, 68, 73, 138
Cardus Benidictus, 9, 16
Carosella, 74
Carrot, 61, 67, 68
Castor oil, 16, 18
Cassidony (see lavender)
Catnip, 5, 7, 57, 68, 138
Cauliflower, 70
Celandine, 73
Chamomile, 5, 10, 14, 59, 60, 68, 88, 109, 123, 138
Chamomile spray, 11
Cherry laurel, 48
Chicory, 9
Cinnamon 82, 111, 116
Chives, 6, 7, 9, 10, 11, 60, 61, 68, 79, 138
Clary sage, 5, 7, 9, 61, 62
Clove, 82, 111, 116
Columbine, 102
Comfrey, 6, 7, 9, 15, 63, 64, 65, 66
Coriander, 9, 17, 22, 39, 68, 74
Cornflower, 16
Corn mint, 96

Corsican mint, 10, 96, 99
Costmary, 22, 123
Cotton lavender, 10
Cowslips, 8, 123, 132
Cress, 22, 101, 102
Cucumber, 51, 54, 68, 70
Cummin, 56, 135
Cypress, 75

Daffodil, 9
Daisy 8, 9, 102, 109, 123
Dandelion, 16
Date, 77
Dill, 5, 7, 14, 16, 18, 40, 56, 57, 69, 70, 138
Dittany, 22
Dock, 22
Dwarf lavenders, 81, 85

Egyptian mint, 96
Elecampane 9, 63, 64, 113
Endive, 7
English lavender, 81, 85
Eau-de-cologne mint, 96

Fennel 2, 5, 7, 9, 22, 49, 56, 57, 67, 68, 69, 70, 71, 72, 73, 74, 102, 118, 123, 138

Feverfew, 9
Fig, 68, 77, 115
Finnochio, 74
Flax, 126
Florence fennel, 74
Flower deluce, 9
Frais du Bois (*see* strawberry)
French lavender, 81, 82, 86

Garlic, 11, 17, 67, 68, 116
Garlic spray, 11
Garlic chives 61
Galium, 16
Germander, 7, 78, 79, 123
Geranium, 7
Gilliflower, 8, 9
Grape hyacinth, 16
Grapes, 68

Hamburg parsley, 106, 108
Haught boy (*see* strawberry)
Hearts ease, 9
Hemlock, 104
Herb of grace (*see* rue)
Holly, 75
Hollyhock, 9, 16
Honeysuckle, 118
Hop, 123

Horehound, 63, 77
Horsemint, 96
Horsetail, 16
Hungary water, 113
Hyssop, 5, 7, 8, 11, 12, 22, 49, 66, 68, 76, 77, 78, 79, 82, 126, 138

Italian lavender, 81, 86
Italian parsley, 105
Iris, 40
Ivy, 75

Jasmine, 36
Juniper, 36, 49

Lad's love, 5, 7, 8, 22, 41, 59, 68, 79, 80, 92, 116, 138
Lavender cotton, 88, 89, 95, 123
Leek, 9, 60
Lemon mint, 96, 99
Lemon thyme, 127, 128
Lemon verbena, 7, 15
Lettuce, 16, 22, 67
Lily, 8, 9, 22, 67
Lovage, 7, 9
Lungwort, 29

Marigold, 5, 7, 9, 10, 68, 75, 89, 90, 91, 132, 138

Marjoram, 5, 7, 9, 10, 92, 93, 95, 100, 102, 123, 128, 138
Meadowsweet, 124
Mercury, 22
Mignonette, 17
Milfoil (*see* yarrow)
Mints, 5, 7, 9, 10, 14, 16, 17, 22, 53, 68, 71, 88, 96, 97, 98, 99, 108, 116, 123, 138
Mugwort, 5, 22, 41, 99, 100, 138
Mulberry, 122
Myrtle, 113

Nasturtium, 6, 11, 68, 101, 102
Nep (*see* catnip)
Nutmeg, 82, 116, 125

Old man, 80
Old woman, 80
Olive, 47
Onion, 8, 9, 66, 68, 118, 126
Oregano, 5, 14, 68, 104, 105, 120, 138
Oxlip, 128

Pansy, 9
Parsley, 5, 6, 10, 22, 39, 48, 54, 68, 79, 105, 106, 107, 108, 138

Parsnip, 8, 67
Pennyroyal, 5, 9, 10, 57, 68, 98, 104,
 108, 109, 110, 123, 138
Pea, 5, 7, 67, 68
Peony, 8, 22
Peppermint, 96
Pimpinella (*see* burnet)
Pinks, 8
Plantain, 22, 118
Poppy, 16, 100, 104, 132
Pot marigold, 94
Potatoes, 67, 68, 102
Prickly comfrey, 65
Primrose, 125
Privet, 78
Purslane, 67

Radish, 66, 67, 68
Rigani, 105
Rocket, 126
Roman wormwood, 133, 134
Rose, 8, 14, 15, 22, 49, 68, 73, 78,
 82, 85, 95, 98, 123, 130
Rosemary, 3, 5, 7, 8, 10, 12, 14, 31,
 36, 49, 68, 84, 87, 95, 102, 110,
 113, 114, 116, 118, 138
Rosemary, prostrate, 10, 110, 114

Rosemary water, 113
Rue, 6, 7, 17, 22, 36, 66, 67, 68, 73,
 76, 102, 115, 116, 117, 133, 138
Russian comfrey, 63

Safflower, 14
Saffron, 9, 17
Sage, 5, 7, 8, 22, 59, 68, 78, 85, 113,
 116, 117, 118, 119, 123
St John's wort, 37
Salad burnet (*see* burnet)
Savory, 3, 5, 7, 9, 22, 66, 68, 76,
 95, 120, 121, 123, 138
Santolina (*see* Cotton lavender)
Scabious, 118
Senna, 18
Siberian chives, 61
Sicilian fennel, 74
Sorrel, 16, 22
Southerwood (*see* Lad's love)
Sowthistle, 64
Spearmint, 57, 97, 99
Spike lavender (Spikenard), 81, 82,
 83, 85, 118, 123, 133
Spinach, 119, 125
Star anise, 40
Stoechas, 81, 83

Strawberry, 6, 9, 51, 66, 67, 68,
 122, 123
Sunflower, 10, 14, 67
Sweet cicely, 9, 107
Sweet marjoram, 92, 93, 94
Tansy, 5, 7, 9, 11, 68, 88, 113, 123,
 124, 125, 138
Tarragon, 5, 7, 14, 41, 126, 127, 138
Thyme, 3, 5, 7, 8, 12, 14, 17, 36,
 48, 49, 53, 68, 78, 79, 82, 88, 95,
 113, 121, 127, 128, 129, 130
Tomato, 68, 70
Vervain, 22, 73
Violet, 6, 7, 14, 20, 75, 102, 109,
 123, 125, 128, 130, 131, 132,
 138
Wallflower, 9
Water mint, 87, 98
Willow, 29, 36
Winter marjoram, 94
Wisteria, 36
Wormwood, 5, 7, 11, 41, 67, 68, 79,
 100, 116, 126, 133, 134, 138
Woolly thyme, 130
Yarrow, 5, 7, 10, 16, 17, 68, 135,
 136, 138.

10
INDEX
of Authors

Addison, Richard, 70
Agnus Castus (*14th C*), 23, 34, 41, 51, 53, 57, 63, 76, 82, 92, 115, 118, 120, 141
Arber, Agnes, 25, 146
Apuleium, *Herbarium* (*1050*), 22, 41, 135, 141
Askham, Anthony, *A Lytel Herball* (*1550*), 24, 59, 64, 79, 89, 122, 133, 141

Bacon, Francis, 1, 35, 53, 78, 116, 131, 146
Bald, *Leech Book* (*900*), 22, 141
Banckes' Herball (*1525*), 24, 111, 135, 141
Bardswell, Frances, *The Herb Garden* (*1911*), 42, 45, 59, 120
Bartholomaeus Anglicus, *De propriet-atibus* (*1495*), 24, 130, 141
Beeton, Isabella, *Household Manage-ment* (*1861*), 39, 56, 73, 98, 101, 107, 118, 120, 129, 146
Broadbent, John, *The Australian Botanic Guide* (*1887*), 65, 146
Brunswyke, Jherom, 124, 146

Cavendish, George, 78
Charlemagne, *Capitulare de Villis* (*812*), 20, 40, 74, 141
Cervantes, Miguel de, *Don Quixote* (*1605*), 113
Charles 1, 90
Chaucer, Geoffrey, 31, 34, 35, 71, 91
Cod. med. gr. 1 (*see* Discorides)
Coghan, Thomas, *Haven of Health* (*1584*), 28, 69, 73, 76, 79, 88, 106, 111, 118, 131, 134, 144
Coles, William, *Art of Simpling* (*1656*), *Adam in Eden* (*1657*), 2, 29, 51, 52, 58, 73, 75, 94, 100, 101, 116, 138, 144, 156
Cooks Oracle (*1821*), 119
Cooper, Joseph, *Receipt Book* (*1640*), 70, 146
Cran, Marian, *Garden of Ignorance* (*1917*), 51, 113, 116, 146
Crescentiis, Petrus de, 76, 115
Culpeper, Nicholas, *The English Physician* (*1652*), *The English Physician Enlarged* (*1653*), 12, 24, 28, 29, 34, 37, 42, 45, 47, 56, 58, 59, 61, 62, 65, 66, 69, 73, 90, 93,

105, 111, 125, 126, 134, 138, 144

Dawson, Thomas, *Good Housewifes Jewell* (*1587*), 73, 113, 132, 146
Digby, Sir Kenelm, 49
Dioscorides, Pedacius, *Materia Medica* (*60 A.D.*), 10, 18, 19, 22, 23, 31, 32, 34, 38, 41, 44, 45, 59, 69, 76, 82, 87, 99, 110, 111, 115, 120, 135, 140
Dodoens, Rembert, *A Niewe Herball* (*1578*), 25, 26, 27, 32, 36, 39, 60, 64, 69, 90, 98, 111, 124, 125, 128, 131, 144
Douglas, Neil, 51

Earle, Alice Morse, 84
Earth Garden, 10, 51, 64
Ecclesiastes, 136
Elizabeth, Queen of Hungary, 113
Elyot, Sir Thomas, 39, 141
Evelyn, John, *Kalendarium Hortense* (*1664*), *Acetaria* (*1699*), 30, 42, 45, 51, 59, 62, 70, 90, 100, 102, 126, 146

Fernie, Dr W.T., *Herbal Simples* (*1897*), 37, 59, 84, 90, 101, 146
Fortunatus, Venantius, 20
Fox, Helen, 85
Friend, Rev. Hilderic, *Flowers & Flower Lore* (*1884*) 84, 146

Gerard, John, *The Herball* (*1597*), 1, 20, 24, 27, 31, 32, 34, 36, 39, 42, 45, 46, 47, 49, 51, 53, 56, 62, 64, 73, 82, 89, 90, 93, 98, 100, 101, 102, 106, 110, 111, 116, 118, 120, 122, 124, 126, 128, 131, 134, 135, 138, 144
Goodyer, John, 20, 32
Grete Herball (*1526*), 24, 100, 111, 130, 141

Harington, Sir John, *The Englishmans Doctor* (*1607*), 39, 73, 76, 110, 116, 118, 144
Hawkes, Stephen, 75
Hill, Sir John, *The British Herbal* (*1756*), 12, 80, 100, 134, 146
Hills, Lawrence, 65
Hindley, Charles, *Cries of London* (*1885*), 80, 81, 113, 146

Holland, Philemon, 18 (*see* Pliny)
Homer, 16, 107, 116
Hyll, Thomas, *A most brief and plesaunt treatyse* (*1563*), *The proffitable Arte of Gardening* (*1568*), *The Gardeners Labyrinth* (*1577*), 1, 8, 9, 10, 11, 29, 30, 35, 39, 41, 44, 48, 76, 82, 90, 92, 95, 98, 102, 106, 108, 111, 115, 120, 122, 136, 138, 146

Jekyll, Gertrude, 48
Johnson, Thomas, 20, 27
Joyce, James, 31
Juliana Anicia Codex, 18, 19, 20, 22, 140 (*see* Dioscorides)

Keats, John, 44
Knight, Joseph, 84, 87
Lacnunga (*10th C*), 23, 100, 141
Langham, William, 82, 111
Langland, William, 71
Lawson, William, *The Countrie Housewifes Garden* (*1617*), *A New Orchard and Garden* (*1618*), 8, 30, 37, 39, 61, 62, 76, 78, 82, 95, 107, 113, 116, 120, 123, 128, 146

Lemnius, Levimus, 123
Linneaus, Carolus, 5, 101
Longfellow, Henry, 73
Lydgate, John, 122
Lyte, Henry, 32, 144 (*see* Dodoens)

Macers Herbal (*12th C*), 23, 24, 54, 59, 62, 71, 89, 106, 115, 118, 130, 133, 141
McDonald, Donald, 80, 134, 136, 146
Maison Rustique, 30, 146 (*see* Surflet)
Maplet, John, *A greene Forest* (*1567*), 59, 92, 135, 144
Markham, Gervaise, 9, 14, 30, 49
Matthew, 97
Mattioli, Pierandrea, 19
Middleton, John, 85
Monardes, Nicholas, 101
More, Sir Thomas, 31, 111
Morgan Cod. 652 (*see* Dioscorides)
MS. 136, *Medical Society of London* (*1444*), 23, 39, 47, 57, 63, 79, 135, 141

Neckham, Alexander, 22

Nicander of Colophon, 131
Nott, John, 94, 125

Parkinson, John, *Paradisus* (*1629*),
   Theatrum Botanicum (*1640*), 24, 28,
   35, 42, 45, 47, 51, 53, 56, 58, 69,
   73, 78, 80, 84, 89, 90, 93, 98, 101,
   107, 113, 116, 118, 124, 126, 128,
   129, 114, 156
Pechey, John, *The Compleat Herbal*
   (*1694*), 58, 110, 134, 144
Pfeiffer, Ehrenfried, 67
Piesse, G., 85, 116
Pindar, 105
Plat, Sir Hugh, 132
Pliny the Elder, *Naturall History*
   (*77 A.D.*), 11, 17, 18, 19, 23, 24,
   30, 39, 40, 42, 44, 47, 57, 59, 66,
   71, 75, 84, 88, 92, 97, 98, 100,
   101, 102, 106, 107, 108, 111, 115,
   120, 123, 124, 128, 141
Proverbs, 133

Psalms, 76
Pynsen, Richard, 52
Pythagoras, 40

Ram, William, *Ram's Little Dodoen*
   (*1606*), 11, 27, 59, 98
Robinson, Clement, 109, 111
Robinson, William, 47, 129
Rohde, E. S., 30, 147

Shakespeare, William, 31, 35, 47,
   56, 59, 66, 92, 102, 115, 128, 131,
   132, 156
Steiner, Rudolf, 136
Stevens, Charles, 30
Strabo, Walafrid, *Hortulus* (*840*
   A.D.), 22, 34, 71, 79, 97, 108, 118,
   133, 141
Surflet, Richard, *The Countrie Farme*
   (*1600*), 30, 34, 36, 39, 45, 64, 82,
   98, 107, 120, 123, 128, 131, 146

Theocritus, 106
Theophrastus, *Enquiry into Plants*
   (*300 B.C.*), 3, 17, 30, 43, 99, 105,
   128, 140
Thomas, Edward, 80
Turner, William, *A New Herball*
   (*1551*), 25, 32, 45, 47, 48, 53, 69,
   92, 108, 133, 143, 144
Tusser, Thomas, *Five hundred points*
   (*1573*), 30, 45, 56, 122, 124, 133,
   138, 146

Virgil, 70, 75, 128, 140

Walton, Izzak, 84
Walsh's Domestic Economy (*1857*), 119
W.M., Cook to Queen Henrietta
   Maria, *Queen's Closet Opened* (*1655*),
   52, 77, 84, 146
Worlidge, John 98
Wyer's Herball, 25

And thus have I led you through all my Garden of Pleasure, and shewed you all the varieties of nature housed therein, pointing unto them and describing them one after another. And now lastly (according to the use of our old ancient Fathers) I bring you to rest on the Grasse, which yet shall not be without some delight, and that not the least of all the rest.

JOHN PARKINSON, *Paradisus*, 1629

I hope you will think it no dishonour to follow the steps of our grandsire Adam, who is commonly pictured with a Spade in his hand, to march through the Quarters of your Garden with the like Instrument, and there to rectify all the disorders thereof, to procure as much as in you lyes the recovery of the languishing Art of Simpling . . . There is no better way to understand the benefit of it, than by being acquainted with Herballs and Herbarists and by putting this Gentle and ingenious Exercise in practise.

WILLIAM COLES, *The Art of Simpling*, 1656

Gardener from *The Herball*, 1597

There is no ancient gentlemen
but gardeners, ditchers and
grave-makers: they hold up
Adam's profession.
(Clown), Hamlet, Act V,
Scene I